CONTENTS

PAGE

English

ABOUT THE AUTHOR

Leesa C Keys graduated from Warwick University July 2000 with an honours degree in Biological Sciences. After graduation she bought and managed her own beauty salon before selling the business for a considerable profit. In 2005 Leesa formed SkinBase Microdermabrasion Systems where she remains partner and senior trainer.

SKINBASE MICRODERMABRASION TRAINING

SkinBase microdermabrasion training is provided in addition to existing beauty qualifications. The minimum requirement for training is NVQ Level 2 in Facials or an equivalent. The training will cover both the theoretical and practical aspects of microdermabrasion.

The SkinBase MDPro is a professional microdermabrasion system engineered and manufactured in the UK. We have worked with experienced beauty therapists who have years of experience working with alternative products on the market to help us design a system with exceptional performance, quality and proven reliability.

SECTION 1 - LEARNING OUTCOMES:

- Understand your responsibilities under the Health and Safety at Work Act (1974) and how to implement them
- The ability to recognise different skin disorders and diseases and how they contraindicate treatment
- A basic understanding of the Anatomy and Physiology of the face and neck

HEALTH & SAFETY IN THE WORKPLACE

This section will cover your responsibilities to yourself, employees (where applicable), and clients with regards to health, safety and welfare in the workplace. It is important that you are aware of these responsibilities and that they are implemented where reasonably possible. Knowledge of health and safety issues will help you to perform treatments safely and demonstrate a professional appearance and attitude at work.

The Health & Safety at Work Act 1974 outlines the minimum standards of health, safety and welfare required in the workplace. When working in a service industry you are legally obliged to provide a safe and hygienic environment.

TO AVOID POTENTIAL HAZARDS AND RISKS IN THE WORKPLACE YOU SHOULD:

- Know your legal responsibility with regards to implementing workplace health & safety policy
- Ensure your personal presentation at work meets health & safety and legislative requirements in accordance with workplace policies
- Follow workplace policies for your job role and manufacturers' instructions for the safe use of resources
- Immediately report or deal with any risk that could be a hazard in the workplace
- Have first aid arrangements in place in the event of an accident or illness
- Have a workplace fire evacuation procedure in place and ensure all employees are aware of how to implement this procedure
- Minimise the possibility of spreading infection or disease by maintaining high levels of hygiene

Electricity at Work Regulations 1989

The regulations cover the installation, maintenance & use of electrical equipment in the workplace. Electrical equipment should be tested regularly by a qualified electrician to make sure it complies with health & safety. You should keep records of these checks. Also be aware of potential hazards associated with electrical equipment; exposed wires, cracked plugs and overloaded sockets.

Although it is the responsibility of the employer to ensure all equipment is safe to use, it is also the responsibility of the employee to ALWAYS check that equipment is safe before use, and to NEVER use it if it is faulty.

POTENTIAL ELECTRICAL HAZARDS

- Exposed wires in flexes
- Cracked plugs or broken sockets
- Overloaded sockets

First Aid

Even if you have taken all precautions to make sure the workplace is as safe as possible accidents can happen. Make sure you have a first aid procedure in place so everyone in the workplace knows what to do in the event of accident, illness or emergency.

Every workplace should have a first aid box and a nominated person to be responsible for the maintenance of the box. Keep a record of any injuries in an accident log book.

KNOW:

Where to locate the first aid book
Who is responsible for maintenance of the first aid box
Who to inform in the event of accident/illness/emergency occurring

Disposal of Waste

Waste should be disposed of in an enclosed waste bin fitted with a polythene bin liner, durable enough to resist tearing. The bin should be regularly sanitised with disinfectant, wearing protective gloves.

All the relevant publications regarding health and safety in the workplace can be downloaded from: The Health and Safety Executive (HSE) website: www.hse.gov.uk ensure you obtain and read these.

Hygiene in the Workplace

Sterilising equipment between clients is essential to destroy any harmful bacteria, fungi and viruses which could cause infection. Good hygiene in the workplace will prevent cross infection and secondary infection.

Cross infection occurs when micro-organisms are transferred through personal contact or by contact with an infected nozzle that has not been sterilised.

Secondary infection can occur as a result of injury to the client during the treatment, or if the client already has an open cut bacteria can penetrate the skin & cause infection.

Personal Hygiene

A high standard of personal hygiene is essential. You should wash your hands regularly and before and after each client. Long hair should be tied back and you should avoid touching your face. Cover any cuts or abrasions on the hands with a clean dressing.

SKIN DISORDERS & DISEASES

Infectious diseases that are contagious contraindicate beauty treatment. People with certain skin disorders, even though these are not contagious, should likewise not be treated by the therapist as treatment might lead to secondary infection. The therapist must be able to distinguish a healthy skin from one suffering from any skin disease or disorder.

IMPORTANT:

If you are uncertain or unable to identify a skin condition you should not treat the client and advise them to consult their doctor.

Certain skin disorders and diseases contraindicate a beauty treatment: the treatment would expose the therapist and other clients to the risk of cross-infection it is therefore vital that you are familiar with the skin diseases & disorders with which you may come into contact.

Bacterial Infections

Bacteria can be present in large numbers on the skin without causing us any ill harm. However, certain types of bacteria are harmful to us and these are known as 'pathogenic'. Pathogenic bacteria can cause skin diseases which are infectious and therefore a client **should not be treated if found to be suffering from the following bacterial infections:**

Impetigo
Extremely infectious and is easily spread through contact. Impetigo usually appears on the face first; around the nose, mouth & ears, and can spread to other areas. Initially red and itchy, blisters appear and these become crusty and weep.

Conjunctivitis
Conjunctivitis is not always infectious as it can be caused by an allergic reaction or as a result of an irritant. However, it would be impossible for you to determine this so it should always be treated as infectious. The eye will appear red and inflamed; eyes might also be watery or have pus coming from the eye area.

Styes/Hordolea
Styes are an infection of the sebaceous gland at the root of an eyelash. This causes a swelling which can leave the adjacent area red and the affected follicle with a small lump filled with pus.

Boil/Furuncle
A boil or furuncle is caused by the inflammation of hair follicles, resulting in an accumulation of pus and dead tissues. Boils are red, pus-filled lumps that are tender, warm, and/or painful. A yellow or white point at the centre of the lump can be seen when the boil is ready to drain.

Viral Infections

The particles of a virus are so small they cannot grow and reproduce on their own so they require a 'host' cell. Viruses invade healthy living cells in the body so they can reproduce. They enter the body any way they can; by inhalation, through saliva, sexual contact. Our immune system is designed to deal with most viruses and we will naturally fight off most infections. Clients suffering from the following viral infections should not receive microdermabrasion treatment.

Herpes Simplex (cold sores)

Cold sores are caught by close contact with someone who already has cold sores. They are characterised by a tingling feeling in the skin followed by sores which scab. Commonly found on the mucous membranes of the nose or lips they can also occur on other areas of the skin.

Herpes Zoster (shingles)

Shingles is an infection of the nerve and the area supplied by the nerve. The virus usually affects one nerve, commonly the chest, abdomen or the upper face. Symptoms occur in the area of skin supplied by the nerve causing redness, blisters and scabs.

Fungal Infections

Fungi are parasitic, microscopic plants feeding off the waste products of the skin. Some fungal infections are found on the skin's surface others are deeper within the skin tissue. Clients with fungal infections should not be treated as these diseases are infectious and can be spread.

Tinea Corporis/Ring Worm

Ringworm is a fungal infection of the skin found on the trunk of the body, the limbs & face. They appear as scaly red patches on the skin which spread outwards. The patches heal from the centre leaving a ring.

Other skin disorders are not infectious however they should be treated with some caution and in some cases avoided altogether.

Sebaceous Gland Disorders

The sebaceous glands are small glands which secrete an oily substance called sebum in the hair follicle to lubricate the skin, they are found in greatest abundance on the face and scalp. Sebaceous gland disorders include acne, rosacea and milia. Sebaceous gland disorders are generally caused by an over production of sebum.

Milia

Also known as 'milk spots' or 'oil seeds' they are benign, keratin filled cysts usually found around the nose and eyes. They are small, hard, white or pale yellow in appearance and can be removed using a sterile needle to pierce the overlying skin and release the keratin.

Comedones/Blackheads

Caused by excess sebum and keratinised cells blocking the hair follicle.They are found on the face, the upper back and chest.

Seborrhoea
Caused by excessive secretion of sebum, usually occurs during puberty because of hormonal changes. Sufferers will have enlarged follicles and excessive sebum. It is not infectious and usually found on the face and scalp. It can also affect the back and chest.

Sebaceous Cysts
These form in the hair follicle when sebum becomes blocked and a lump forms.

Acne Vulgaris
Hormonal imbalances during puberty cause an increase in the production of sebum. This in turn causes congestion in the sebaceous ducts resulting in; inflammation of the skin, comedones, pustules and papules. It is not infectious, commonly found on the face, nose, chin and forehead. It may also occur on the chest and back. Active acne should be avoided during microdermabrasion treatment.

Rosacea
Caused by a combination of excessive sebum secretion and chronic inflammatory condition, skin becomes coarse, pores enlarge, cheeks and nose become red and inflamed. The skin can look purplish in appearance because of slow blood circulation. Rosacea cannot be treated with microdermabrasion.

Pigmentation

Hyperpigmentation - Increased Pigmentation
Chloasmata 'liver spots' - increased pigment production can be caused by UV light, often occurs during pregnancy. Oestrogen is believed to stimulate the production of melanin and so may also occur as a result of taking the contraceptive pill. They occur on the hands, forearms, upper chest, temples and forehead.

Ephelides 'freckles' - caused by exposure to UV light which stimulates the production of melanin. Found on the nose and cheeks of fair skinned people, also can occur on the hands, arms, shoulders, and back.

Lentigo - patches of hyperpigmentation larger than freckles, occurring either in childhood or middle age due to sun exposure. Found on the face, hands and shoulders.

Hypopigmentation - Loss of Pigment
Vitiligo - patches of skin which have no pigment in them so appear completely white.

Albinism - skin with no pigment whatsoever and so the skin, hair, and eyes lack colour. Skin is very pale pink, eyes are also pink and hair is white.

Vascular Naevi
These are areas of pigmentation caused by permanent dilation of blood capillaries.

Dilated Capillaries – small red capillaries visible in areas that are neglected or dry like the cheeks.
Spider Naevi – dilated blood vessels with dilated capillaries spreading out around them.
Naevi vasculosis 'strawberry marks' – red or purplish raised marks that appear on the skin at birth
Capillary Naevi 'Port-wine stain' – large areas of dilated capillaries

Erythema

Erythema is the reddening of the skin caused by dilation of the blood vessels controlling capillary networks in areas of the skin affected by injury or infection.

Telangiectasia (Broken Capillaries)

Any form of broken capillary can be made worse by the vacuum action of microdermabrasion. These "thread veins" are quite common around the nose and cheek area. The area would have to be avoided completely or the treatment would have to be performed at a very low level.

Keloids

Keloids are scar tissue with excess deposits of collagen. Skin is raised in appearance and red with ridges. This type of scar tissue cannot be treated with microdermabrasion. Stretch marks and post-operative scars can be treated, however scar tissue should not be treated until all the inflammation has disappeared (6 months post surgery for example).

Dermatitis

An inflammation of the skin caused by an irritant or allergen. There are several types of dermatitis, symptoms can include skin which is red, itchy, flaking, scaling, weeping, swollen and possibly blistered depending on the severity.

Irritant contact dermatitis occurs quickly after contact with a strong irritant or over a longer period after prolonged and repeated exposure to a weak irritant. Common causes of this type of dermatitis are; soaps, shampoos and detergents, dust, oil and grease, repeated and prolonged contact with water.

Allergic contact dermatitis is caused when the sufferer develops an allergy to a substance. Common causes are hair dyes, adhesives and food such as shellfish.

Eczema

There are two main types of eczema, atopic and contact. Atopic eczema tends to develop in childhood and many children grow out of it. Contact eczema usually affects adults and is caused by contact with an allergen such as nickel, detergent, soap or perfume.

When suffering from eczema the skin becomes itchy, dry and flaky, and is often red and painful. Sometimes it weeps or bleeds. Areas commonly affected are the face, neck and skin particularly in the inner creases of the elbows and behind the knees.

Psoriasis

Psoriasis is a chronic autoimmune disease affecting the skin and joints. Psoriasis causes scaly patches of skin called psoriatic plaques which are areas of inflammation and excessive skin production which rapidly becomes silvery white in appearance due to the build up of skin.

ANATOMY AND PHYSIOLOGY

It is important to have some basic understanding of anatomy and physiology as a therapist carrying out treatment.

BONES OF THE HEAD & NECK

The face is made up of 14 facial bones, these are indicated in the diagram below.

Facial Bones

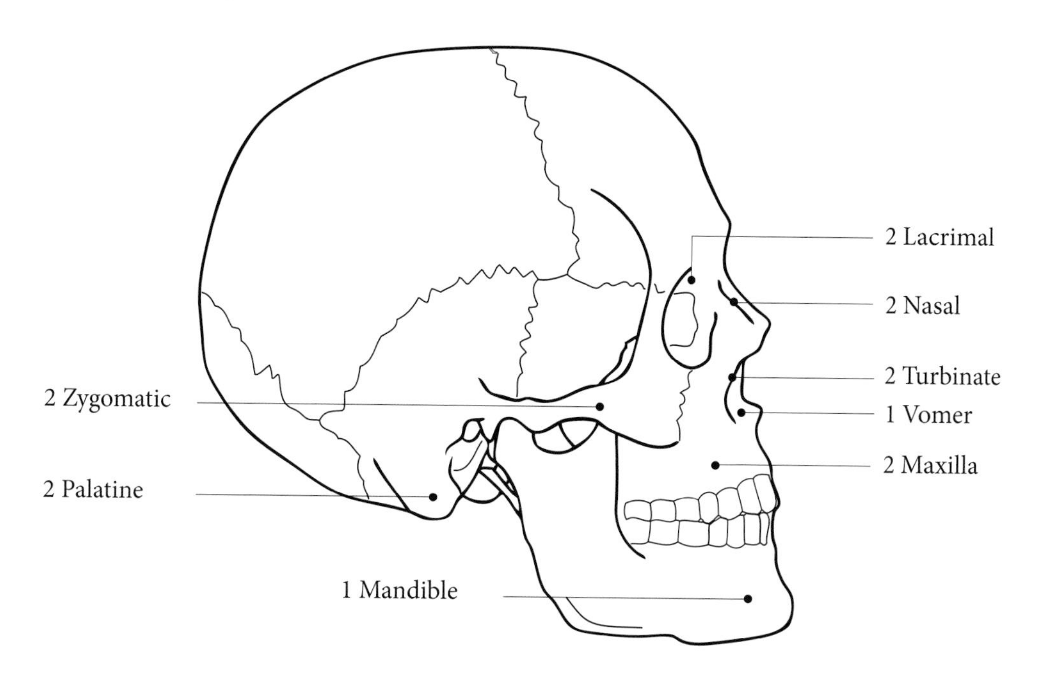

Bone	Description
Palatine	x 2 Forms the floor and wall of the nose and the mouth roof
Nasal	x 2 Form the bridge of the nose
Turbinate	x 2 These two bones form the outer walls of the nose
Vomer	This is the dividing wall of the nose
Lacrimal	x 2 The inner walls of the eye sockets
Maxilla	x 2 Fused to form the upper jaw
Mandible	The lower jaw
Zygomatic	x 2 Cheekbones

The rest of the skull is made up of the cranial bones, there are eight in total shown in the diagram below.

Cranial Bones

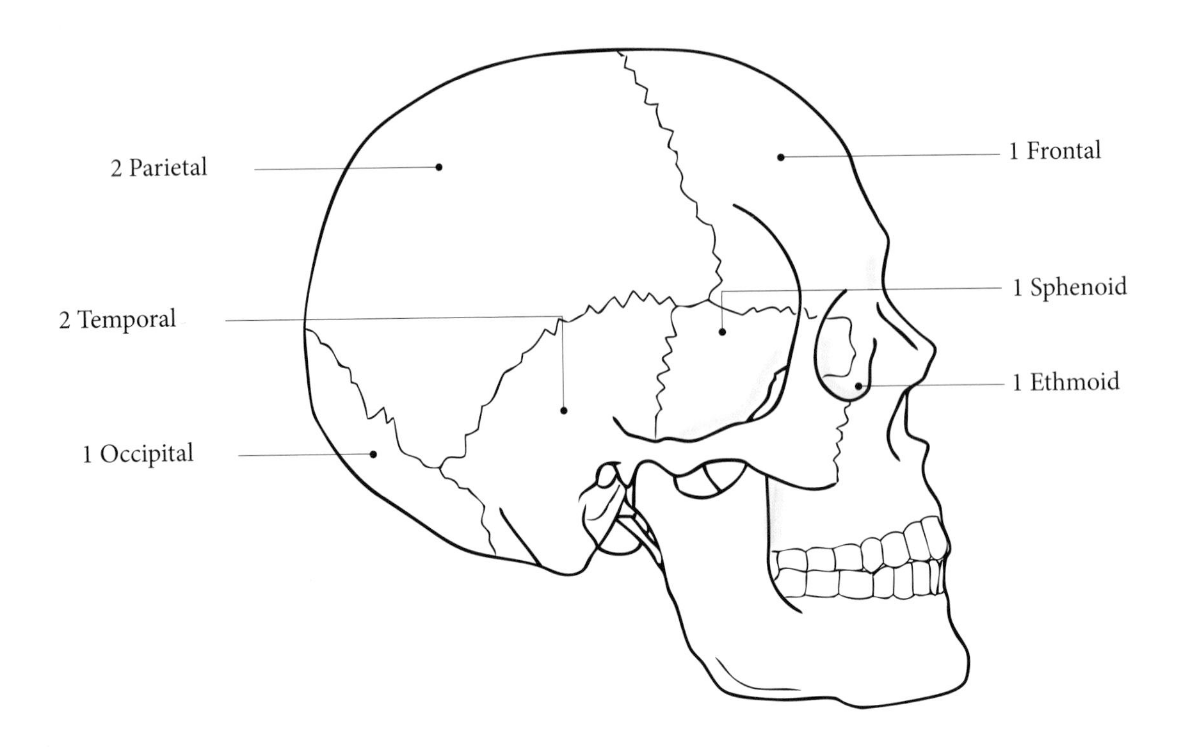

Bone	Description
Occipital	Located at the back of the skull, contains the hole for the spinal chord, nerves and blood vessels to pass through
Parietal	x 2 fused together to form the crown
Frontal	Forehead and upper eye sockets
Temporal	x 2 The sides of the head
Ethmoid	Forms part of the nasal cavities
Sphenoid	Bat-shaped bone joining all the cranial bones together

Neck, Chest and Shoulder Bones

Front

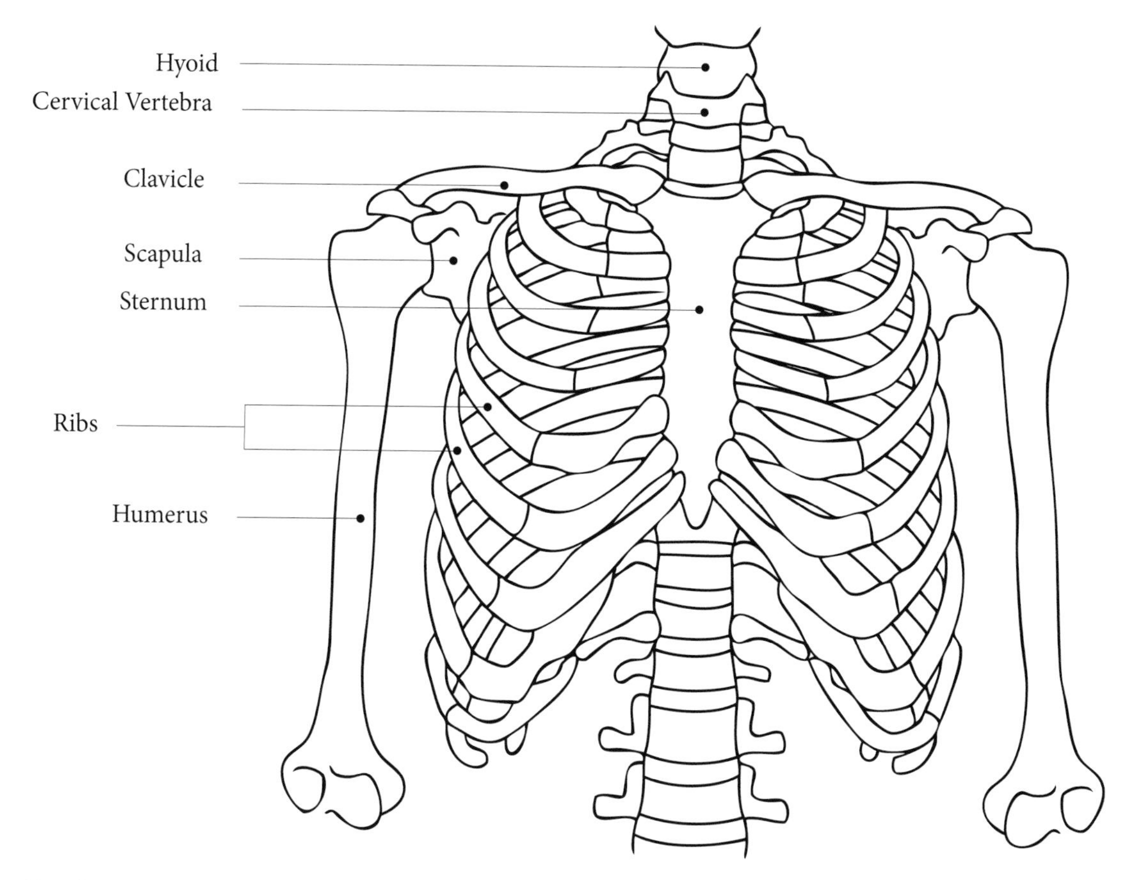

Back

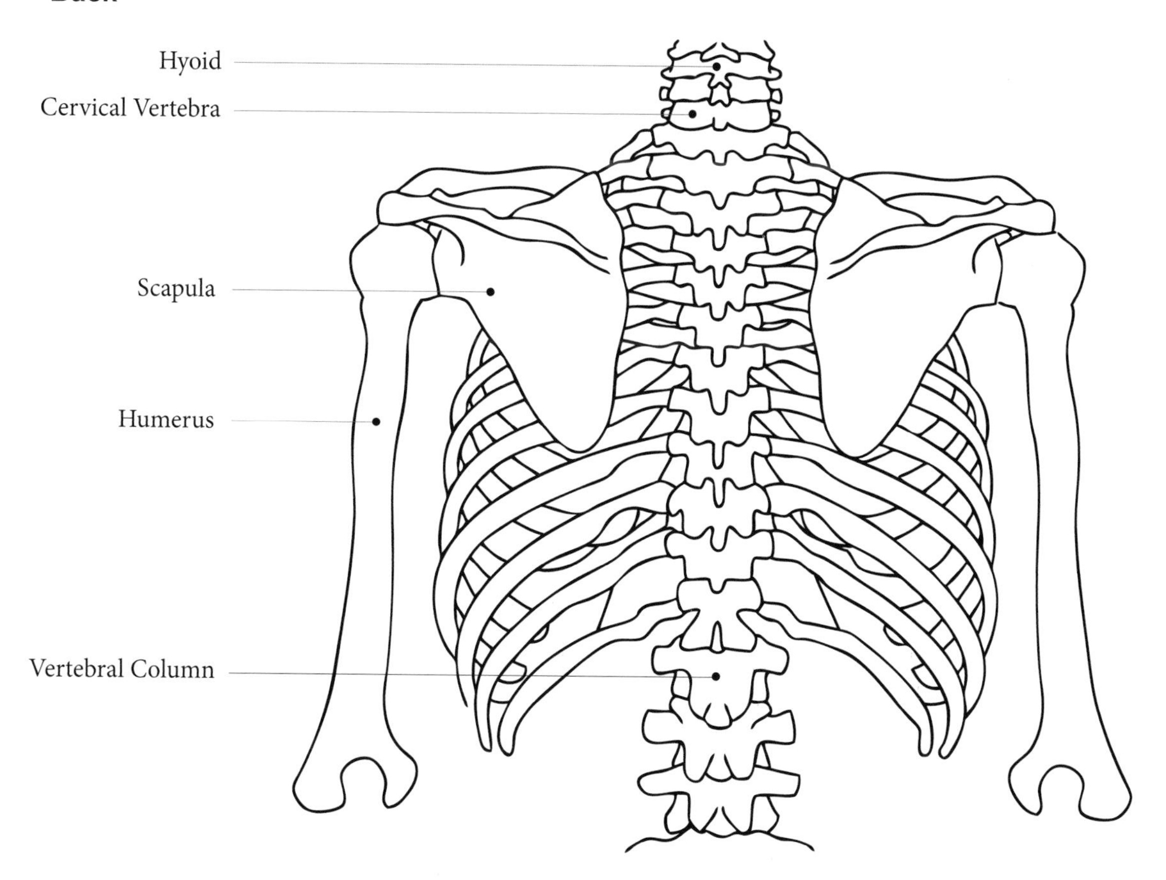

English

MUSCLES OF THE FACE AND NECK

The muscles in the face and neck are responsible for our facial expressions. As we age the expressions that we use on a daily basis produce lines on the skin and we begin to show the outward signs of ageing. Microdermabrasion removes the dead skin cells from the epidermis improving the appearance of these fine lines and wrinkles.

Facial Muscles

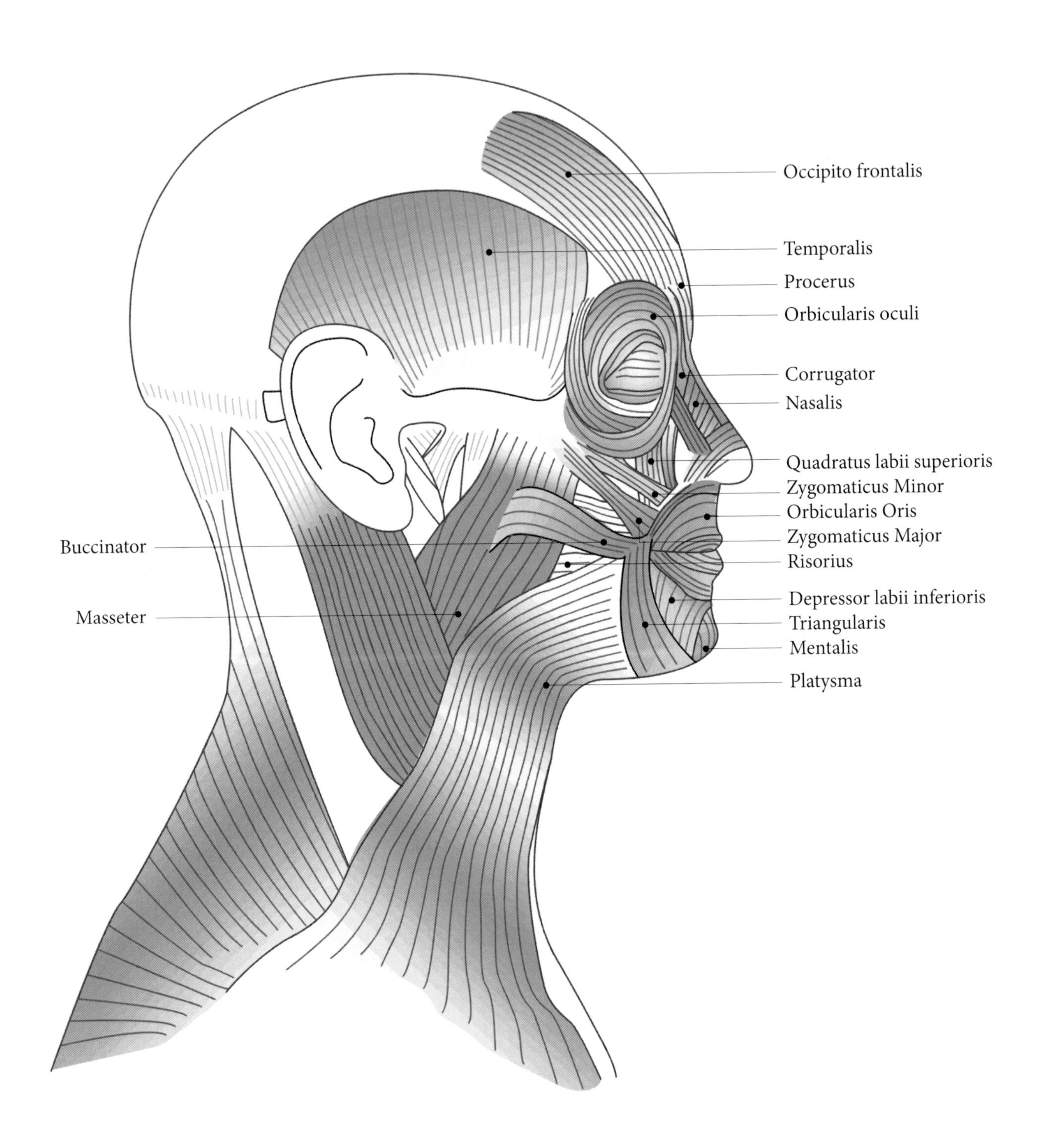

Muscles of the Neck

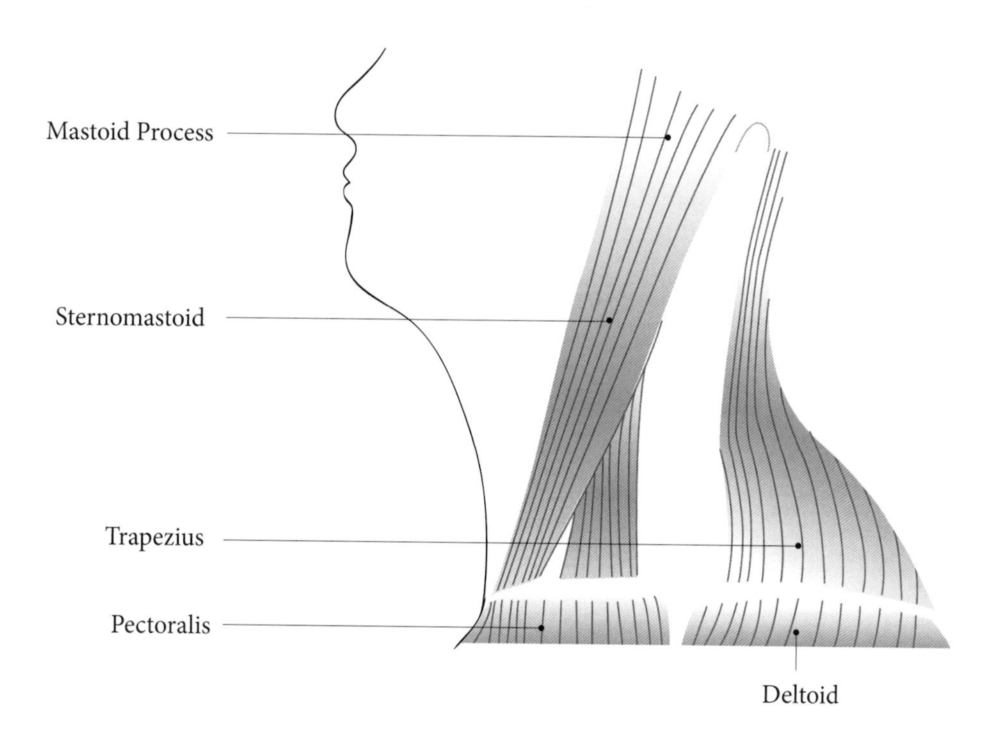

CRANIAL NERVES

The nervous system is the body's method of sending 'information' messages from the brain to other parts of the body. The nerves of the face and neck or 'cranial' nerves control the muscles in the head and neck or carry nerve impulses (sensory information) from sense organs to the brain. The 5th, 7th and 11th cranial nerves are those that we are concerned with as therapists when performing facial treatments.

5th Cranial Nerve - 'Trigeminal'

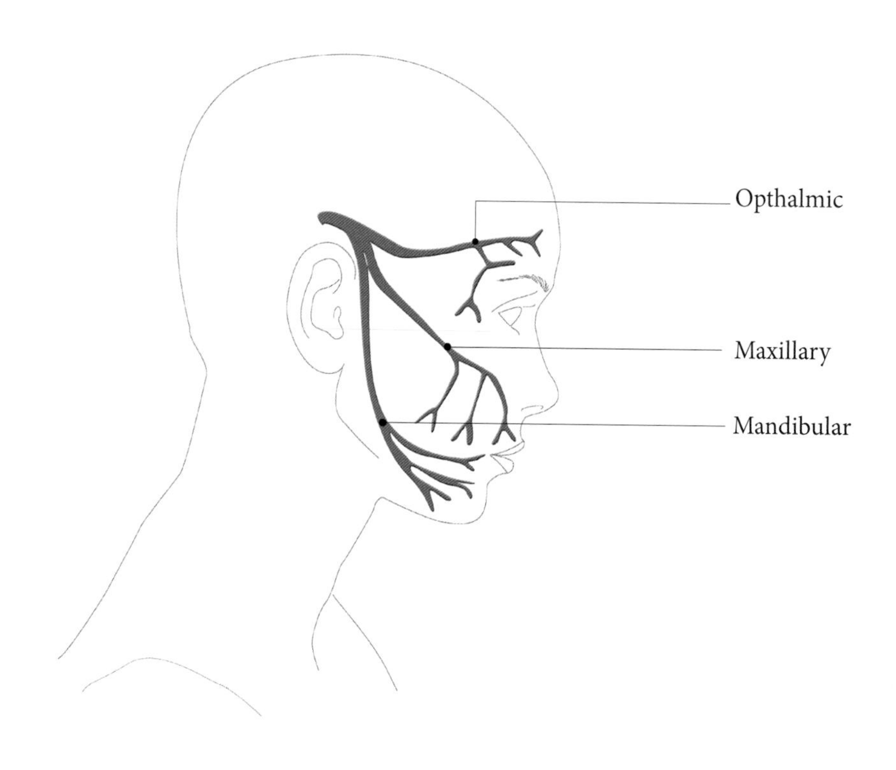

7th Cranial Nerve - 'Facial' **11th Cranial Nerve - 'Accessory'**

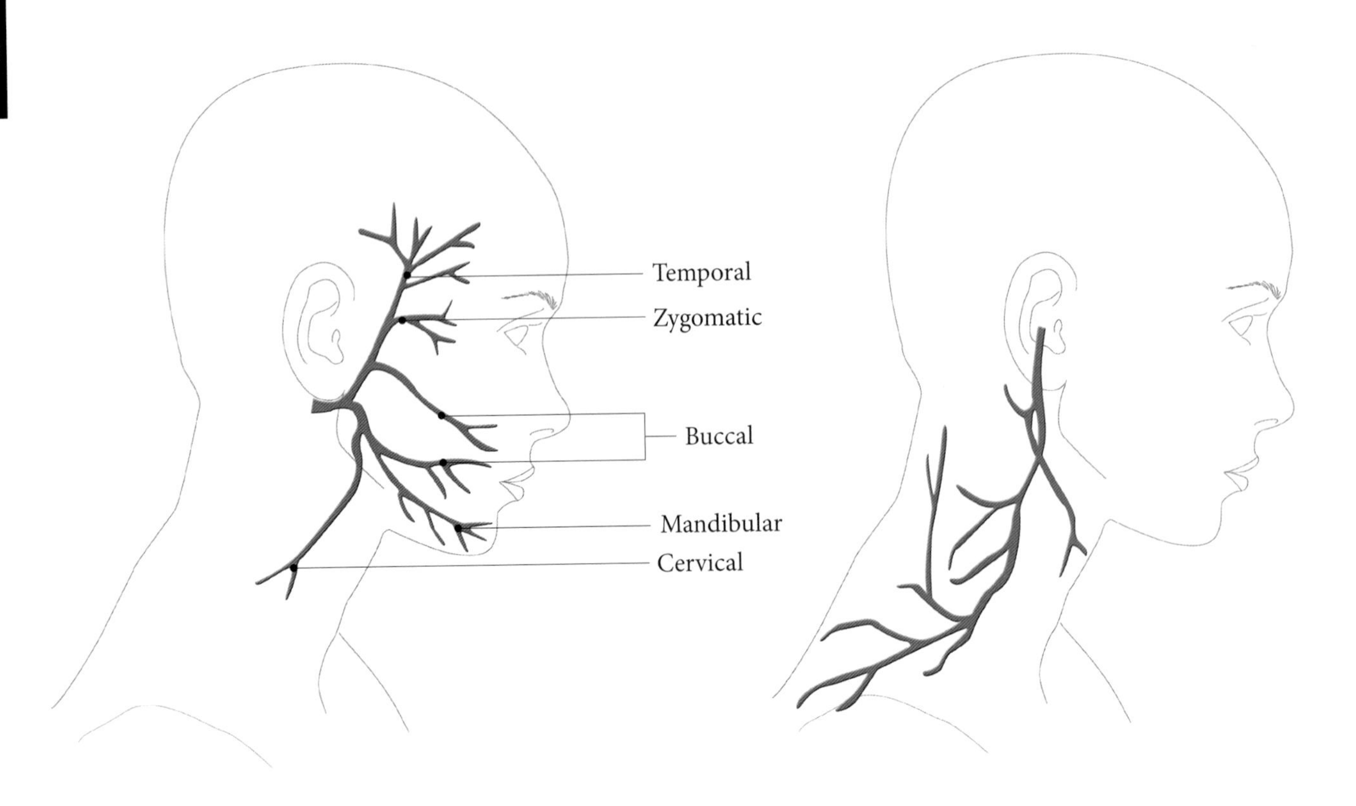

Nerve	Function	Nerve Branches	Sends Messages to:
5th 'Trigeminal'	Controls muscles for chewing	Opthalmic	Tear glands Skin of forehead Upper cheeks
	Passes on sensory info from the face	Maxillary	Upper jaw muscle Mouth
		Mandibular	Lower jaw muscle Teeth Muscles for chewing
7th 'Facial'	Controls muscles used for facial expressions	Temporal	Muscle surrounding the eye Muscles on the forehead
		Zygomatic	Eye muscles
		Buccal	Upper lip Sides of the nose
		Mandibular	Lower lip Chin
		Cervical	Sides of neck and chin
11th 'Accessory'	Moves the neck and shoulders		

SECTION 2 - LEARNING OUTCOMES:

- A basic knowledge and understanding of the structure and function of the skin
- You will be able to identify the different skin types
- Good understanding of microdermabrasion theory
- You will be able to identify the problem areas that can be treated with microdermabrasion treatment
- Understand how a course of microdermbrasion treatment works

THE SKIN

The skin is the largest organ of the body. The skin functions in a number of ways to protect us from external elements.

- Prevents the absorption of harmful substances
- Helps regulate body temperature
- Acts as a barrier to keep out infection
- Melanin in the skin protects us from the harmful effects of UV light
- Provides a waterproof coating that prevents us from becoming dehydrated
- Provides an energy reserve in the form of stored fat

The Structure of the Skin

The skin is made up of two distinct layers; the epidermis and the dermis. Between them is the basement membrane which keeps the two layers together. Beneath these layers is the subcutaneous layer, a layer of fat that protects, cushions, insulates and stores extra energy for the body.

The Epidermis

The epidermis is the outermost layer of the skin. It is composed of five layers. Each layer of the epidermis can be recognised by its shape and by the function of its cells. The main type of cell found in the epidermis is the keratinocyte, which produces the protein keratin.

Cell renewal happens over a period of approximately four weeks. Cells move from the bottom layer of the epidermis (basal layer) to the top layer (horny layer) changing in shape and structure as they progress. The top layer of the epidermis is the layer that dies and which is shed from the skin 'desquamation'. This is the layer that is removed in microdermabrasion treatment and also the layer that helps to reflect UV light away from the skin, which is why it is important that clients use sun protection after microdermabrasion treatment.

The Epidermis

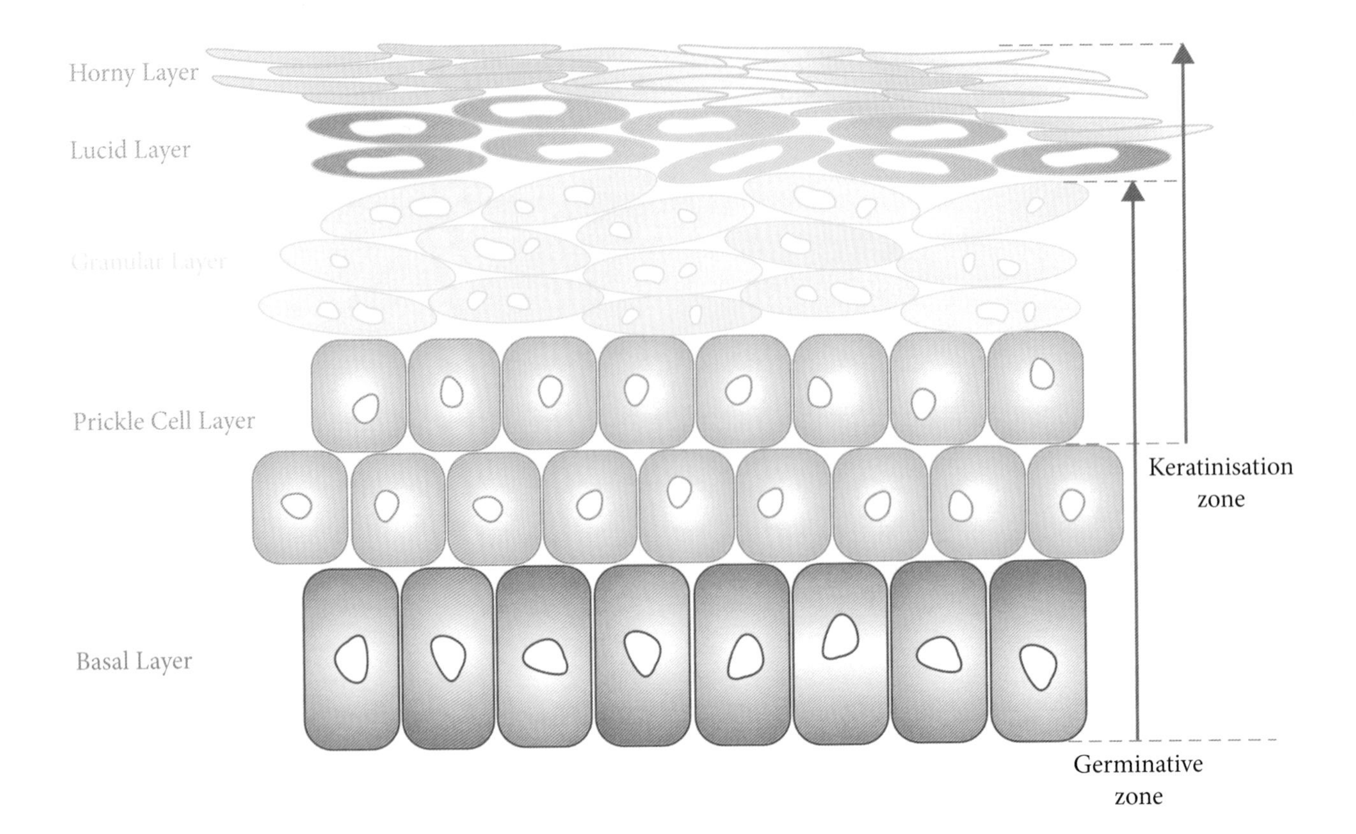

1. Stratum Corneum or 'Horny Layer'

This is the outermost layer of the epidermis, made up of several layers of flattened, mostly dead, overlapping cells. These cells help to reflect UV light. Black skin, which evolved to withstand strong UV light, has a thicker stratum corneum than caucasian skin. It takes about three weeks for the epidermal cells to reach the stratum corneum from the stratum germinativum. The cells are then shed; a process called desquamation.

2. Stratum Lucidum or 'Lucid Layer'

This layer is only found in thicker areas of the skin such as the palms of the hands or soles of the feet.

3. Stratum Granulosum or 'Granular Layer'

In this layer cells begin to die. These cells have what look like granules within them caused by the nuclei breaking up. These granules are known as keratohyaline granules and later form keratin.

4. Stratum Spinosum or 'Prickle Cell Layer'

The stratum spinosum is made up of cells which have a spiky surface (hence the name) to connect with surrounding cells. This is the layer that begins to synthesise keratin.

5. Stratum Germinativum or 'Basal Layer'

Column shaped cells responsible for producing new epidermal cells. Cells divide and move up to higher layers. The remaining cells divide to fill the gaps. This process of cell division is known as Mitosis. The germinative zone of the epidermis also contains two other important cells, Langerhan and Melanocyte cells.

Langerhan cells absorb & remove foreign bodies that enter the skin. They move out of the epidermis and into the dermis below then finally enter the lymph system; the body's 'waste disposal system'. Melanocyte cells are responsible for the production of melanin in the skin. These protect the other epidermal cells from the harmful effects of UV. Melanin helps determine our skin colour, the more melanin present the darker our skin tone.

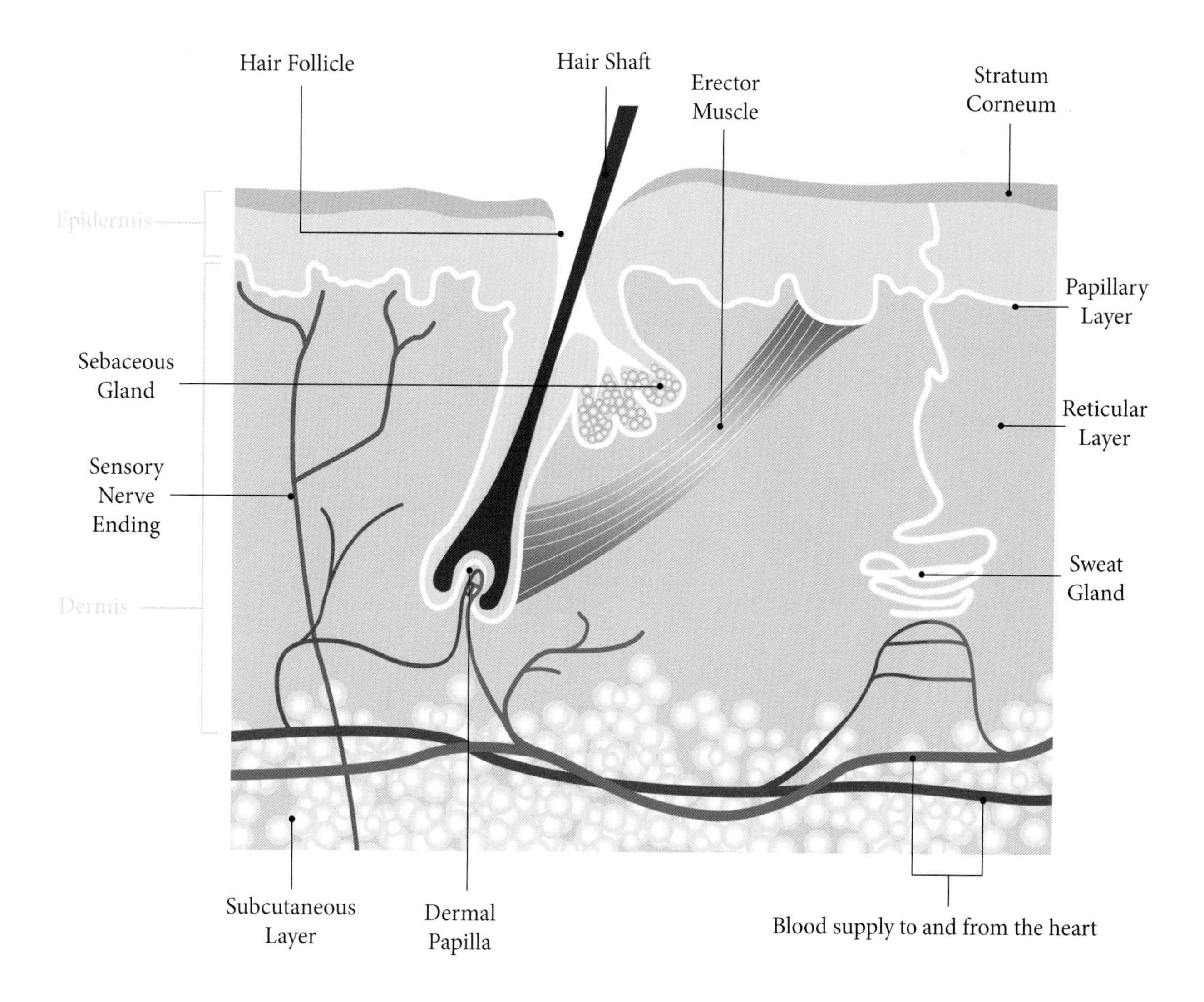

The Dermis

The dermis is the layer found beneath the epidermis and is responsible for the strength and elasticity of the skin. It also contains lots of specialised cells and structures including nerves, blood vessels, glands & hair follicles. The dermis consists of two layers, the papillary and reticular layers. The upper, papillary layer contains a thin arrangement of collagen fibres. The reticular layer beneath is made of dense collagen fibres arranged parallel with the skin's surface.

The Reticular Layer

The reticular layer consists of two sorts of protein: elastin fibres which give the skin its elasticity and collagen fibres which give the skin its strength. These fibres are held in a gel-like substance called 'ground substance'. The elastin and collagen fibres form a strong network which gives us our youthful appearance.

As we age these fibres in the skin begin to harden and fragment; the network starts to break down and our skin starts to lose its elasticity and show visible signs of ageing. Blood circulation to the skin declines; nutrients do not reach the surface, resulting in sallow skin. The fatty layer beneath the skin grows thinner so we look more drawn as our bone structure is more prominent. The reticular layer is vital to our skin's health and appearance and so it is essential that it is looked after in order to prevent the signs of ageing.

Blood Flow

The blood circulates through the body to all the cells carrying vital nutrients and energy such as oxygen, glucose and other raw materials essential for the body's health, maintenance and growth. The vacuum action of microdermabrasion treatment assists in the stimulation of the micro-circulation near the skin's surface. This promotes increased blood flow to the area which promotes collagen and elastin production in the skin as well as cell renewal (skin regeneration), aiding tissue repair and revealing smoother and fresher skin.

This diagram shows how the blood flows through the cells; first delivering nutrients and energy and then removing waste products such as carbon dioxide.

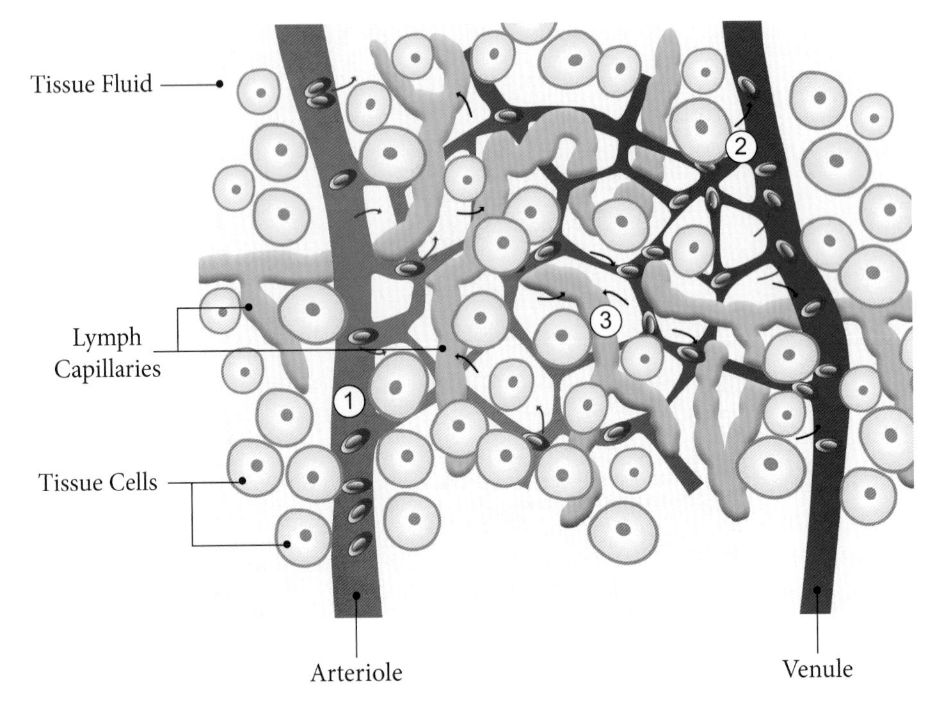

① Blood is under high pressure as it flows through the capillary network forcing fluid out into the tissue and becoming tissue fluid. This fluid contains useful substances like oxygen and nutrients essential for the cells. Blood cells and large proteins remain in the capillary.

② As the blood becomes deoxygenated pressure is reversed and some of the fluid containing waste products will re-enter the capillaries and be carried away.

③ Excess fluids, waste products and large molecules like proteins that were unable to re-enter the blood are taken up by lymph capillaries and carried to lymph nodes where the fluid is processed and enters back into the blood nearer to the heart.

Blood Flow through the Skin

Normal body temperature is 37°c. The body will work to maintain this temperature. If body temperature starts to rise, blood will pass close to the skin to release some of its heat. When body temperature falls, capillaries are constricted and blood will pass through 'shunt vessels' deeper in the dermis instead, reducing the amount of heat lost through the skin.

Vaso-dilation happens when you are:
Hot – blood passes close to the surface – heat is released

Vaso-constriction happens when you are:
Cold – blood flows through shunt vessels away from the surface – heat is retained

Skin Types

There are six basic skin types. However, a person's facial skin can vary at different times during their life due to illness or hormonal imbalance.

Dry skin types

Dry skin is caused by under or inactive oil glands that do not produce enough sebum to keep the skin naturally hydrated. It usually has a dull appearance, feels dry and itchy and is sometimes sensitive. Dry skin must be hydrated regularly from the inside (drinking water) and outside with rich hydrating creams or lotions.

Oily skin types

Oily skin is caused by glands that produce too much sebum, resulting in skin that appears shiny and has large open pores. Oily skin types are prone to develop comedones (blackheads) and acne. Despite these drawbacks oily skin generally remains younger looking and remains suppler over time than other skin types. Oily skin benefits hugely from microdermabrasion with the application of light moisturisers.

Sensitive skin types

Sensitive skins can be dry, normal or oily and are characterised by their delicacy. Sensitive skin frequently reacts adversely to environmental conditions and often requires special treatment in order to remain in good condition. Sensitive skin benefits greatly from natural skin care products and treatments.

Normal skin types

Normal skin produces sebum at a moderate rate, resulting in a balanced state. Normal skin looks consistently plump, moist and vibrant. A great blessing but still requires no less attention. It benefits from regular cleansing, toning and moisturising.

Combination skin types

Combination skin is the most common skin type. Combination skin is frequently characterised by an oily T zone area that covers the forehead, nose and chin. While the skin around the cheeks, eyes and mouth is normal to dry. People with combination skin should assess their skin regularly and use different products on different areas of the face.

Mature skin types

Mature skin has the following characteristics: skin becomes dry as sebaceous glands become less active. Skin loses elasticity; fine lines and wrinkles appear. Skin appears thinner with broken capillaries, especially on the cheek area and around the nose. Facial contours become slack as muscle tone is reduced. Underlying bone structure becomes more obvious, as the fatty layer beneath the skin grows thinner. Blood circulation becomes poor, which interferes with skin nutrition making skin appear sallow. Due to the decrease in metabolic rate, waste products are not removed as quickly leading to puffiness of the skin. Mature skin must be hydrated well by drinking water regularly and using nourishing moisturisers.

Skin Colour Types

The tone of human skin can vary from dark brown to nearly a colourless pigmentation, which may appear reddish due to blood in the skin. Europeans generally have lighter skin, hair and eyes than any other group, although this is not always the case. For practical purposes, six types are distinguished following the Fitzpatrick scale (1975). Skin colours are listed in decreasing lightness.

English

The Fitzpatrick Scale

TYPE	ALSO CALLED	TANNING BEHAVIOUR	HAIR AND EYE COLOUR
I	Very light, also 'Nordic'	Often burns, rarely tans	Tend to have freckles, red or blonde hair, blue or green eyes
II	Light or light skinned	Usually burns	Tend to have light hair, blue or green eyes
III	Light intermediate, or dark skinned European or 'average caucasian'	Sometimes burns Usually tans	Tends to have brown hair Dark eyes
IV	Dark intermediate, also 'Mediterranean' or 'Olive'	Sometimes burns Often tans	Tends to have dark brown hair and eyes
V	Dark or 'Brown' Type	Naturally black-brown skin	Often has dark brown hair and eyes
VI	Very dark or 'Black' Type	Naturally black-brown skin	Usually has black-brown hair and eyes

MICRODERMABRASION – WHAT IS IT?

Microdermabrasion is a safe, controlled system of intense exfoliation and resurfacing using ultra fine crystals that rejuvenate the skin. The crystals work as a gentle abrasive on the skin to remove dead skin cells layer by layer. The irregular shape of the crystals helps to work on hard to reach areas without any damage to the skin. The treatment is progressive meaning clients will continue to see results over the course of treatment.

The degree of epidermal abrasion can be varied by altering the crystal's speed when impacting on the skin. The removal of the stratum corneum results in skin that feels instantly smoother and fresher, whilst promoting new skin and collagen growth. Over a course of treatment skin will be left 'glowing' and will feel rejuvenated.

The vacuum action draws away used crystals and dead skin cells and also works to stimulate the circulation and promotes increased blood flow to the area. The production of collagen and elastin is stimulated, which results in a firmer, more youthful looking skin.

Microdermabrasion can be used for all skin types on all areas of the body and face. SkinBase recommend a course of 8, usually performed every 7 to 10 days. People with acne or acne scarring might need more treatments and we recommend a monthly maintenance treatment after the course has finished to help maintain the results achieved. After the treatment, the skin may feel tight with mild redness. Therefore it is important that clients use a good moisturiser. These effects normally subside within 24 hours of treatment.

What are the benefits of using microdermabrasion over other methods of treatment?

There is minimal discomfort experienced during a microdermabrasion treatment and the patient is able to carry on with their normal day afterwards. Crystal microdermabrasion uses a completely inert and sterile compound with zero risk of allergic reaction.

- Eliminates possible adverse reactions often associated with chemical solutions
- Client can return to their normal lifestyle immediately after treatment i.e., no extreme reddening of the skin
- Can safely treat all skin colours and skin types
- Immediate visible results even after the first treatment, helps keep client motivated
- Helps treat early signs of ageing and offers an overall rejuvenation for aged skin
- Vacuum action offers improved elasticity and muscle tone of the skin and also stimulates fibroblasts for collagen production
- Enhances penetration of approved products after treatment
- Perfect for congested skin with open pores and comedones and acne prone skin
- Variable control allowing for deeper exfoliation of thickened blemished skin and acne scarring
- Successfully helps remove unwanted pigmentation marks
- Perfect for sun-damaged skin
- Total body exfoliation offers a cellulite treatment as the vacuum action helps with lymphatic drainage

Are there any risks associated with microdermabrasion?

Improper use or unhygienic conditions pose a risk when having microdermabrasion treatment, that is why we advocate the importance of good hygiene in the workplace. The MDPro uses disposable nozzles; eliminating any risk of cross-contamination between clients as the nozzle is the only component that will come into contact with the skin during treatment.

THE CRYSTALS

Crystals are made of Aluminium Oxide; a naturally occurring mineral. Sterile and non-toxic with no adverse skin contact reactions, we would however recommend a skin allergy test prior to treatment as a precautionary measure.

Aluminium Oxide is considered a low health risk by inhalation and industry standards treat any inhalation of this nature as a nuisance dust. The inhalation of any fine particle dust, for example artificial nail dust, may cause irritation and coughing if exposed to them over long periods. Aluminium Oxide contains no free silica which means it poses no respiratory risk from inhalation.

Crystal sensitivity – Patch test

It is important to perform a skin patch test to check the client is not sensitive to the crystals employed. It is most unusual for a client to be sensitive to the crystals employed however a skin test should be performed prior to treatment on the back of the forearm. If the area becomes irritable or swollen do not proceed with treatment. If the client develops red marks on the skin after treatment it is normally due to the therapist applying too much pressure.

WHAT SKIN CONDITIONS CAN MICRODERMABRASION BE USED TO TREAT?

Anyone can benefit from microdermabrasion treatment. It improves the overall appearance of the skin giving skin a healthy glow and youthful appearance. Microdermabrasion is also extremely effective at treating a number of skin problems. It can be used on the face and body making it a good treatment for acne scarring on the back for example.

Acne & Acne Scarring

Microdermabrasion works by removing the top layers of dead skin cells from the skin's surface making it particularly effective in treating acne. Getting rid of the dead skin cells from the surface of the skin unclogs the pores reducing the chance of new spots developing.

Fine Lines and Wrinkles
Ageing Skin

The vacuum action of the microdermabrasion treatment works to stimulate the production of collagen in the skin. As we age elastin and collagen production starts to slow down. The combination of collagen stimulation and increased skin renewal will improve the condition of the skin's surface smoothing out fine lines and wrinkles.

Dry and Dehydrated Skin
Uneven Skin Tone

Normally skin renews itself approximately every 28 days. Removing the dead cells from the top layers of skin, microdermabrasion speeds up the rate at which the skin would normally renew itself revealing new, fresh skin and giving a radiant glow.

Cellulite, 'orange peel' Effect

Microdermabrasion can't cure cellulite however it will stimulate the circulation improving blood flow to the area. To improve the appearance of cellulite clients should drink plenty of water and exercise regularly.

Stretch Marks
Pigmentation and Blemishes

Microdermabrasion can vastly improve the appearance of pigmentation and stretch marks. The microdermabrasion treatment stimulates the area being targeted to produce more collagen and speed up the skin renewal process, improving skin condition and diminishing the appearance of stretch marks and discolouration of the skin.

Microdermabrasion treatment will not remove the stretch mark. However, regular treatment will show an improvement to the treated area making the marks less obvious. Scar tissue should not be treated until all the inflammation has disappeared from the area (6 months post surgery for example).

Regular treatment with microdermabrasion will help improve the appearance of stretch marks by creating a blending effect to the surrounding scar tissue, also reducing any pigmentation problems that often make the stretch mark more noticeable.

Hyper-Pigmentation (Melasma) and the Cause

Most obvious causes are the oral use of birth control pills or hormone replacement therapy, pregnancy or interaction with certain medications. Repeated sun exposure or over exposure also plays a part as does inflammation or trauma caused to the skin. Certain chemicals found in perfumes etc., can also result in pigmentation marks occurring. Regular microdermabrasion treatment will show significant benefits to sun-damaged skin and help remove unwanted pigmentation marks.

A course of SkinBase microdermabrasion treatments can achieve beneficial results in the treatment of pigmentation marks. Clients should be advised that a course of between 10-15 treatments might be needed. It is also imperative that the client is advised to wear a sun block cream at all times.

Please note microdermabrasion treatment cannot help clients with the vitiligo skin disorder.

Melasma and chloasma (darkening of the skin due to hormone changes) can be helped by microderm-abrasion treatment. It will help the trapped pigment move up through the epidermal layers to be shed in its normal organised way. However, many treatments may be needed to improve the affected area.

HOW THE TREATMENT COURSE WORKS

Microdermabrasion is a progressive rather than aggressive treatment. The epidermal layers are removed gently and safely over a course of treatments. In a course, the treatment is performed every 7 to 10 days. This means that the stratum corneum layer that was removed in the previous treatment has not had the chance to rebuild and also the client's tolerance to the treatment increases. Therefore, with each subsequent treatment, the intensity of the treatment can be increased in order to reach deeper down the layers of the epidermis to successfully remove acne scarring, lift pigmentation and smooth fine lines.

Generally a client will opt for a course of six treatments to be performed every 7-10 days to get maximum effect. After completing a course the client can then go on to have a monthly maintenance treatment to help them maintain the results achieved.

Clients with more problematic skin may need a longer course of treatment, however 15-20 treatments is considered to be a maximum, after which they must go on to a monthly maintenance program of one treatment every 4-6 weeks.

SECTION 3 - LEARNING OUTCOMES:

- You will have the ability to carry out a full client consultation prior to treatment
- You will know what the contraindications to microdermabrasion treatment are
- You will understand the aftercare required and the possible reactions to the treatment

CLIENT CONSULTATION

1. Check client's suitability for treatment using the list of contraindications.
2. Check for known allergies, e.g., metal allergies.
3. Carry out a skin analysis pinpointing any areas to avoid during treatment i.e., minor contraindications such as telangiectasia (broken capillaries).
4. Pinpoint areas that require special attention such as acne scarring or pigmentation, open pores or uneven skin tone.
5. Suggest a treatment plan making sure you explain the cost, duration and frequency required for the course.
6. Explain to the client what the treatment will do and how it will feel.
7. Explain to the client how the skin might react. Although reactions if any are very minor, make sure clients are aware there may be some sensitivity.
8. Talk the client through the aftercare advice so they are aware of what they should be doing post-procedure to look after their skin.
9. It is vital the client understands the importance of using the correct home regime in between treatments and is committed to achieving results i.e., using the correct sun protection factor, this is crucial to avoid further pigmentation problems.
10. **ALWAYS COMPLETE A CLIENT RECORD CARD:**

    This will ensure special attention is drawn to their specific needs. Explain contraindications of treatment and ask the client to sign the record card.

Parents/Guardians (over 18) <u>must</u> sign the consultation card for children under 16 years of age

CONTRAINDICATIONS TO MICRODERMABRASION TREATMENT

MAJOR CONTRAINDICATIONS - Do not proceed

Pregnancy

An increase in hormones can affect the skin during pregnancy, this can cause pigmentation. For this reason we advise against microdermabrasion as the skin could react in an unexpected manner making the condition worse. Advise clients to use a good sunscreen when outside to help prevent the pigmentation occurring. Wait 6-8 weeks after birth before performing microdermabrasion.

Cancer

We advise that you do not treat a client with Cancer, they should be in remission for at least 6 months prior to commencing a course of treatment. Microdermabrasion stimulates the blood flow and lymphatic drainage.

Grade 4 Acne

Clients with this level of acne should not be treated with microdermabrasion. If the skin is very congested with pustules and papules treatment would irritate the skin and spread bacteria.

"Roaccutane"

Roaccutane causes thinning of the skin, if your client is receiving Roaccutane treatment for acne, you must wait 6 months after discontinuing Roaccutane before performing microdermabrasion treatment.

Auto-immune disease

Used to describe a number of disorders where the body attacks its own cells and tissues, you should avoid treating a client suffering from an auto-immune disease.

Diabetes

Diabetes affects the nerves and circulation and the skin can take much longer to heal than normal. Clients must provide written permission from their GP before treatment can be carried out.

Impetigo

A contagious bacterial skin infection, do not perform microdermabrasion.

Rosacea

Rosacea cannot be treated with microdermabrasion.

MINOR CONTRAINDICATIONS - Proceed with caution and avoid affected areas

Skin Disorders e.g. Active Acne, Seborrheic Dermatitis, Herpes Simplex (cold sores), Eczema, Psoriasis
Keloid Scars
Telangiectasia (broken capillaries)
Raised Moles, Warts, Skin Tags
Cuts, Bruises, Abrasions

If you are uncertain or unable to identify a skin condition you should not treat the client and advise them to consult their GP.

PRE-TREATMENT ADVICE

We recommend that clients adhere to the following advice prior to commencing treatment:

Botox/Dermal fillers

Allow 14 days **before** performing microdermabrasion, including any touch up injections, to allow botox/fillers to settle.

Men

Men should close shave the night before a treatment if the treatment is in the morning, or in the morning if the treatment is in the afternoon.

Laser Treatments

A course of laser treatments cannot run concurrently with a course of SkinBase microdermabrasion treatments. Please allow at least 2 weeks before commencing microdermabrasion after completing a course of Laser.

Dermal Rollers

Do not use for 2 weeks prior to microdermabrasion treatment.

AFTERCARE ADVICE

We recommend that clients adhere to the following advice after treatment:

For 12 Hours after treatment:

No heavy Make-Up.

For 24 Hours after treatment:

No swimming, no facial waxing.

For 48 Hours after treatment:

No sauna, sun beds or sun exposure. No 'Botox', collagen injections or dermal fillers.

For 72 Hours after treatment:

Do not use anti-ageing creams, AHA's, Glycolics or Retinol.
Do not use exfoliating products, the newly abraded skin is receptive to any products applied, so the use of any exfoliants after treatment can irritate the skin.

At all times during a course of treatment:

SPF 15 minimum must be applied and exposure to U.V should be avoided.
Regular moisturiser applications are vital to replenish moisture and prevent the skin from becoming dry and peeling.

Products must be between pH 4.5 and 7

Skin care products that contain a high percentage of botanicals and essential oils are UNSUITABLE for use after microdermabrasion treatment as some of the ingredients contained may cause an allergic reaction. Should this occur, there is a real danger of both the therapist and client thinking that it is the treatment they are allergic to, where it is actually the ingredients within the skin care preparations. It is important that products are used that replace or add moisture back to the skin to stop the skin becoming dry or peeling.

SECTION 4 - LEARNING OUTCOMES:

- Students will be able to identify the parts of the microdermabrasion machine and its functions
- They should be able to set up the equipment and check that it is in good working order
- Students will be able to select the appropriate treatment according to client's skin type

SETTING UP THE SKINBASE MDPRO SYSTEM

1. Always check that your filter jar is empty of any used crystals before starting a treatment.
2. Make sure the handset is connected to the disposal jar with the silver tube and firmly connected at both ends.
3. Attach a clean nozzle and a new bottle of crystal to the handset and screw in firmly.
4. Connect the electrical lead, switch on at the power point and the starting switch on the panel. If you have a PAYG machine follow the instructions inside the machine.

ADJUSTING TREATMENT LEVEL

Make sure a bottle of crystal is connected to the handset and with your fore-finger over the hole in the nozzle, turn the regulator valve until you have your desired pressure for the facial. Please make sure you understand correct pressure levels before commencing any Microdermabrasion treatment.

PLEASE NOTE: UNDER NO CIRCUMSTANCES SHOULD THE METAL CASING BE UN-SCREWED AND LIFTED WITHOUT FULLY DISCONNECTING FROM THE MAINS SUPPLY.

TREATMENT LEVELS

The following descriptions provide a guideline to selecting an appropriate treatment level for your client.

LEVEL ONE - 0.3 bar

This level should be used by newly trained therapists until they are confident about how light their strokes should be. Level one allows gentle all-over exfoliation and should always be selected for the client's first treatment. Always use level one when performing microdermabrasion around the eye (feathering action).

LEVEL ONE
-0.3bar

- Newly trained therapists
- First treatment
- Eye area

LEVEL TWO - 0.4 bar

This level should be gradually selected when working on acne scars or more thickened skin. No higher than this level for black and asian skin types - see Fitzpatrick Scale.

LEVEL TWO
-0.4bar

- Targeting
- NO higher than level 2 for Black/Asian skin

LEVEL THREE - 0.5 bar

This level is only to be used on clients toward the end of their treatment course when the skin is more tolerant. Used for working on acne scars, pigmentation, fine lines and wrinkles. Also for body exfoliation, stretch marks and cellulite.

LEVEL THREE
-0.5bar

- End of a treatment course when skin is more tolerant
- Body exfoliation
- Problematic skin
- Targeting only
- Never for Black/Asian skin

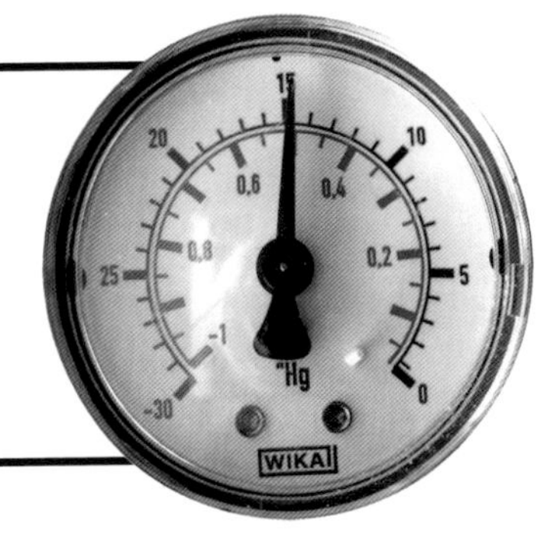

LEVEL FOUR - 0.6 bar

Use for body treatments only. **Never to be used on the face.**

SECTION 5 - LEARNING OUTCOMES:

- Demonstrate the ability to operate the machine and apply the treatment safely and effectively for the advised treatment time
- Demonstrate the ability to work within time limits acceptable to industry

METHOD OF TREATMENT

1. Position client semi-reclining
2. Ensure client's hair is away from the face
3. CLEANSE client's skin thoroughly
   – must use a gel/foaming cleanser
4. Skin must then be completely dry
5. Stretch the skin with thumb and middle finger
6. Hold the handset as if it were a pen, gently move in a sweeping action across the facial area (see diagram on following page)
7. BASE - Perform a gentle exfoliation to the entire facial area and neck
8. TARGET - On completion of a gentle exfoliation you can return to the areas that need further attention such as acne scarring, pigmentation marks, fine lines and wrinkles.
9. On completion of treatment, wipe away any residue of crystals that remain on the skin using damp cotton pads (cold water)
10. Tone using gentle toner
11. Mask optional
12. Moisturise
13. Apply SPF 15

Treatment application directions

The diagram demonstrates the directions you should work in when treating the face. Each arrow (stroke) is approximately 4cms in length.

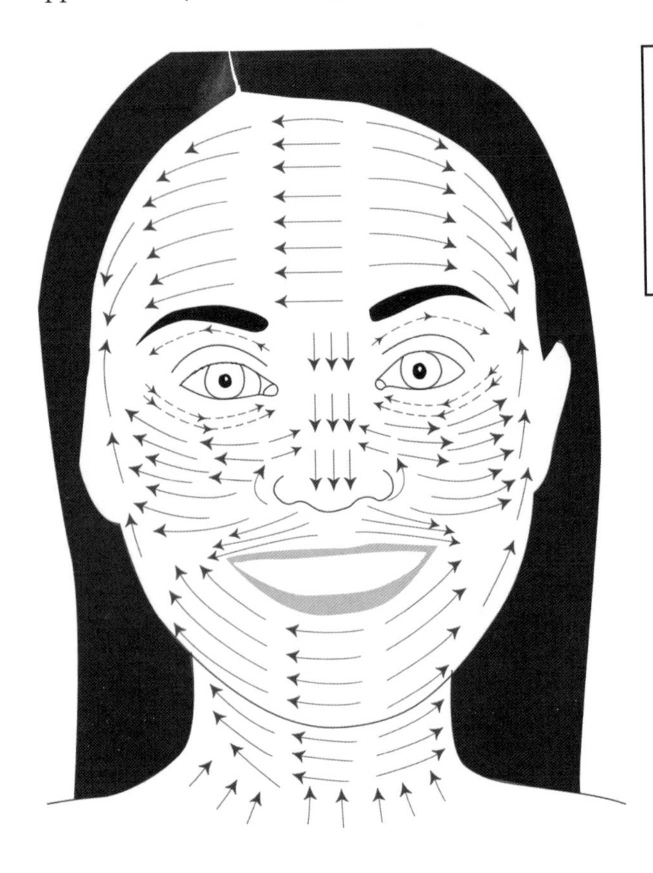

EYE AREA

- Always use Level 1
- Use a feathering action
- quick, light strokes

Tips for treatment

1. You should try to understand the client's skin and how it reacts before becoming too adventurous. Quite often therapists want to impress the client so much on their first treatment that they apply too much pressure and work too aggressively. This results in the client's skin actually becoming sensitive and if the skin has been dragged with too much pressure applied red stripes can be evident. This is due to the therapist being too ambitious and not understanding the client's skin. It is vital that therapists master the gliding movement of the nozzle across the skin in a gentle and controlled manner.

2. Always keep the pressure light during the first treatment then slowly progress to higher levels and a more aggressive treatment as the course progresses. This ensures the client's skin becomes used to the treatment and the client will understand what is happening. A client that goes home with red stripes or red, sensitive skin will be a very unhappy client and will probably cancel the course of treatments because the therapist has failed to explain or perform the treatment properly.

3. N.B. Always use a light vacuum on Black and Asian skin, no higher than level 2 on skin types V and VI of the fitzpatrick scale.

4. The secret of a treatment's success lies in the pressure of the strokes used. Light quick strokes should be used for a gentle exfoliation (feathering around the eyes), slower strokes to concentrate on problem areas. Areas exhibiting minor telangiectasias (broken capillaries) should be treated very gently by performing light quick strokes over the area. Strokes should never be longer than 4cms.

SECTION 6 – LEARNING OUTCOMES:

- You will gain an appreciation of the health and safety issues concerned with treatment and equipment maintenance
- You will be able to accurately update client record cards

VITAL MACHINE MAINTENANCE

- After every treatment – turn off the system and unplug the power cable from the mains supply and the casing.
- Remove the crystal cartridge and tap the handset onto the palm of your hand to remove any residue crystals in the handset chamber. Each time you change the crystal bottle, shake out any excess crystals that may be in the inner canal of the handset. This ensures the inner chamber of the handset is kept clear at all times.
- Remove and dispose of the nozzle.
- Empty disposal jar after EVERY treatment, unscrew the disposal jar from the lid and empty the used crystals carefully and dispose of responsibly.
- Make sure the disposal jar is replaced securely and firmly and is not cross threaded (if it is not secure the vacuum power will be decreased).
- Tidily wrap up all tubing and attachments into the case and make sure everything is clean ready for the next use.

IMPORTANT: When to change your parts

Disposable Jar

The plastic disposable filter jar MUST be changed at least every 80 treatments. Failure to connect a new jar will cause the vacuum power to drop and can cause crystals to be sucked from the paper filter in the jar directly into the pump inside the unit, which may seriously damage your machine and invalidate any warranty.

Handset

The handset piece should be changed immediately when it begins to use 7 bottles of crystal per treatment. Aluminium oxide is an abrasive compound that will gradually wear out the handset. The speed at which this happens can vary depending on the intensity and number of treatments carried out.

INDEX

SkinBase™

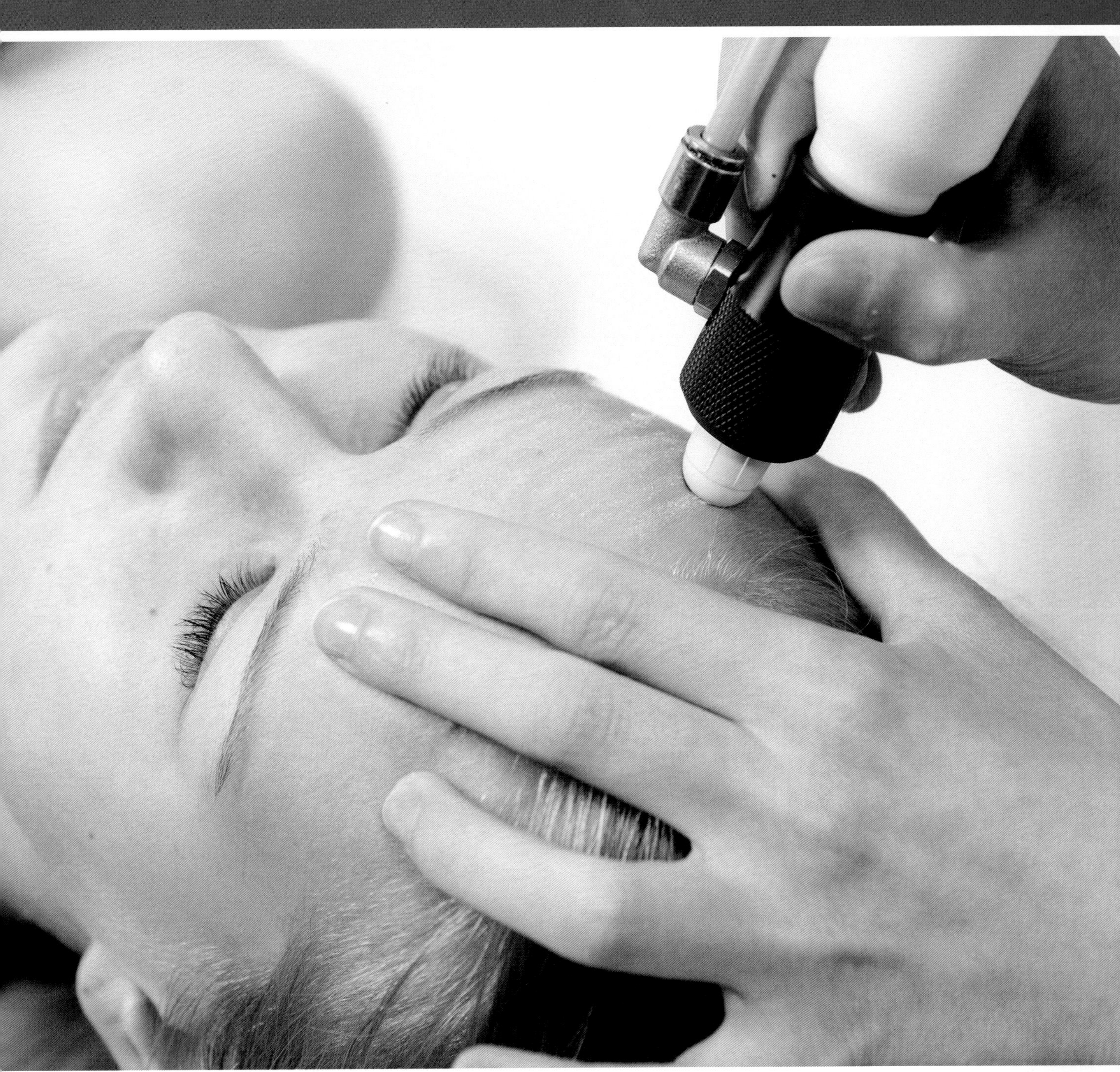

Mikrodermabrasion Ausbildungshandbuch

INHALT SEITE

SKINBASE MIKRODERMABRASION: EINFÜHRUNG ZUR AUSBILDUNG

Die Ausbildung in der SkinBase Mikrodermabrasion wird zusätzlich zu vorhandenen kosmetischen Qualifizierungen angeboten. Für die Ausbildung ist eine Qualifizierung in Gesichtsbehandlungen oder entsprechendes Voraussetzung. Die Ausbildung befasst sich mit theoretischen und praktischen Aspekten der Mikrodermabrasion.

Das SkinBase MDPRo ist ein System der professionellen Mikrodermabrasion, das in Großbritannien entwickelt und hergestellt wurde. Wir haben mit erfahrenen Kosmetiktherapeuten gearbeitet, die jahrelange Erfahrung mit alternativen Produkten im Vertrieb haben. Mit dieser Hilfe haben wir ein System entworfen, das außergewöhnliche Leistungsfähigkeit, Qualität und nachgewiesene Funktionssicherheit gewährleistet.

LEKTION 1 - LERNERGEBNISSE

- Erkenntnisse über die Gesundheits- und Sicherheitsrichtlinien am Arbeitsplatz erlangen, sowie deren praktische Umsetzung verstehen.
- In der Lage sein verschiedene Hautstörungen und Hautkrankheiten zu erkennen und Kontraindikationen einer Behandlung zu deuten.
- Ein grundlegendes Verständnis für Anatomie und Physiologie des Gesichts und des Nackens aneignen.

GESUNDHEIT UND SICHERHEIT AM ARBEITSPLATZ

Diese Lektion wird sich um Ihre Pflichten, wie auch die Pflichten gegenüber Arbeitnehmern (wenn zutreffend) und Kunden, in Bezug auf Gesundheit, Sicherheit und das Gemeinwohl am Arbeitsplatz befassen. Es ist wichtig, dass ihnen die Pflichten bewusst sind und, dass diese möglichst vernünftig angewendet werden. Die Kenntnisse von Gesundheits- und Sicherheitsbelangen werden Ihnen dabei helfen, Behandlungen gefahrlos durchzuführen und ihnen Professionalität am Auftreten, wie auch in Ihrer Einstellung am Arbeitsplatz anzueignen.

Die Gesundheits- und Sicherheitsrichtlinie stellt die geforderten Mindeststandards für Gesundheit, Sicherheit und das allgemeine Wohlbefinden am Arbeitsplatz auf. In einer Dienstleistungsbranche zu arbeiten bedeutet, dass Sie rechtlich verpflichtet sind ein sicheres und hygienisches Umfeld zu schaffen.

UM MÖGLICHE GEFAHREN UND RISIKEN AM ARBEITSPLATZ ZU VERMEIDEN, SOLLTEN SIE:

- Ihre gesetzliche Verantwortung hinsichtlich der Umsetzung von Gesundheits- und Sicherheitsvorschriften am Arbeitsplatz kennen
- Sicherstellen, dass Ihr persönliches Auftreten am Arbeitsplatz den Gesundheits- und Sicherheitsschutz, wie auch rechtlichen Vorschriften in Übereinstimmung mit den Richtlinien am Arbeitsplatz gerecht wird
- Die Richtlinien Ihres Berufes am Arbeitsplatz und die Anweisungen des Herstellers befolgen, um die sichere Nutzung der Ausstattung zu garantieren
- Umgehend jede Art von Risiko, die eine Gefahr am Arbeitsplatz darstellen könnte zu melden oder zu beseitigen, wie auch eine Erste Hilfe Ausstattung vor Ort haben, im Falle eines Unfalls oder einer Erkrankung
- Evakuierungsmaßnahmen, im Falle eines Brandes, eingerichtet haben und sicherstellen, dass allen Arbeitnehmern bewusst ist, wie diese umgesetzt werden
- Mögliche Infektions- oder Krankheitsausbreitungen zu minimieren, indem Sie ein hohes Maβ an Hygiene aufrechterhalten

Die Regelungen der Stromnutzung am Arbeitsplatz

Die Regelungen beinhalten die Installation, die Aufrechterhaltung und die Benutzung der elektrischen Ausstattung am Arbeitsplatz. Die elektrische Ausstattung sollte regelmäßig von einem qualifizierten Elektriker überprüft werden, um die Gesundheits- und Sicherheitsstandards zu gewährleisten. Diese Überprüfungen sollten von ihnen festgehalten werden. Seien Sie sich auch möglichen Gefahren bewusst, die mit der elektrischen Ausstattung einhergehen; freiliegende Drähte, gebrochene Stecker und überlastete Steckdosen.

Auch wenn es die Aufgabe des Arbeitgebers ist sicherzustellen, dass die gesamte Ausstattung Anwendungssicher ist, ist es auch die Pflicht des Arbeitnehmers, die Ausstattung vor der Nutzung zu testen und Sie unter keinen Umständen im defekten Zustand zu verwenden.

MÖGLICHE ELEKTRISCHE GEFAHREN:

- Freiliegende Kabeldrähte
- Gebrochene Stecker oder defekte Steckdosen
- Überlastete Steckdosen

Erste Hilfe

Auch wenn Sie alle Schutzmaßnahmen befolgt haben, um sich zu vergewissern, dass der Arbeitsplatz so sicher wie möglich ist, können Unfälle trotzdem passieren. Sorgen Sie dafür, dass Sie Erste-Hilfe-Richtlinien vor Ort haben, damit jeder am Arbeitsplatz weiß, was im Falle eines Unfalls, einer Erkrankung oder eines Notfalls zu tun ist.

Jede Arbeitsstelle sollte einen Sanitätskasten und eine bestimmte Person haben, welche für die Instandhaltung des Sanitätskastens verantwortlich ist. Führen Sie Aufzeichnungen über jegliche Verletzungen und tragen Sie diese in einem Unfalltagebuch ein.

ALLE MITARBEITER SOLLTEN WISSEN:

- wo sich der Sanitätskasten befindet
- wer für die Instandhaltung des Sanitätskastens zuständig ist
- wen im Falle eines Unfalls, eines Notfalls oder einer Erkrankung zu informieren ist

Die Entsorgung von Abfallstoffen

Abfallstoffe sollten in einem geschlossenen Abfalleimer entsorgt werden, der mit einer dauerhaften und reißfesten Polyäthylen Folie ausgestattet ist. Der Abfalleimer sollte regelmäßig mit Desinfektionsmittel desinfiziert werden. Dabei sollten zum Schutz Plastikhandschuehe benutzt werden.

Hygiene am Arbeitsplatz

Es ist notwendig die Ausstattung nach jedem Kunden zu sterilisieren, um schädliche Bakterien, Schimmelpilze und Viren, die zu Infektionen führen könnten, zu zerstören. Kreuzinfektionen und sekundäre Infektionen werden durch gute Hygiene am Arbeitsplatz vermieden.

Kreuzinfektionen können auftreten, wenn Mikroorganismen durch persönlichen Kontakt oder durch Kontakt mit infizierten, nicht sterilisierten Aufsätzen übertragen werden.

Sekundäre Infektionen können als Folge von Verletzungen an Kunden, während der Behandlung auftreten, oder wenn Kunden offene Schnittwunden haben, in die Bakterien durchdringen können und zu Infektionen führen können.

Persönliche Hygiene

Ein hohes Maβ an persönlicher Hygiene ist erforderlich. Sie sollten Ihre Hände regelmäßig waschen, wie auch vor und nach jedem Kunden. Lange Haare sollten zurückgebunden werden und Sie sollten möglichst vermeiden Ihr Gesicht zu berühren. Bedecken Sie jegliche Art von Schnitt- oder Schürfwunden an Ihren Händen mit einem sauberen Verband.

HAUTSTÖRUNGEN UND HAUTKRANKHEITEN

Ansteckende Infektionskrankheiten weisen gegen Schönheitsbehandlungen hin. Kunden mit gewissen Hautstörungen (auch wenn diese nicht ansteckend sind) sollten ebenfalls nicht von einem Therapeuten behandelt werden, da eine Behandlung zu sekundären Infektionen führen könnte. Therapeuten müssen imstande sein, gesunde Haut von Haut zu unterscheiden, die an einer Hautstörung oder Hautkrankheit leidet.

WICHTIG : Falls Sie unsicher oder nicht in der Lage sind den Hautzustand zu erkennen, dann sollten Sie den Kunden nicht behandeln und diesem empfehlen seinen Arzt zu befragen.

Gewisse Hautstörungen und Hautkrankheiten weisen Kontraindikationen für eine Schönheitsbehandlung auf: die Behandlung könnte den Therapeuten und andere Kunden dem Risiko einer Kreuzinfektion aussetzen. Deshalb ist es entscheidend, dass Sie mit Hautstörungen und Hautkrankheiten vertraut sind, mit denen Sie in Kontakt geraten könnten.

Bakterielle Infektionen

Bakterien können in großen Zahlen auf der Haut vorkommen, ohne uns jeglichen Schaden zu verursachen. Trotzdem können einige Bakterienarten schädlich für uns sein. Diese sind unter dem Namen „pathogene Bakterien" bekannt. Pathogene Bakterien können Hautkrankheiten auslösen, die ansteckend sind. Aus diesem Grund sollten Kunden nicht behandelt werden, die unter folgenden bakteriellen Infektionen leiden:

Grindflechte (Impetigo contagiosa)

Äuβerst ansteckend und durch Kontakt leicht übertragbar. Die Grindflechte tritt zunächst häufig im Gesicht und im Bereich Nase, Mund und Ohren auf und kann auf andere Stellen übertragen werden. Anfangs rot und kratzig, können sich später Blasen bilden, die dann verkrusten und nässen.

Konjunktivitis
Konjunktivitis ist nicht immer ansteckend, da es durch eine allergische Reaktion hervorgerufen werden kann bzw. in Folge eines Reizstoffes entstehen kann. Dadurch, dass es aber unmöglich für Sie ist dies festzustellen, sollten Sie stets von der Möglichkeit der Ansteckung ausgehen. Das Auge wird rot und erscheint entzündet; Ebenso können die Augen auch tränen oder Eiter aus dem Augenbereich heraustreten.

Gerstenkorn (Hordeolum)
Gerstenkörner sind eine Infizierung der Talgdrüsen an einer Augenwimpernwurzel. Dies kann eine Schwellung hervorrufen, die die anliegende Fläche rötet und sich im betroffenen Follikel eine kleine mit Eiter gefüllte Geschwulst bildet.

Furunkel
Ein Furunkel ist eine tiefe Entzündung des Haarbalgs, die eine Anhäufung von Eiter und abgestorbenem Gewebe zur Folge hat. Furunkel sind rötliche, mit Eiter gefüllte Auswölbungen, die warm und/oder schmerzhaft sind. Ein gelber oder weißer Punkt in der Mitte der Auswölbung ist zu erkennen, wenn der Furunkel bereit ist sich zu entleeren.

Virale Infektionen

Virenteilchen sind so klein, dass sie nicht selbstständig wachsen und sich reproduzieren können. Um dieses zu erreichen, benötigen sie eine Wirtszelle. Viren befallen gesunde, lebende Zellen im Körper, um sich zu vervielfachen. Sie treten auf vielfache Weise in den Körper ein: Inhalation, Speichel, sexuellen Kontakt. Unser Immunsystem ist dazu ausgelegt mit den meisten Viren umzugehen und wir bekämpfen die meisten Infektionen auf eine natürliche Weise. Kunden mit den folgenden viralen Infektionen sollten keine Mikrodermabrasion Behandlung erhalten:

Fieberbläschen (Herpes Simplex)
Die Ansteckung erfolgt durch engen Kontakt mit jemandem, der Fieberbläschen bereits hat. Kennzeichnend ist ein kribbelndes Gefühl auf der Haut, gefolgt von einer Wunde, die einen Schorf bildet. Gewöhnlich bilden sich Fieberbläschen an der Nasen- oder Lippenschleimhaut, aber sie können auch auf anderen Hautbereichen vorkommen.

Gürtelrose (Herpes zoster)
Gürtelrose ist die Entzündung eines Nervs und seiner umliegenden Fläche. Der Virus befällt meistens einen Nerv, üblicherweise am Brustkorb, Bauchraum oder der oberen Gesichtshälfte. Symptome zeigen sich an der umliegenden Nervenfläche, wie z.B. Errötung der Haut und Bildung von Bläschen und Wunfschorf.

Pilzinfektionen

Pilze sind parasitäre, mikroskopische Pflanzen, die sich von den Abfallstoffen der Haut ernähren. Einige Pilzinfektionen erscheinen an der Hautoberfläche, andere treten tiefer, innerhalb des Hautgewebes auf. Kunden mit Pilzinfektionen sollten nicht behandelt werden, da diese ansteckend und übertragbar sind.

Mattenbrand (Tinea corporis)
Mattenbrand ist eine Pilzinfektion der Haut, die am Rumpf des Körpers, an den Gliedmaßen und im Gesicht vorkommt. Sie zeigt sich in schuppigen, roten Flecken auf der Haut, die sich nach auβen verteilen. Die Flecken heilen von der Mitte aus und hinterlassen einen Ring.

Andere Hautstörungen sind nicht ansteckend, allerdings sollten sie mit Vorsicht betrachtet werden und in einigen Fällen sogar gemieden werden.

Deutsch

Störungen der Talgdrüsen

Talgdrüsen sind kleine Drüsen, die eine ölige Substanz „Talg", oder auch „Sebum" genannt, am Haarfollikel absondern, um die Haut zu ölen. Die größte Menge kann man am Gesicht oder in der Kopfhaut finden. Störungen der Talgdrüsen sind Akne, Rosacea und Milien. Verursacht werden sie meistens durch eine Überproduktion von Talg.

Milien

Auch „Hautgrieß" oder „Grießkörner" genannt, sind gutartige, mit Keratin gefüllte Zysten, die sich meistens im Augen- und Nasenbereich bilden. Sie sind vom Aussehen her klein, hart, weiß oder blassgelb. Sie sind nicht ansteckend und können beseitigt werden, indem die darüberliegende Haut mit einer sterilen Nadel durchstochen wird, um das Keratin freizusetzen.

Mitesser (Komedonen)

Mittesser werden durch überschüssigen Talg und verhornte Zellen verursacht, die die Haarfollikel blockieren. Diese lagern sich am Gesicht, an der oberen Hälfte des Rückens und am Brustkorb an und sind nicht ansteckend.

Seborrhö

Dies wird durch überschüssige Talgproduktion verursacht und tritt meistens, auf Grund der hormonellen Umstellung, während der Pubertät auf. Erkrankte haben erweiterte Follikel und produzieren überschüssiges Hautfett. Es ist nicht ansteckend und ist gewöhnlich auf dem Gesicht oder auf der Kopfhaut zu finden. Rücken und Brustkorb können ebenso davon betroffen sein.

Talgzysten

Talgzysten bilden sich in Haarfollikeln, wenn die Talgdrüse verstopft ist und einen Pfropf bildet. Sie sind nicht ansteckend.

Gewöhnliche Akne (Akne vulgaris)

Ein hormonelles Ungleichgewicht während der Pubertät löst eine erhöhte Talgproduktion aus. Dies wiederum verursacht eine Stauung in den Talgdrüsen, was zu Hautentzündungen, Mitessern, Pusteln und Knötchen führen kann. Es ist nicht ansteckend und tritt meistens in Gesicht, Nase, Kinn und Stirn auf.

Rosacea

Rosacea wird durch eine Kombination von überflüssiger Talgabsonderung und chronischem Entzündungszustand verursacht. Die Haut wird rau, die Poren weiten sich, Wangen und Nase röten und entzünden sich. Die Haut kann sich, auf Grund der langsamen Durchblutung, violett verfärben. Rosacea kann nicht mit Mikrodermabrasion behandelt werden.

Pigmentierung

Hyperpigmentierung - übermäßige Pigmentierung

- Chloasma „Altersflecken" - eine Zunahme der Pigmentierung kann durch UV-Licht Bestrahlung, oft auch während der Schwangerschaft (man nimmt an, dass Östrogen die Melanin Produktion ankurbelt) und auch durch die Einnahme der empfängnisverhütenden Pille verursacht werden. Sie treten an den Händen, Unterarmen, dem oberen Brustkorb, der Schläfe und der Stirn auf.

- Epheliden „Sommersprossen“ – verursacht durch UV-Licht Aussetzung, welches die Melanin Produktion stimuliert. Sommersprossen findet man auf Nase und Wangen hellhäutiger Menschen. Sie können auch auf Händen, Armen, Schultern und Rücken auftreten.

- Lentigo: Hyperpigmentierungsflecken, größer als Sommersprossen, erscheinen auf Grund hoher Sonnenausstzung entweder während der Kindheit oder im mittleren Alter. Treten an Gesicht, Händen und Schultern auf.

Hypopigmentierung - Pigmentverlust

- Vitiligo „Weißfleckenkrankheit“ – Hautflecken ohne Pigmente, die völlig weiß erscheinen.
- Albinismus – Haut ohne Pigmente, sodass die Haut, Haare und Augen farblos erscheinen.

Vaskuläre Naevi - Muttermale

Dies sind pigmentierte Flächen, die durch dauerhafte Erweiterung der Blutkapillaren verursacht wurden:

- Erweiterte Kapillaren – kleine, rote Kapillaren, die an vernachlässigten oder trockenen Zonen, wie z.B. Wangen sichtbar werden

- Spider Naevi „Lebersternchen“ – erweiterte Kapillaren, die sich um erweiterte Blutgefäße ausbreiten

- Hämangiom „Erdbeerfleck“ – rotes oder violettes Mal, das bei der Geburt auf der Haut auftritt

- Naevus flammeus „Feuermal“ oder „Portweinfleck“ – große Fläche erweiterter Kapillaren

Erythema

Ein Erythem ist die Rötung der Haut, die durch die Ausdehnung von Blutgefäßen hervorgerufen wird. Diese Blutgefäße steuern die Kapillarnetze an Hautflächen, die durch eine Verletzung oder eine Infektion betroffen wurden.

Teleangiektasie - beschädigte Kapillaren

Jegliche Form von beschädigten Kapillaren kann durch das Vakuum-Therapie der Mikrodermabrasion weiter beschädigt werden. „Besenreiser“ sind im Nasen- und Wangenbereich bekannt. Diese Fläche sollte bei der Behandlung völlig vermieden werden oder sollte in einer sehr niedrigen Stufe ausgeführt werden.

Keloid Narben

Keloide sind Narbengewebe mit überschüssigen Kollagenablagerungen. Die Haut wirkt angehoben, rötlich und mit Linien durchzogen. Diese Art von Narbengewebe kann nicht mit Mikrodermabrasion behandelt werden. Dehnungsstreifen und Operationsnarben können behandelt werden, allerdings sollte das Narbengewebe nicht behandelt werden, bis die Entzündung ganz abgeklungen ist (z.B. 6 Monate nach Operation).

Deutsch

Dermatitis

Dies ist eine Entzündung der Haut, die durch einen reizenden oder allergieauslösenden Stoff verursacht wurde. Es gibt verschiedene Arten von Dermatitis. Symptome beinhalten errötende, juckende, abschuppende, nässende, geschwollene und möglicherweise Bläschen bildende Haut, je nach Schweregrad der Erkrankung.

Irritative Kontaktdermatitis erfolgt umgehend nach der Berührung eines starken Reizmittelsoder über einen längeren Zeitraum nach lang anhaltender und wiederholter Aussetzung eines schwächeren Reizmittels. Gewöhnliche Ursachen für diese Dermatitis Art sind: Seife, Haarwaschmittel, Reinigungsmittel, Staub, Öle und Fette, wiederholter und längerer Kontakt mit Wasser.

Allergische Kontaktdermatitis wird ausgelöst, wenn der Erkrankte eine Allergie gegen eine Substanz entwickelt. Gewöhnliche Ursachen sind: Haarfärbemittel, Klebemittel und Nahrung, wie z.B. Krustentiere.

Ekzeme

Es gibt zwei Hauptarten von Ekzemen: Atopische Ekzeme und Kontaktekzeme.

Atopische Ekzeme neigen dazu sich in der Kindheit auszubilden, wobei es sich bei vielen Kindern herauswächst.

Kontaktekzeme betreffen meistens Erwachsene und werden durch allergieauslösende Stoffe verursacht, wie z.B. Nickel, Reinigungsmittel, Seifen und Parfums.

Wenn man an Ekzemen leidet, juckt die Haut, sie wird trocken und schuppig, rötet sich häufig und schmerzt. Manchmal nässt oder blutet die Haut. Gesicht, Hals und Haut (vor allem an der inneren Ellenbogenfalte und auf der Rückseite der Knie) sind normalerweise davon betroffen.

Psoriasis-Schuppenflechte

Psoriasis ist eine chronische Autoimmunerkrankung, die sich auf die Haut und die Gelenke auswirkt. Es verursacht beschuppte Flecken „psoriatic Plaketten". Dies sind entzündete, überschüssige Haut produzierende Flächen, die auf Grund der Hautanhäufung eine sofortige,silbrig-weiße Farbe annehmen.

ANATOMIE UND PHYSIOLOGIE

Dadurch, dass Sie als Therapeut/in die Mikrodermabrasion Behandlung durchführen, ist es notwendig, dass Sie ein grundlegendes Verständnis über die Anatomie und Physiologie des Kopfes haben.

KNOCHEN AN KOPF UND NACKEN

Das Gesicht ist aus 14 Gesichtsknochen zusammengesetzt. Diese können dem nachstehenden Diagramm entnommen werden.

Knochen an Kopf und Nacken

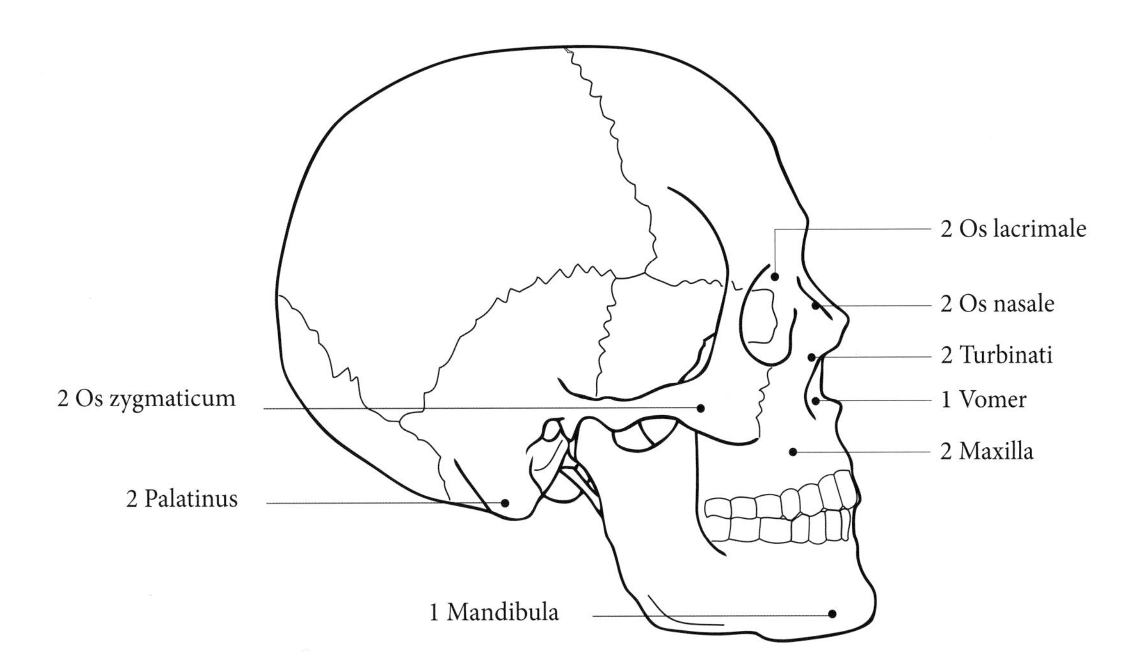

Knochen	
Palatinus	x 2 Formt den Nasenboden, Nasenwand und Gaumen
Os nasale	x 2 Formt den Nasenrücken
Turbinati	x 2 Diese zwei Knochen formen die äußeren Nasenwände
Vomer	Dies ist die Nasentrennwand
Os lacrimale	x 2 Die inneren Wände der Augenhöhlen
Maxilla	x 2 Verwachsen, um den Oberkiefer zu formen
Mandibula	Der Unterkiefer
Os zygomaticum	x 2 Die Wangenknochen

Der restliche Schädel ist aus Schädelknochen zusammengesetzt. Insgesamt gibt es 8 davon. Diese sind im nachstehenden Diagramm aufgezeichnet.

Schädelknochen

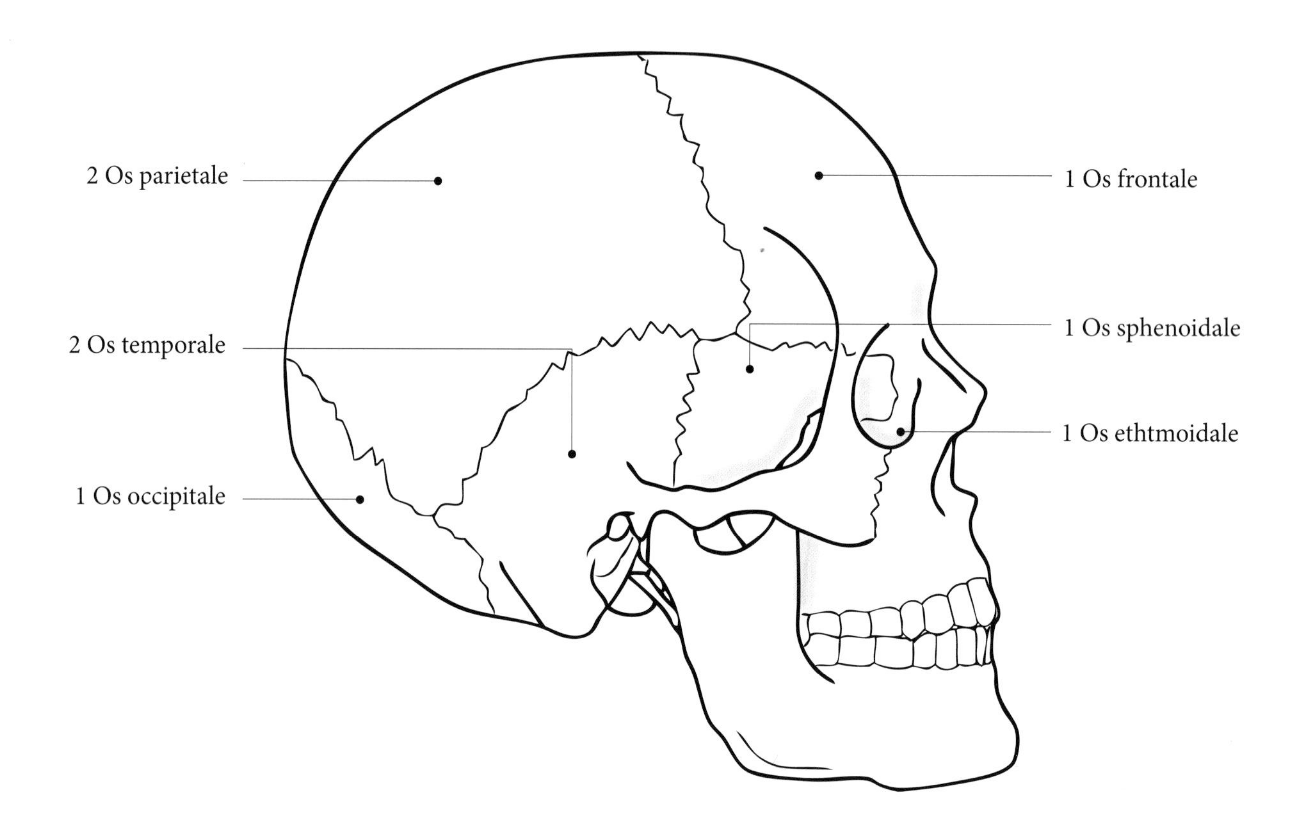

Knochen	
Os occipitale	Liegt auf der Hinterseite des Schädels und umschließt die Öffnung, durch die Rückenmark, Nerven und Blutgefäße fließen
Os parietale	Verwachsen, um die Schädeldecke zu formen
Os frontale	Stirn und obere Augenhöhlen
Os temporale	x 2 Schädelseiten
Os ethtmoidale	Teil der Nasenhöhle
Os sphenoidale	Ähnlich einem Fledermausflügel geformter Knochen, der alle Schädelknochen miteinander verbindet

Nacken, Brust und Schulterknochen

Vorne

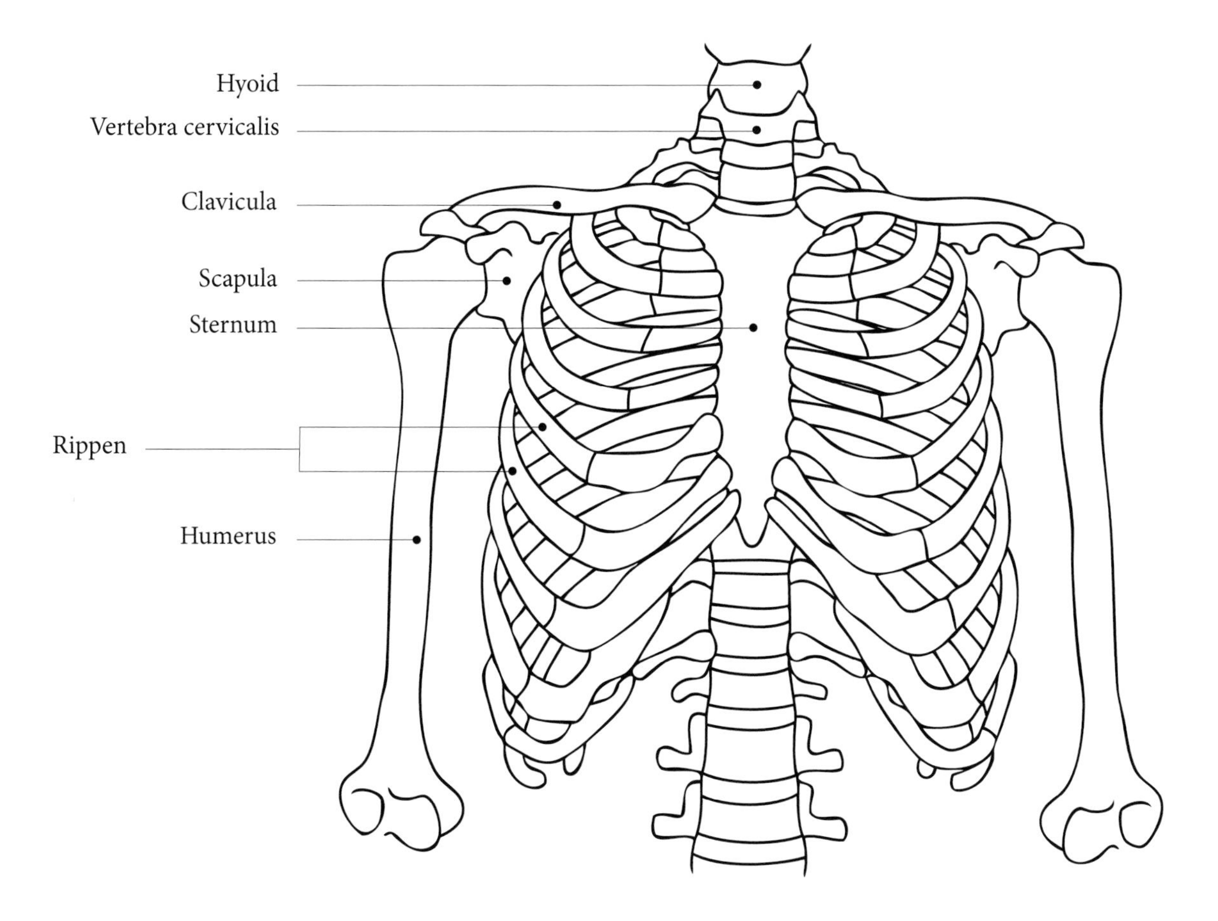

Hinten

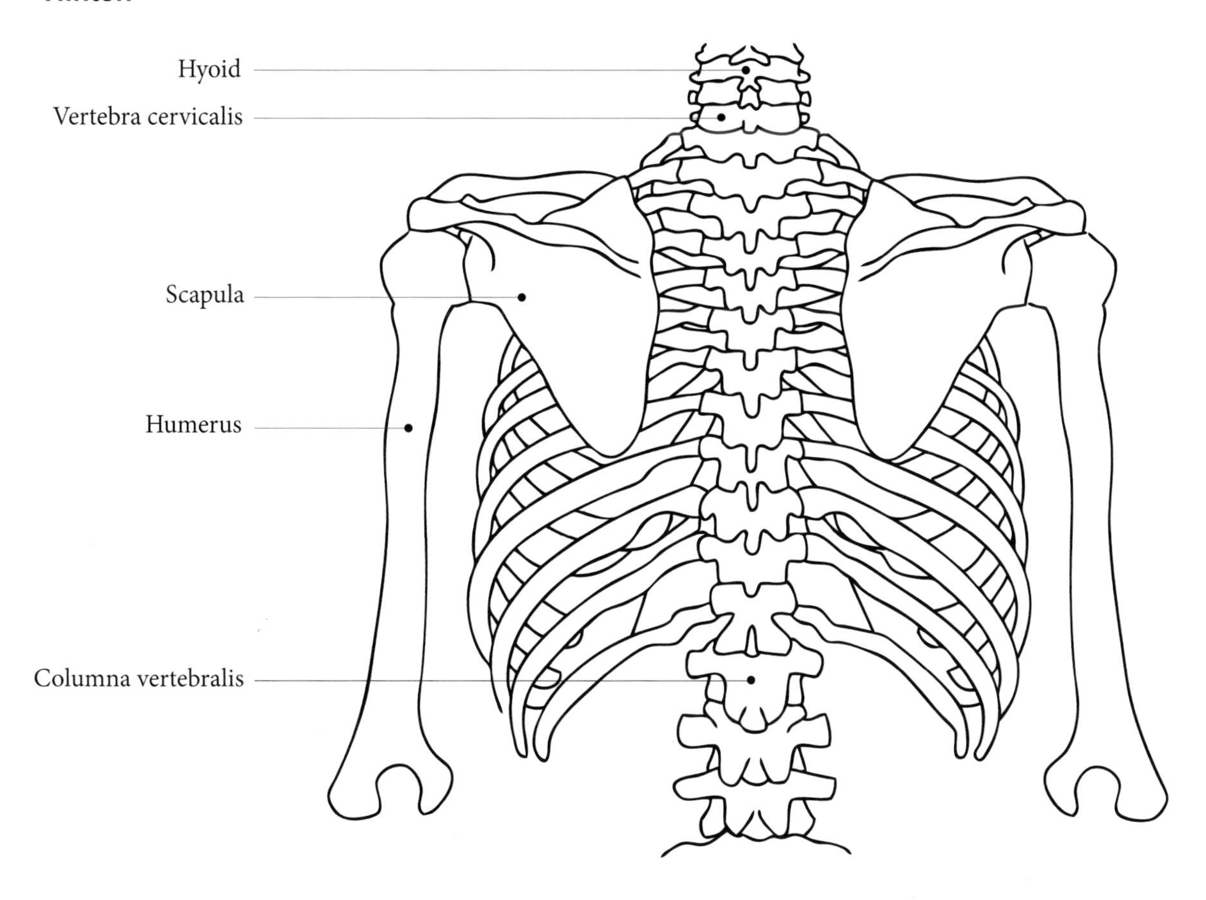

Deutsch

Deutsch

GESICHTS- UND NACKENMUSKULATUR

Die Gesichts- und Nackenmuskulatur ist für unsere Gesichtsausdrücke verantwortlich. Mit zunehmendem Alter erzeugen die Gesichtsausdrücke, die wir tagtäglich benutzen Fältchen und Linien und wir beginnen die äußeren Anzeichen des Alterns aufzuweisen. Mikrodermabrasion beseitigt die abgestorbenen Hautzellen der Epidermis und verbessert das Aussehen dieser feinen Linien und Falten.

Gesichtsmuskeln

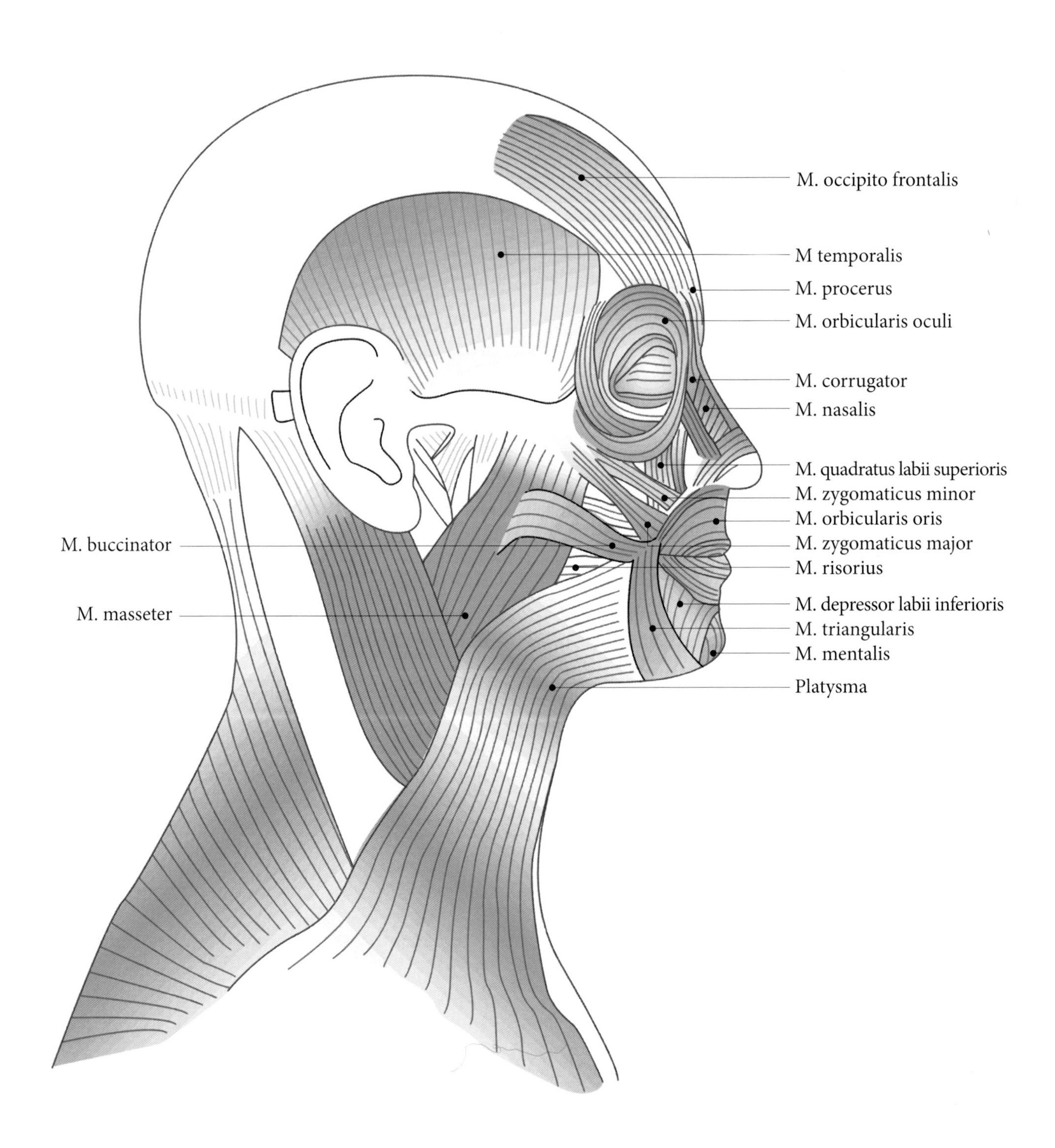

Nackenmuskeln

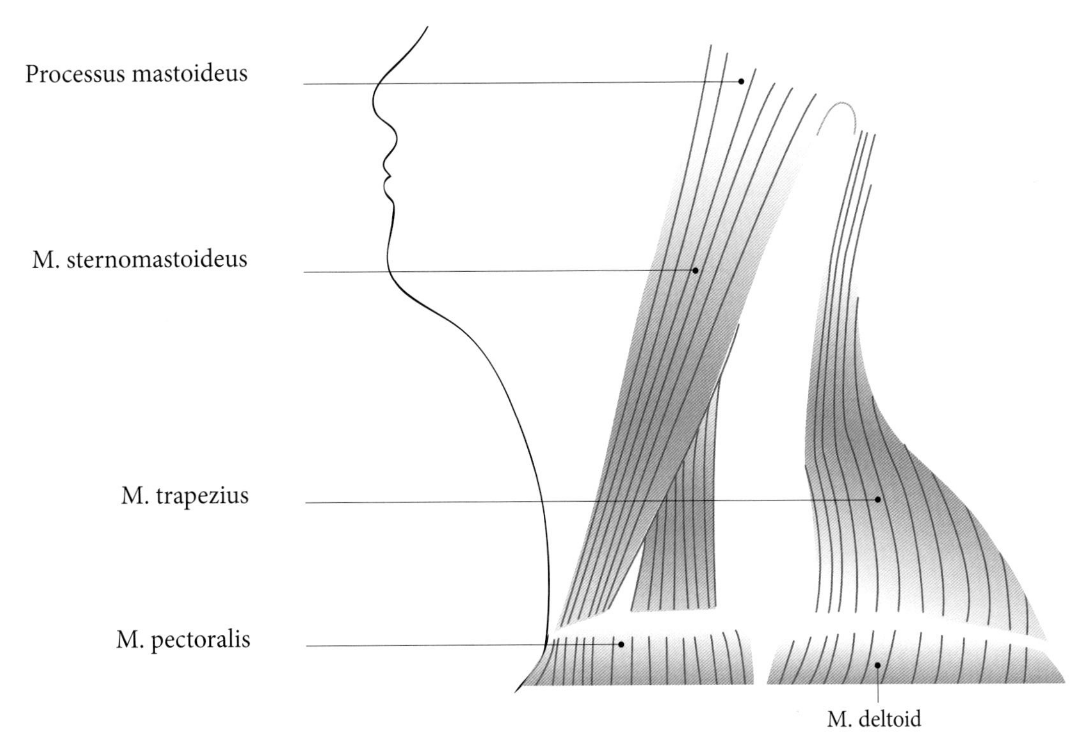

Deutsch

HIRNNERVEN

Durch das Nervensystem sendet der Körper Informationssignale vom Gehirn an andere Körperteile. Die Gesichts- und Hirnnerven steuern die Muskeln an Kopf und Nacken oder übertragen Nervenimpulse (sensorische Informationen) von den Sinnesorganen an das Gehirn. Der 5., 7. Und 11. Hirnnerv ist besonders kritisch für Therapeuten/innen, die die Gesichtsbehandlung durchführen.

Der 5. Hirnnerv - N. trigeminus

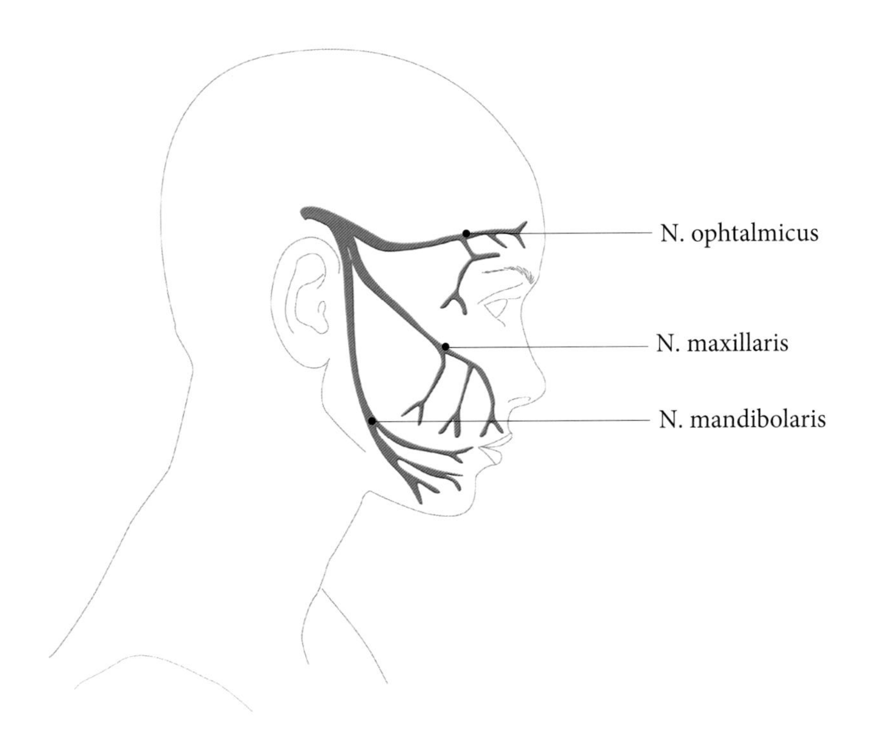

Der 7. Hirnnerv - N. facialis **Der 11. Hirnnerv - N. accessorius**

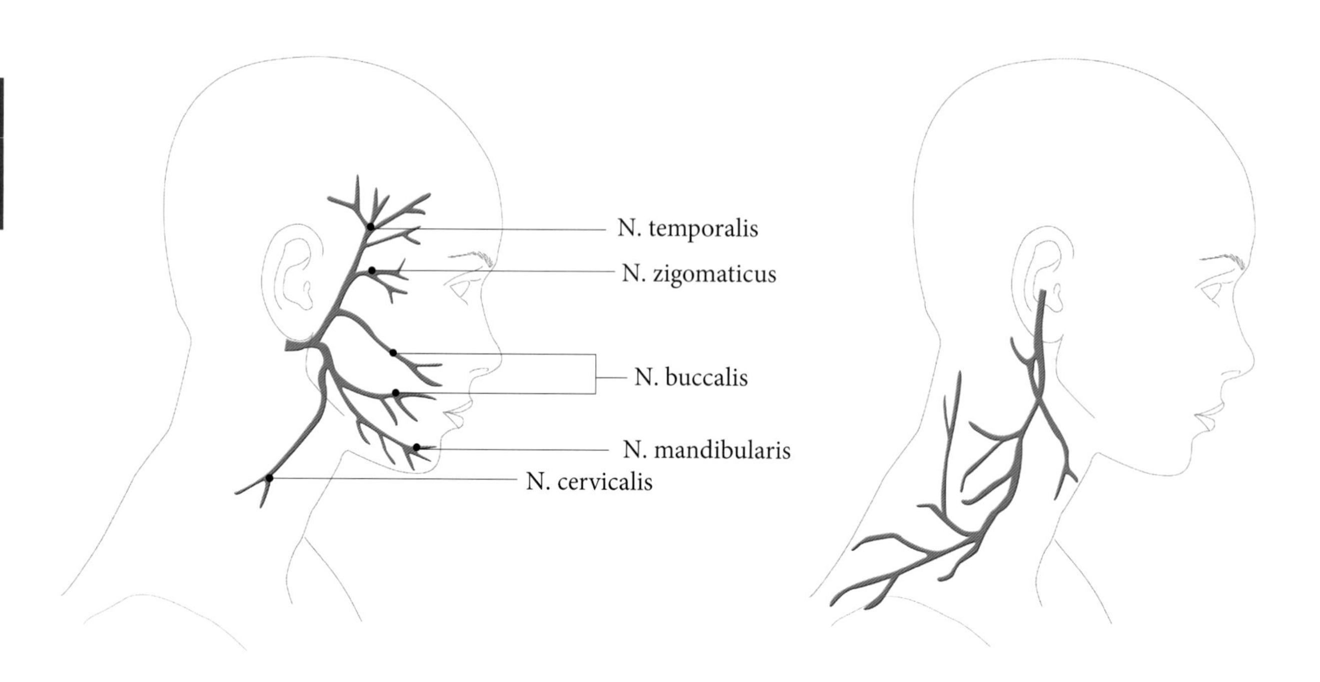

Nervo	Funktion	Nervenast	Sendet Informationen an:
5. N. trigeminus	Steuert die Kaumuskeln	N. ophtalmicus	Tränendrüsen Stirnhaut Obere Wangen
	Überträgt sensonirische	N. maxillaris	Oberer Kiefermuskel
	Informationen vom Gesicht	N. mandibularis	Unterer Kiefermuskel Zähne Kaumuskeln
7. N. facialis	Steuert Muskeln, die für die Gesichtsausdrücke verantwortlich sind	N. temporalis	Muskeln um das Auge herum Stirnmuskeln
		N. zygomaticus	Augenmuskeln
		N. buccalis	Obere Lippe Nasenflügel
		N. mandibularis	Untere Lippe Kinn
		N. cervicalis	Nacken-und Schulterseiten
11. N. accessorius	Bewegt Nacken und Schultern		

LEKTION 2 - LERNERGEBNISSE

- ein grundlegendes Verständnis der Struktur und Funktion der Haut erlangen
- fähig sein die verschiedenen Hauttypen zu unterscheiden
- ein gutes Verständnis über die Theorie der Mikrodermabrasion besitzen
- in der Lage sein die Problembereiche, die mit Mikrodermabrasion behandelt werden können, zu erkennen
- verstehen, wie eine Mikrodermabrasion Behandlung abläuft

DIE HAUT

Die Haut ist das größte Organ des Körpers. Sie wirkt auf vielfache Weise, um uns vor Äußeren Einflüssen zu beschützen:

- Verhindert die Absorbierung schädlicher Substanzen
- Hilft die Körpertemperatur zu regulieren
- Wirkt wie eine Barriere, um Infizierungen fernzuhalten
- Melanin in der Haut schützt uns vor den schädlichen Wirkungen des UV-Lichts
- Bietet eine wasserdichte Beschichtung, die uns vor Dehydrierung bewahrt
- Liefert einen Energiespeicher in Form von eingelagertem Fett

Die Struktur der Haut

Die Haut ist aus zwei unterschiedlichen Schichten zusammengesetzt: der Epidermis und der Dermis. Zwischen diesen liegt die Basalmembran, die beide Schichten zusammenhält. Unter diesen Schichten liegt die subkutane Schicht (Unterhaut), eine Fettschicht, die schützt, abdämpft, isoliert und zusätzliche Energie für den Körper speichert.

Die Epidermis

Die Epidermis ist die äußerste Schicht der Haut. Sie besteht aus 5 weiteren Schichten. Jede einzelne Schicht der Epidermis kann an Ihrer Form und Zellenfunktion erkannt werden. Der Hauptzelltyp in der Epidermis ist der Keratinozyt, der das Protein Keratin erzeugt.

Zellerneuerung ereignet sich in einem Zeitraum von ungefähr 4 Wochen. Zellen bewegen sich von der untersten Schicht der Epidermis (Basalschicht) bis hin zur obersten Schicht (Hornschicht), wobei sie Ihre Form und Struktur während des Verlaufes verändern. Die oberste Schicht der Epidermis ist die Schicht, die abstirbt und sich durch Desquamation (Abschuppung) häutet. Es ist diese Schicht, die während der Mikrodermabrasion Behandlung beseitigt wird und auch die Schicht, die hilft UV-Licht von der Haut zu reflektieren. Aus diesem Grund ist es wichtig, dass Kunden nach der Behandlung Sonnenschutzmittel benutzen.

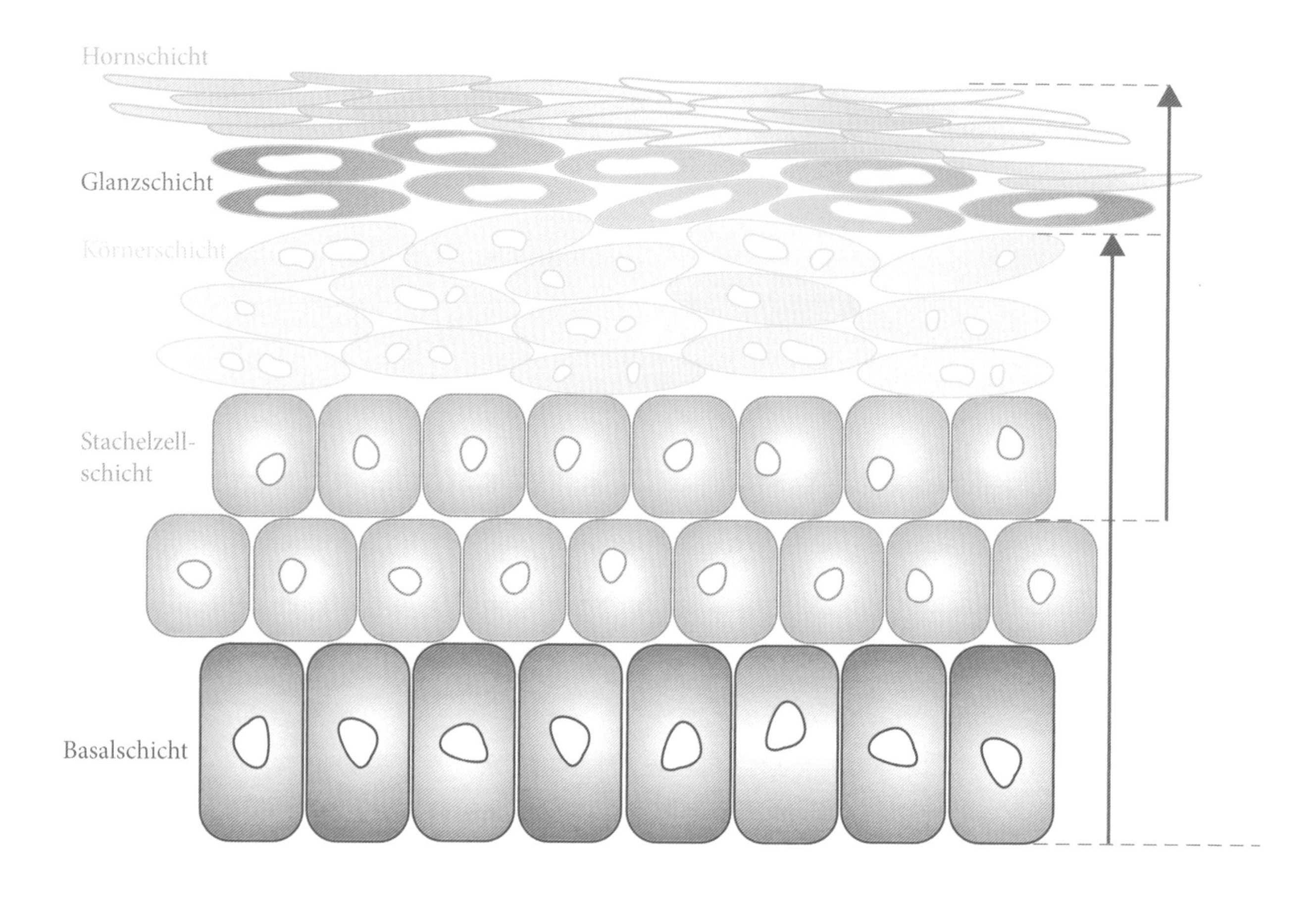

Die Fünf Schichten der Epidermis

1. Stratum Corneum oder „Hornschicht“

Diese Schicht ist die äußerste Schicht der Epidermis und besteht aus verschiedenen Schichten abgeflachter, hauptsächlich abgestorbener, übereinanderliegenden Zellen. Diese Zellen verhelfen ebenso, das UV-Licht zu reflektieren.

Schwarze Haut, die sich entwickelt hat, um starker UV-Licht Bestrahlung standzuhalten, besitzt eine dickere Hornschicht als kaukasische Haut. Es dauert ungefähr drei Wochen bis, die an der Basalschicht liegenden epidermalen Zellen, die Hornschicht erreichen. Diese Zellen werden dann abgeworfen, ein Verlauf, der als Desquamation bezeichnet wird.

2. Stratum Lucidum oder „Glanzschicht“

Diese Schicht findet man nur an dickeren Stellen der Haut, wie z.B. Handinnenfläche oder an den Fuβsohlen.

3. Stratum Granulosum oder „Körnerschicht“

In dieser Schicht beginnen die Zellen abzusterben. Diese Zellen besitzen im Innern eine Körnchen-artige Substanz, die durch das Auflösen der Zellkerne erzeugt wird. Diese Körnchen bezeichnet man als „Keratohyalin-Granula“, die später Keratin bilden.

4. Stratum Spinosum oder „Stachelzellschicht“

Die Stachelzellschicht besteht aus Zellen, die eine zugespitzige Oberfläche haben, um sich mit anderen umliegenden Zellen zu verknüpfen. Diese Schicht beginnt mit der Keratin Synthese.

5. Stratum Germinativum oder „Basalschicht"

Zellen in dieser Schicht sind Säulenartig und verantwortlich für die Produktion neuer epidermaler Zellen. Einige Zellen teilen sich und bewegen sich zu darüber gelegenen Schichten. Die restlichen Zellen teilen sich, um die Lücken zu füllen. Der Ablauf der Zellteilung ist bekannt als Mitose.

Die Basalschicht der Epidermis enthält auch zwei weitere wichtige Zellen: Langerhans Zellen und Melanozyten Zellen.

Langerhans Zellen – absorbieren und beseitigen die Fremdkörper, die in die Haut eindringen. Diese verlassen die Epidermis und dringen unter die Dermis, wo sie das Lymphsystem betreten, das der „Entsorgungsanlage" des Körpers entspricht.

Melanozyten Zellen – sind für die Melanin Produktion in der Haut verantwortlich. Diese schützen andere epidermale Zellen vor der schädlichen Wirkung des UV-Lichts. Melanin verhilft unseren Hauttypen zu bestimmen. Je mehr Melanin vorhanden ist, desto dunkler unser Hautton.

Deutsch

Die Dermis

Die Dermis ist die Schicht, die unter der Epidermis zu finden ist und die für die Festigkeit und Elastizität der Haut verantwortlich ist. Sie enthält auch spezialisierte Zellen und Strukturen, einschließlich Blutgefäße, Drüsen und Haarfollikeln. Die Dermis besteht aus zwei Schichten, der Papillarschicht oder auch Zapfenschicht genannt und der Netzschicht. Die obere Zapfenschicht enthält eine dünne Anordnung von Kollagenfasern. Die darunterliegende Netzschicht besteht aus dicht gelagerten Kollagenfasern, die parallel zur Hautoberfläche angeordnet sind.

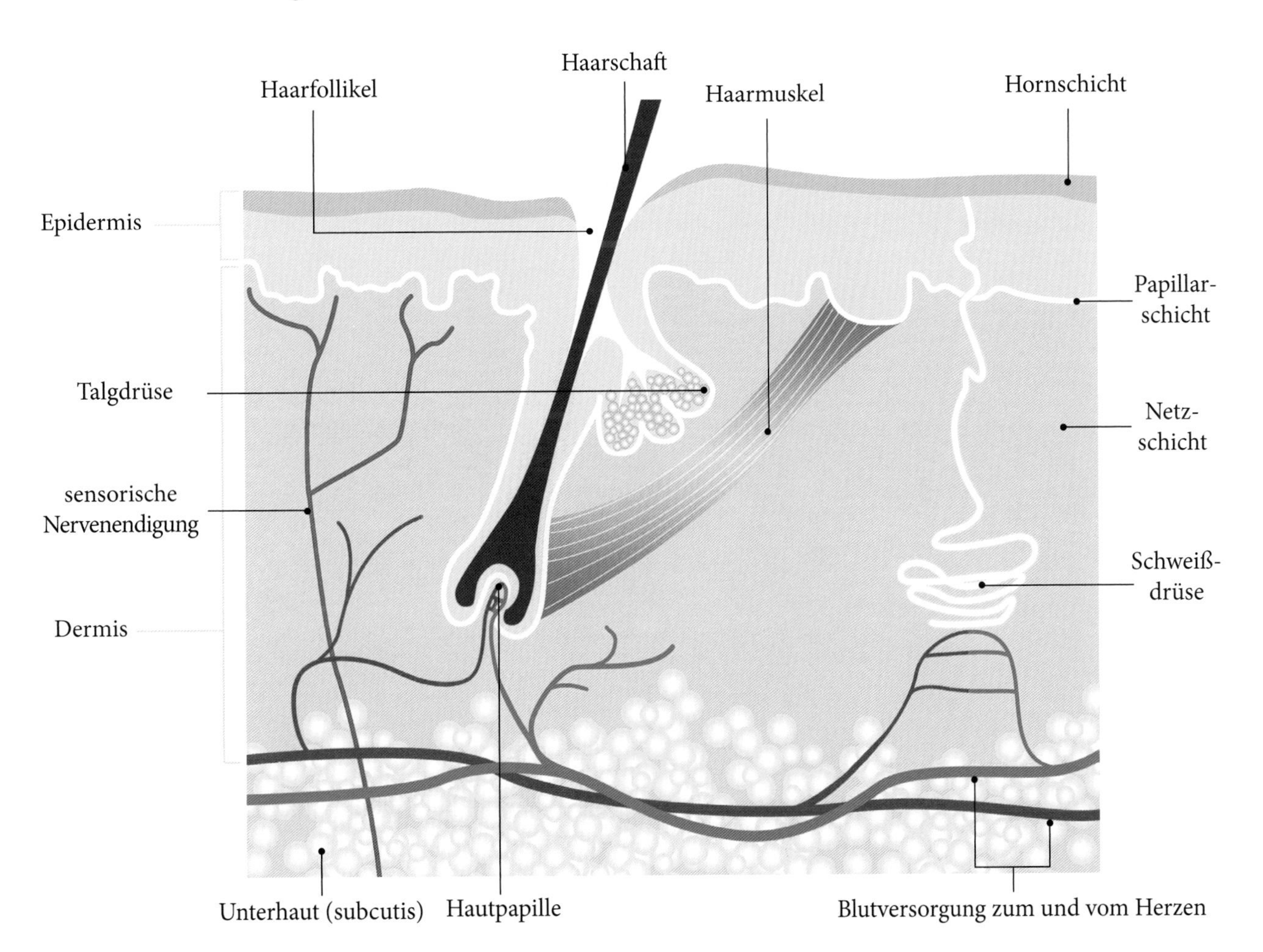

Die Netzschicht

Die Netzschicht besteht aus zwei Proteinarten: Elastin Fasern, die für die Elastizität der Haut sorgen und Kollagenfasern, die der Haut ihre Festigkeit verleihen. Beide Fasernarten werden in einer gallert-artigen Substanz gehalten, die sogenannte „Grundsubstanz". Die Elastin- und Kollagenfasern bilden ein starkes Netzwerk, das uns ein jugendliches Aussehen verleiht.

Mit zunehmendem Alter erhärten sich diese Hautfasern und beginnen sich zu fragmentieren. Das Netzwerk fängt an zusammenzubrechen und unsere Haut beginnt ihre Elastizität zu verlieren, wobei Zeichen des Alterns sichtbar werden. Die Blutzirkulation der Haut nimmt ab. Dadurch gelangen Nährstoffe nicht zur Hautoberfläche und dies wiederum führt zu fahler Haut. Die Fettschicht unter der Haut wird dünner und wir erhalten durch hervortreten unserer Knochenstruktur ein weniger gestrafftes Äußeres. Die Netzschicht ist unerlässlich für die Gesundheit und das Aussehen unserer Haut. Deshalb ist es wichtig sie zu pflegen, um die Zeichen des Alterns zu vermeiden.

Der Blutfluss

Das Blut fließt durch den Körper in alle Zellen und transportiert essentielle Nährstoffe, wie z.B. Sauerstoff, Glukose und andere Elemente, die für die Gesundheit, die Aufrechterhaltung und das Wachstum des Körpers notwendig sind.

Die Vakuum Behandlung der Mikrodermabrasion unterstützt die Anregung der Mikrozirkulation nahe der Hautoberfläche. Dies begünstigt zweierlei: Zellerneuerung (Hautregeneration) und die Zunahme des Blutflusses in die Zone, die die Elastin- und Kollagenproduktion der Haut fördert. Dadurch wird das Gewebe repariert und eine sanfte und frische Haut wird enthüllt.

Dieses Diagramm zeigt, wie das Blut durch die Zellen fließt: Es ist zuständig für die Lieferung von Nährstoffen und Energie, bis hin zu der Beseitigung von Abfallstoffen, wie z.B. Kohlendioxid.

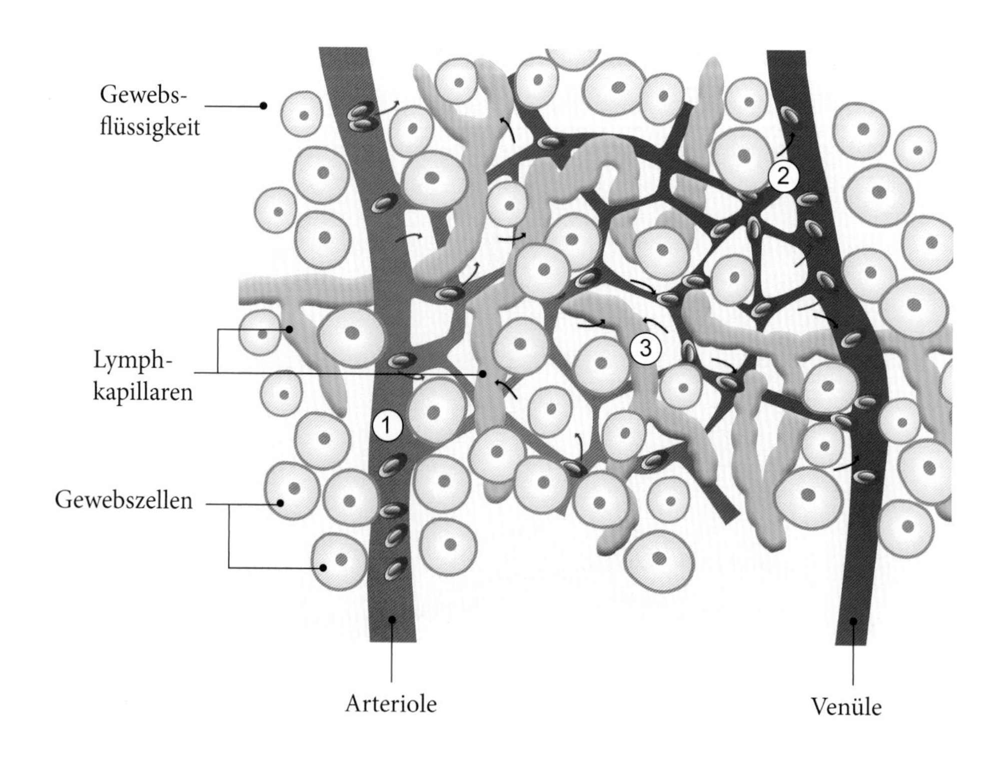

① Das Blut ist unter hohem Druck und fließt durch das Kapillarnetz. Dadurch wird Flüssigkeit in das Gewebe abgesondert, wo es sich dann zu Gewebeflüssigkeit entwickelt. Diese Flüssigkeit enthält nützliche Substanzen, wie z.B. Sauerstoff und Nährstoffe, die für die Zellen notwendig sind. Blut körperchen und große Proteine verbleiben in den Kapillaren.

② Mit dem Sauerstoffentzug des Blutes wird der Druck umgekehrt, wobei etwas Flüssigkeit, die Abfallstoffe enthält, in die Kapillaren erneut eindringt und mitgerissen wird.

③ Überschüssige Flüssigkeit, Abfallstoffe und große Moleküle, wie z.B. Proteine, die außerstande waren in das Blut einzudringen, werden von Lymphkapillaren aufgenommen und zu den Lymphknoten transportiert, wo die Flüssigkeit verarbeitet wird und wieder zurück in das Blut (in Herznähe) gelangt.

Der Blutfluss durch die Haut

Die normale Körpertemperatur beträgt 37° C. Der Körper arbeitet daran diese Temperatur aufrechtzuerhalten. Wenn sich die Körpertemperatur erhöht, dann fließt das Blut dicht an der Haut entlang, um einen Teil der Wärme abzugeben. Wenn die Körpertemperatur sinkt, dann ziehen sich die Kapillare zusammen und das Blut fließt stattdessen durch sogenannte „Shuntgefäße", die tiefer in der Haut liegen, um den Wärmeverlust durch die Haut zu verringern.

Vasodilatation erfolgt wenn Ihnen:
Heiß ist - Blut fließt nah an der Oberfläche entlang - Wärme wird abgegeben

Vasokonstriktion erfolgt wenn ihnen:
Kalt ist - Blut fließt durch „Shuntgefäße" von der Oberfläche weg -Wärme wird aufrechterhalten.

Hauttypen

Es gibt sechs grundlegende Hauttypen. Allerdings ändert sich die Gesichtshaut in den verschiedenen Lebensabschnitten, bedingt durch Erkrankungen oder hormonelles Ungleichgewicht.

Trockene Hauttypen

Trockene Haut wird durch mangelnden- oder inaktive Talgdrüsen verursacht, die nicht genug Talg produzieren, um die Haut auf eine natürliche Weise zu hydratisieren. Die Haut hat meist ein mattes Erscheinungsbild, fühlt sich trocken an, juckt, und ist zuweilen empfindlich. Trockene Haut muss regelmäßig von Innen (Wasser trinken) und von auβen (hydratisierende Cremes oder Lotionen) hydratisiert werden.

Fettige Hauttypen

Fettige Haut wird durch Drüsen verursacht, die zu viel Talg produzieren, was eine glänzend erscheinende Haut mit großen, offenen Poren hervorruft. Fettige Hauttypen sind anfällig für die Bildung von Mitessern und Akne. Trotz dieser Nachteile, bleibt fettige Haut, im Gegensatz zu anderen Hauttypen, jung aussehend und geschmeidig im Verlauf der Jahre. Fettige Haut profitiert enorm von Mikrodermabrasion im Zusammenhang mit der Verwendung von leichten Feuchtigkeitsmitteln.

Sensible Hauttypen

Sensible Haut kann trocken, normal oder fettig sein und ist durch ihre Empfindsamkeit gekennzeichnet. Sensible Haut reagiert häufig nachteilig auf Umweltbedingungen und benötigt oft bestimmte Behandlungen, um den guten Zustand aufrechtzuerhalten. Sensible Haut profitiert sehr von natürlichen Hautpflegeprodukten und Behandlungen.

Normale Hauttypen

Normale Haut produziert Talg in mäßigen Mengen, was zu einem ausgeglichenen Zustand führt. Normale Haut wirkt einheitlich füllig, feucht und pulsierend. Ein großer Segen, jedoch benötigt diese Art von Haut ebensoviel Aufmerksamkeit. Sie profitiert von regelmäßiger Reinigung, Tönung und feuchtigkeitsspendender Pflege.

Mischhauttypen

Mischhaut ist die gewöhnlichste aller Hauttypen. Mischhaut ist oft durch eine fettige T-Zone gekennzeichnet, die den Stirn-, Nasen- und Kinnbereich umfasst. Die Haut um Wangen, Augen und Mund ist eher trocken. Menschen mit Mischhaut sollten ihre Haut regelmäßig untersuchen lassen und unterschiedliche Produkte auf den verschiedenen Gesichtszonen verwenden.

Reife Hauttypen

Reife Haut hat folgende Eigenschaften: die Haut wird trocken, da die Talgdrüsen an Leistung verlieren. Die Haut verliert Elastizität: feine Linien und Falten entstehen. Haut erscheint dünner und beschädigte Kapillaren treten hervor, vor allem im Wangenbereich und um die Nase herum. Gesichtskonturen lassen nach, sobald der Muskeltonus abnimmt. Die darunterliegende Knochenstruktur wird sichtbar, während die Fettschicht unter der Haut dünner wird. Die Blutzirkulation wird schwächer, was die Anreicherung der Haut verhindert, was wiederum die Haut blässlich erscheinen lässt. Durch die Verringerung der Metabolismuszirkulation, werden Abfallstoffe nicht schnell genug beseitigt, was zu Hautschwellung führt. Reife Haut muss sehr gut hydratisiert werden, indem man viel Wasser trinkt und regelmäßig nahrhafte, feuchtigkeitsspendende Produkte anwendet.

Hautfarbtypen

Der Farbton der Haut kann von dunkelbraun bis hin zu einer fast farblosen Pigmentierung variieren, die durch das Vorhandensein von Blut in der Haut, rötlich erscheint. Europäer haben im Vergleich zu den anderen Gruppen, generell hellere Haut, Haare, und Augen, obwohl dies nicht immer der Fall ist. Aus praktischen Gründen wird zwischen sechs verschiedenen Typen, gemäß der Fitzpatrick Skala (1975), unterschieden. Die Hautfarben werden nach abnehmender Helligkeit aufgeführt.

Scala Di Fitzpatrick

TYP	ANDERE BEZEICHNUNG	BRÄUNUNGSVERHALTEN	HAAR UND AUGENFARBE
I	Sehr hell, auch „nordisch“	Verbrennt oft, bräunt selten	Neigen dazu Sommersprossen zu haben; rotes oder blondes Haar; blaue oder grüne Augen
II	Hell oder hellhäutig	Verbrennt generell	Neigen dazu helle Haare zu haben; blaue oder grüne Augen
III	Mittelhell, oder dunkel häutiger Europäer oder „ durchschnittlicher Kaukasier“	Verbrennt manchmal, bräunt gewöhnlich	Neigen dazu braune Haare und dunkle Augen zu haben
IV	Mitteldunkel, auch „südländisch“ oder „mediterran-oliv“	Verbrennt manchmal, bräunt sich häufig	Neigen dazu dunkle Haare und Augen zu haben
V	Dunkel oder „Braun Typ“	Natürliche schwarz-braune Haut	Haben oft dunkel-braune Haare und Augen
VI	Sehr dunkel oder „Schwarz Typ“	Natürliche schwarz-braune Haut	Haben normalerweise schwarz-braune Haare und Augen

MIKRODERMABRASION - WAS GENAU IST DAS?

Mikrodermabrasion ist ein sicheres und kontrolliertes System intensiven Peelings, das durch die Anwendung Ultra feiner Kristalle, der Hautverjüngung verhilft. Die Kristalle wirken wie milde Schleifmittel auf der Haut, die abgestorbene Hautzellen Schicht für Schicht beseitigen. Die unregelmäßige Form der Kristalle verleiht Zugriff auf Zonen, die sonst schwer zu erreichen sind, ohne der Haut jeglichen Schaden zuzufügen. Die Behandlung verläuft progressiv, d.h. dass Kunden die Ergebnisse mit fortführendem Behandlungsverlauf wahrnehmen.

Das Ausmaß der epidermalen Abschleifung kann man variieren, indem man die Geschwindigkeit ändert, mit der die die Kristalle auf die Haut treffen. Die Beseitigung der Hornschicht ergibt eine Haut, die sich augenblicklich geschmeidiger und frischer anfühlt. Gleichzeitig wird das Wachstum neuer Haut, wie auch das von Kollagen gefördert. Während des Behandlungsverlaufes wird die Haut strahlend wirken und sich verjüngt anfühlen.

Die Vakuumbehandlung stößt benutzte Kristalle und abgestorbene Hautzellen ab, stimuliert den Kreislauf/ Zirkulation und fördert die Erhöhung des Blutflusses in dieser Zone. Die Elastin- und Kollagenproduktion werden angeregt, was zu einer festeren und jünger-aussehenden Haut führt.

Deutsch

Mikrodermabrasion kann an allen Hauttypen und allen Körper- und Gesichtsbereichen verwendet werden. SkinBase empfiehlt 8 Abläufe, die alle 7 bis 10 Tage ausgeführt werden sollten. Es könnte sein, dass Kunden mit Akne oder Akne Narben mehr Behandlungen benötigen werden und wir empfehlen, am Ende der Abläufe, eine monatliche Behandlung zur Aufrechterhaltung durchzuführen, um die erzielten Ergebnisse beizubehalten. Nach der Behandlung kann es sein, dass die Haut sich etwas gespannt anfühlt und leicht gerötet ist. Daher ist es wichtig, dass Klienten ein gutes feuchtigkeitsspendendes Produkt verwenden. Diese Auswirkungen lassen aber normalerweise innerhalb 24 Stunden nach Behandlung nach.

Was sind die Vorteile der Anwendung von Mikrodermabrasion im Vergleich zu anderen Behandlungsmethoden?

Es wurden selten Unannehmlichkeiten empfunden während der Mikrodermabrasion Behandlung und der Patient ist danach auch imstande mit der normalen Alltagsroutine fortzufahren. Kristall-Mikrodermabrasion benutzt ein träges und keimfreies Gemisch, sodass kein Risiko auf allergische Reaktionen besteht.

- Beseitigt mögliche Nebenwirkungen, die oft mit chemischen Lösungen in Verbindung stehen.
- Die Kunden können direkt nach der Behandlung mit ihren normalen Lebensgewohnheiten fortfahren (die Behandlung ruft z.B. keine extreme Errötung der Haut hervor).
- Kann gefahrlos alle Hautfarben und Hauttypen behandeln.
- Sofortige, sichtbare Ergebnisse sogar nach der ersten Behandlung (hilft Kunden motiviert zu bleiben).
- Verhilft die ersten Zeichen des Alterns zu bekämpfen und bietet eine allgemeine Verjüngung der gealterten Haut.
- Die Vakuumbehandlung bietet eine Besserung der Elastizität und Muskelspannung der Haut und stimuliert auch Fibroblasten für die Kollagenproduktion.
- Erhöht die Wirkung zugelassener Produkte nach der Behandlung.
- Ideal für gestaute Haut mit offenen Poren und Mitessern, wie auch für zu Akne neigende Haut.
- Variable Steuerung ermöglicht ein tieferes Peeling an verdickter, unreiner Haut , wie auch an Akne Vernarbung.
- Hilft unerwünschte Pigmentflecken erfolgreich zu beseitigen
- Ideal für sonnengeschädigte Haut
- Ganzkörper-Peelings ermöglichen eine Cellulite-Behandlung, da durch das Vakuum die Lymphdrainage unterstützt

Gibt es irgendwelche Risiken, die mit Mikrodremabrasion in Verbindung stehen?

Unsachgemäße Verwendung oder unhygienische Bedingungen stellen währen der Mikrodermabrasion Behandlung ein Risiko dar. Aus diesem Grund betonen wir, wie bedeutend gute Hygiene am Arbeitsplatz ist. Das MDPro gebraucht Einwegaufsätze, sodass das Risiko von Kreuzkontamination von Kunden zu Kunden vermieden wird. Diese Aufätze sind das Einzige, das während der Behandlung in Kontakt mit der Haut kommt.

DIE KRISTALLE

Die Kristalle bestehen aus Aluminiumoxiden, die natürlich vorkommende Minerale sind. Diese sind steril und unschädlich und verursachen deshalb keine Nebenwirkungen bei Hautkontakt. Trotzdem empfehlen wir zur Vorbeugung, einen Haut-Allergie-Test vor der Behandlung durchzuführen.

Man betrachtet das Einatmen von Aluminiumoxiden als niedriges Gesundheitsrisiko und geltende Industrienormen sehen jegliches Einatmen dieser Art als Staubbelastung an. das Einatmen feiner Staubpartikel, (z.B. künstlicher Fingernagelstaub) kann bei längerer Aussetzung zu Irritation und Husten führen. Aluminiumoxide enthalten keine freie Kieselsäure, d.h. es besteht keine Gesundheitsgefährdung der Atemwege beim Einatmen dieser Substanz.

Die Durchführung eines Haut-Patch-Tests ist wichtig, um herauszufinden, ob der Kunde empfindlich auf die angewandten Kristalle reagiert.

Empfindlichkeit gegenüber Kristallen - Patch Test

Obwohl es sehr unüblich ist, dass ein Kunde auf die Kristalle empfindlich reagiert, sollte trotzdem vor der Behandlung ein Hauttest auf der Rückseite des Unterarmes vollzogen werden. Bitte fahren Sie im Falle einer Irritation oder Schwellung nicht mit der Behandlung fort. Falls nach der Behandlung auf der Haut des Kunden rote Markierungen entstehen, so ist dies auf einen zu hohen Druck durch den Therapeuten zurückzuführen.

WELCHE HAUT KANN ANHAND VON MIKRODERMABRASION BEHANDELT WERDEN?

Jeder kann von Mikrodermabrasion Behandlungen profitieren. Es verbessert allgemein das Erscheinungsbild der Haut, in dem es der Haut ein gesundes Strahlen und ein jugendliches Aussehen verleiht. Mikrodermabrasion ist auch höchst effektiv bei vielfältigen Hautproblemen. Es kann an Gesicht und Körper angewendet werden, was es z.B. zu einer guten Behandlungsmethode gegen Akne Vernarbung am Rücken macht.

Akne und Akne Vernarbung

Mikrodermabrasion beseitigt die oberen Schichten abgestorbener Hautzellen an der Hautoberfläche, d.h. es ist besonders effektiv zur Akne Behandlung. Durch das Entfernen der abgestorbenen Hautzellen auf der Oberfläche der Haut, werden verstopfte Poren geöffnet, was die Möglichkeiten neuer Pickelentwicklung verringert.

Leichte Linien und Falten
Alternde Haut

Das Vakuum der Mikrodermabrasion Behandlung stimuliert die Kollagenproduktion in der Haut. Mit zunehmendem Alter verlangsamt sich die Elastin- und Kollagenproduktion. Die Kombination von Kollagenstimulierung und erhöhter Hauterneuerung wird den Zustand der Hautoberfläche verbessern, indem feine Linien und Falten geglättet werden.

Trockene und Dehydrierte Haut
Unregelmäßiger Haut Ton

Normalerweise erneuert sich die Haut selbst ungefähr alle 28 Tage. Indem die abgestorbenen Hautzellen von den oberen Hautschichten beseitigt werden, beschleunigt die Mikrodermabrasion die Häufigkeit, in der sich die Haut normalerweise selbst erneuert. Somit wird neue, frische Haut enthüllt, die ein strahlendes Aussehen verleiht.

Zellulitis, „Orangenhaut"-Effekt

Mikrodermabrasion kann nicht Zellulitis heilen, aber es kann die Zirkulation anregen und die Durchblutung in dieser Zone verbessern. Um das Erscheinungsbild von Zellulitis zu verbessern, sollten Kunden reichlich Wasser trinken und sich regelmäßig bewegen.

Dehnungsstreifen
Pigmentierung und Unreinheiten

Mikrodermabrasion kann erheblich das Erscheinungsbild von Pigmentierung und Dehnungsstreifen verbessern. Die Mikrodermabrasion Behandlung stimuliert Zonen, um eine höhere Kollagenproduktion zu erzielen und, um den Hauterneuerungsvorgang zu beschleunigen. Dies wird den Hautzustand verbessern und das Auftreten von Dehnungsstreifen, wie auch die Farblosigkeit der Haut reduzieren.

Die Mikrodermabrasion Behandlung wird nicht in der Lage sein die Dehnungsstreifen komplett zu beseitigen. Trotzdem wird regelmäßige Behandlung, die zu behandelnde Zone verbessern, indem diese weniger sichtbar wird. Narbengewebe sollte nicht behandelt werden, bis in dieser Zone keine Entzündung mehr vorhanden ist (z.B. 6 Monate nach Operation).

Regelmäßige Mikrodermabrasion Behandlungen werden das Erscheinungsbild von Dehnungsstreifen verbessern, indem das herumliegende Narbengewebe angeglichen wird, wodurch auch Pigmentierungsprobleme verringert werden, die oft die Dehnungsstreifen sichtbarer machen.

Hyperpigmentierung und ihre Ursache (Melasma)

Die meist offensichtlichen Ursachen sind die Einnahme der Antibabypille oder die Hormonersatztherapie, wie auch Schwangerschaft oder die Beeinträchtigung durch bestimmte Medikamente. Wiederholte Sonnenaussetzung oder übermäßige Aussetzung spielt eine große Rolle, genauso wie Entzündungen oder Traumen, die der Haut zugeführt wurden.

Gewisse Chemikalien, die z.B. in Parfums enthalten sind, können auch zu Pigmentierung führen. Regelmäßige Mikrodermabrasion Behandlungen werden sonnengeschädigter Haut bedeutende Verbesserungen bringen und unerwünschte Pigmentierungsspuren beseitigen.

Eine Anwendung der SkinBase Mikrodermabrasion Behandlung kann positive Ergebnisse erzielen in der Behandlung von Pigmentierungsspuren. Den Kunden sollte mitgeteilt werden, dass Eine Anwendung zwischen 10-15 Behandlungen benötigt wird. Es ist auch notwendig, dass den Kunden geraten wird zu jeder Zeit Sonnenschutz zu tragen.

Bitte berücksichtigen Sie, dass Mikrodermabrasion Behandlungen Kunden mit der Weiβfleckenkrankheit (Vitiligo) nicht helfen kann.

Melasma und Chloasma (Hautverdunklung durch Hormonveränderungen) können von Mikrodermabrasion Behandlungen profitieren. Es unterstützt das eingeklemmte Pigment dabei sich durch die epidermalen Schichten zu bewegen, um dann auf normale und natürliche Weise abgestoßen zu werden. Allerdings kann es sein, dass eine große Anzahl an Behandlungen benötigt wird, um die betroffene Zone zu verbessern.

WIE DER BEHANDLUNGSABLAUF FUNKTIONIERT

Die Mikrodermabrasion ist eher eine progressive als eine aggressive Behandlung. Die epidermalen Schichten werden behutsam und gefahrlos im Verlauf mehrerer Behandlungsabläufe beseitigt. Ein Behandlungsablauf wird alle 7 bis 10 Tage durchgeführt. Dies bedeutet, dass die Hornschicht, die beseitigt wurde, noch nicht die Möglichkeit hatte sich zu erneuern und auch, dass der Kunde sich an die Behandlung gewöhnt. Dadurch kann man, mit jeder Folgebehandlung, die Intensität der Behandlung erhöhen, um tiefer in die Schichten der Epidermis zu gelangen und erfolgreich Akne Vernarbung zu beseitigen, Pigmentierung zu beheben und feine Fältchen zu glätten.

Gewöhnlich entscheiden sich Kunden für die Anwendung von 6 Behandlungen, die alle 7-10 Tage durchgeführt werden, um maximale Ergebnisse zu erzielen. Nach der Ausführung eines Behandlungsablaufes, kann der Kunde sich dafür entscheiden eine monatliche Aufrechterhaltungsbehandlung zu erhalten, um die erlangten Ergebnisse beizubehalten.

Kunden mit einer eher problematischen Haut mögen einen längeren Behandlungsablauf benötigen, allerdings betrachtet man 15 -20 Behandlungen als das Maximum. Danach müssen Sie zu einen monatlichen Aufrechterhaltungsprogramm übergehen, das alle 4-6 Wochen durchgeführt wird.

Deutsch

LEKTION 3 - LERNERGEBNISSE

- fähig sein eine komplette Kundenberatung vor der Behandlung durchzuführen
- wissen was die Gegenanzeigen der Mikrodermabrasion Behandlungen sind
- verstehen welche Nachbehandlung erforderlich ist und welche möglichen Reaktionen die Behandlung verursachen können

KUNDENBERATUNG

1. Testen Sie, wie geeignet der Kunden für die Behandlung ist, indem Sie die Liste der Gegenanzeichen verwenden.
2. Analysieren Sie die Haut auf Zonen, die Sie während der Behandlung vermeiden sollten, wie z.B. geringe Gegenindikationen durch Teleangiektasie (beschädigte Kapillare).
3. Legen Sie Zonen fest, die besondere Vorsicht benötigen, wie z.B. Akne Vernarbung oder Pigmentierung, offene Poren oder unregelmäßiger Haut Ton.
4. Schlagen Sie einen Behandlungsplan vor und stellen Sie sicher, dass Sie die volle Kost, Dauer und Häufigkeit der Anwendung erklären.
5. Erklären Sie dem Kunden was die Behandlung tun wird und wie es sich anfühlen wird.
6. Erklären Sie wie Haut darauf reagieren könnte. Obwohl Reaktionen (wenn überhaupt) sehr geringfügig sind, vergewissern Sie sich, dass dem Kunden bewusst ist, es könne Empfindlichkeit bestehen.
7. Besprechen Sie mit dem Kunden die Nachsorgeberatung, sodass dem Kunden bewusst ist, was nach der Behandlung zu tun ist, um die Haut zu pflegen.
8. Es ist entscheidend, dass der Kunde die Bedeutung der korrekten Anwendung der Regeln zu Hause zwischen Behandlungen versteht und sich dafür einsetzt, Ergebnisse zu erzielen und beispielsweise die richtigen Sonnenschutzfaktoren zu benutzen, um weitere Pigmentierungsprobleme zu vermeiden.
9. **Füllen Sie immer einen Kundenbericht aus:**
   Dies wird gewährleisten, dass Sie besondere Vorsicht für die besonderen Bedürfnisse der Kunden haben walten lassen.

Eltern/Vormunde müssen den Beratungsbericht für Kinder unter 16 Jahre unterschreiben

Bedeutende Gegenindikationen – Nehmen Sie die Behandlung nicht vor, bei

Schwangerschaft

Ein Anstieg der Hormone kann die Haut während der Schwangerschaft beeinflussen. Dies kann zu Pigmentierung führen. Aus diesem Grund raten wir von Mikrodermabrasion ab, da die Haut auf eine unerwartete Weise reagieren könnte und sich der Zustand verschlimmern könnte. Raten Sie Kunden guten Sonnenschutz zu benutzen, wenn diese draußen sind, um Pigmentierung zu vermeiden.

Krebs

Wir raten Ihnen keine krebskranke Kunden zu behandeln. Diese sollten mindestens seit 6 Monaten geheilt sein, bevor Sie mit einem Behandlungsablauf anfangen. Mikrodermabrasion stimuliert die Durchblutung und die Lymphdrainage.

Akne Stufe 4

Kunden mit dieser Akne Stufe sollten nicht mit Mikrodermabrasion behandelt werden. Wenn die Haut mit Pusteln und Papeln sehr verstopft ist, dann würde eine Behandlung die Haut irritieren und Bakterien ebenfalls verbreiten.

„Roaccutan“

Roaccutan verursacht die Verdünnung der Haut. Falls Ihr Kunde mit Roaccutan gegen Akne behandelt wird, müssen Sie 6 Monate nach dem Abbrechen der Roaccutan Behandlung warten, bevor Mikrodermasion Behandlung durchgeführt werden kann.

Autoimmunerkrankung

Dieser Begriff beschreibt viele Störungen, in denen der Körper seine eigenen Zellen, wie auch sein eigenes Gewebe angreift. Sie sollten es vermeiden Kunden mit Autoimmunerkrankungen zu behandeln.

Diabetes

Diabetes wirkt sich auf die Nerven und die Durchblutung aus und die Haut kann eine längere Weile dauern zu verheilen, als gewöhnlich. Kunden müssen eine schriftliche Genehmigung von Ihrem Arzt beibringen, bevor die Behandlung durchgeführt werden kann.

Rosacea

Rosacea kann nicht mit Mikrodermabrasion behandelt werden.

Geringfügige Gegenindikationen –
Gehen Sie mit besonderer Vorsicht vor und vermeiden Sie betroffene Zonen

- Augeninfektionen z.B. Konjunktivitis (Bindehautentzündung), Gerstenkörner, Zysten
- Hautkrankheiten z.B. aktive Phasen der Akne, seborrhoische Dermatitis, Herpes Simplex (Fieberbläschen), Ekzeme, Psoriasis (Schuppenflechte)
- Keloid Narben
- Teleangiektasie (beschädigte Kapillare)
- Erhabene Muttermale, Warzen, Stielwarzen
- Schnittwunden, blaue Flecken, Schürfwunden

Falls Sie unsicher oder nicht in der Lage sind den Hautzustand zu identifizieren, dann sollten Sie den Kunden nicht behandeln und diesen raten einen Arzt aufzusuchen.

Deutsch

HINWEISE ZUR NACHBEHANDLUNG

Wir empfehlen Kunden folgende Hinweise nach der Behandlung zu befolgen:

Bis zu 12 h nach Behandlung
Tragen Sie kein dickes Make-Up auf

Bis zu 24 h nach Behandlung
Kein schwimmen
Keine Gesichtsenthaarung

Bis zu 48 h nach Behandlung
Keine Sauna, intensive Sonneneinstrahlung (z.B Solarium) oder Sonnenaussetzung
Keine „Botox-Injektionen ", Kollageninjektionen oder Hautfüller

Bis zu 72 h nach Behandlung
Benutzen Sie keine Anti-Falten-Cremes oder Cremes, die AHA's, Glykol säure oder Retinol enthalten. Benutzen Sie auch keine Haut-Peeling-Produkte, denn die neuerdings abgescheuerte Haut ist sehr empfindlich auf jegliche angewandten Produkte. Die Anwendung von Peeling-Produkten nach der Behandlung kann die Haut irritieren.

Zwischen den Behandlungsabläufen:
müssen Sie zu jeder Zeit ein LSF 15 (mindestens) auftragen und UV-Licht Aussetzung sollte vermieden werden.Die regelmäßige Anwendung von Feuchtigkeitscremes ist notwendig, um Feuchtigkeit wiederaufzustocken und die Haut vor dem Austrocknen und Abschälen zu schützen.

Produkte müssen einen pH-Wert zwischen 4.5 und 7 haben
Hautpflegeprodukte, die einen hohen Prozentsatz an pflanzlichen Stoffen und ätherischen Ölen haben, sind für die Nachbehandlung der Mikrodermabrasion ungeeignet, da einige der enthaltenen Inhaltsstoffe eine allergische Reaktion auslösen könnten. Sollte dies geschehen, kann die Gefahr erscheinen, dass beide, der Therapeut und der Kunde denken, dass die allergische Reaktion durch die Behandlung hervorgerufen wurde, dabei sind die Inhaltsstoffe der Hautpflege daran schuld. Es ist wichtig, dass Produkte verwendet werden, die Feuchtigkeit ersetzen oder hinzufügen, um die Haut vor Austrocknung und Abschälen zu schützen.

Botox/Hautfüller
Warten Sie 14 Tage nach einer Botox- oder Hautfüllerbehandlung, bevor Sie eine Mikrodermabrasion Behandlung durchführen, um diese abklingen zu lassen. Dies gilt auch für Wiederholungsbehandlungen.

Männer
Männer sollten sich am Abend vor der Behandlung gründlich rasieren, falls die Behandlung in der Früh ist. Wenn die Behandlung aber am Nachmittag ist, sollten diese sich in der Früh rasieren.

Laser Behandlungen
Laserbehandlungsabläufe können nicht zur gleichen Zeit mit Abläufen der SkinBase Mikrodermabrasion Behandlung durchgeführt werden. Bitte warten Sie mindestens 2 Wochen nach einem Laserbehandlungsablauf, bevor Sie mit Mikrodermabrasion beginnen.

Deutsch

LEKTION 4 - LERNERGEBNISSE

- fähig sein die verschiedenen Teile der Mikrodermabrasionsmaschine zu erkennen und ihre Funktionen zu verstehen.
- imstande sein das Gerät aufzubauen und testen können, dass alles richtig funktioniert.
- fähig sein die geeignete Behandlung gemäß des Hauttypen des Kunden zu bestimmen

WIE MAN DAS SKINBASE MDPRO SYSTEM AUFBAUT

1. Prüfen Sie immer, dass der Filterbehälter keine benutzten Kristalle enthält
2. Stellen Sie sicher, dass das Handset am Entsorgungsbehälter mit dem silbernen Schlauch verbunden ist und an beiden Enden fest angeschlossen ist.
3. Befestigen Sie einen sauberen Aufsatz mit einem neuen Kristallfläschchen an das Handset und schrauben Sie ihn fest ein.
4. Schließen Sie den elektrischen Draht an, betätigen Sie den Einschaltknopf und das Bedienfeld. Falls Sie eine „Pay-per-Use" Maschine haben, befolgen Sie die Anweisungen im Inneren der Maschine.

Wie man die Behandlungsstufe anpasst

Vergewissern Sie sich, dass das Kristallfläschchen mit dem Handset angeschlossen ist und drehen Sie das Regulierventil auf, während Sie den Zeigefinger über die Düsenöffnung halten, bis Sie den gewünschten Druck für das Gesicht haben.

Bitte stellen Sie sicher, dass Sie die geeigneten Druckstufen verstehen, bevor Sie mit der Mikrodermabrasion Behandlung beginnen.

BITTE BERÜCKSICHTIGEN:
Unter keinen Umständen sollte das Metallgehäuse abgeschraubt und angehoben werden, bevor die Stromzufuhr unterbrochen wurde.

BEHANDLUNGSSTUFEN

Die nachfolgenden Beschreibungen liefern eine Richtlinie, die eine geeignete Behandlungsstufe für Ihre Kunden zu bestimmen verhilft.

STUFE EINS - 0.3 bar

Frisch ausgebildete Therapeuten sollten diese Stufe benutzen, bis Sie mit dem anzuwendenden Druck vertraut. Stufe eins erlaubt ein sanftes, allgemeines Peeling und sollte immer für die erste Behandlung des Kunden gewählt werden. Verwenden Sie immer Stufe eins, wenn Sie Mikrodermabrasion im Augenbereich ausführen (federnde Wirkung).

STUFE EINS

-0.3 bar

- Frisch, ausgebildete Therapeuten
- Erste Behandlung
- Augenbereich

STUFE ZWEI - 0.4 bar

Diese Stufe sollte schrittweise bei der Behandlung von Aknenarben und dickeren Hautbereichen angewandt werden. Verwenden Sie keine höhere Stufe als Stufe zwei an schwarzen und asiatischen Hauttypen (siehe Fitzpatrick Skala).

STUFE ZWEI

-0.4 bar

- Zielgerichtet
- Nicht höher als Level zwei für schwarze/asiatische Haut

STUFE DREI - 0.5 bar

Diese Stufe sollte nur gegen Ende eines Behandlungsablaufs an Kunden ausgeübt werden, wenn deren Haut mehr verträgt. Diese Stufe wird für Akne Vernarbungen, Pigmentierung, feine Linien und Falten verwendet. Ebenfalls kann diese Stufe für Körperpeelings, Dehnungsstreifen und Zellulite angewendet werden.

STUFE DREI

-0.5 bar

- Am Ende des Behandlungsablaufes, wenn die Haut mehr toleriert
- Körperpeelings
- Problematische Haut
- Nur Zielgerichtet
- Niemals an schwarzer/asiatischer Haut anwenden

STUFE VIER - 0.6 bar

Nur für Körperbehandlungen anwendbar. **NIEMALS AM GESICHT AUSÜBEN**

LEKTION 5 – LERNERGEBNISSE

- In der Lage sein die Maschine zu bedienen und die Behandlung in der empfohlenen Behandlungszeit gefahrlos und effektiv durchführen können
- In der Lage sein innerhalb eines wirtschaftlich angemessenem Zeitrahmen zu arbeiten

BEHANDLUNGSMETHODE

1. Bringen Sie de Kunden in eine halb angewinkelte Liegeposition.
2. Vergewissern Sie sich, dass die Haare des Kunden nicht im Gesicht liegen.
3. Reinigen Sie das Gesicht des Kunden gründlich – Sie müssen ein gelartiges/schäumendes Reinigungsmittel verwenden.
4. Die Haut muss völlig abgetrocknet werden.
5. Dehnen Sie die Haut mit Ihrem Daumen und Mittelfinger aus.
6. Halten Sie das Handset, als ob es ein Stift wäre und machen Sie fegende Bewegungen quer über dem Gesichtsbereich (siehe Diagramm)
7. GENERELL – Führen Sie ein sanftes Peeling im gesamten Gesichts- und Nackenbereich durch.
8. ZIELGERICHTET – Nach Vervollständigung des sanften Peelings können Sie zu den Zonen zurückkehren, die weitere Zuwendung brauchen, wie z.B. Akne Vernarbung, Pigmentierungsanzeichen, feine Linien und Falten.
9. Nach Beendigung der Behandlung wischen Sie jegliche Überreste ab, die auf der Haut zurückbleiben, indem Sie angefeuchtete Wattepads verwenden (kaltes Wasser).
10. Wenden Sie sanftes Gesichtswasser an.
11. Nach Wusch können Sie dem Kunden eine Maske auflegen.
12. Legen Sie einen Feuchtigkeitspflegemittel auf.
13. Streichen Sie LSF 15 auf.

Anwendungsvorschriften der behandlung

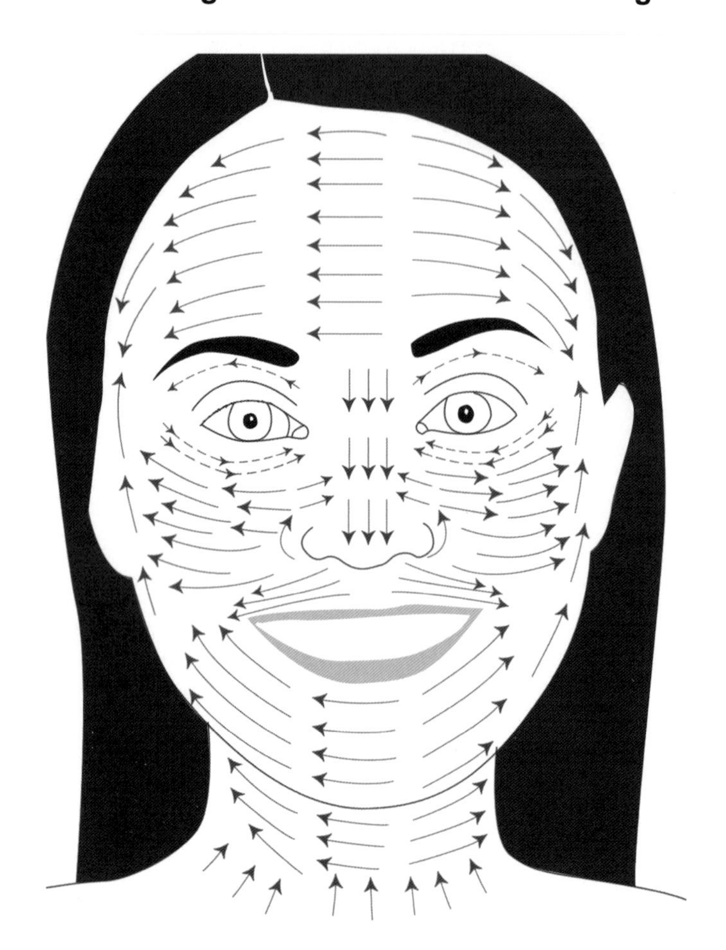

Das Diagramm zeigt die Vorschriften auf, die bei Gesichtsbehandlungen befolgt werden sollen.

Die gestrichelten Linien um den empfindlichen Augenbereich bedeuten schnelle und leichte Streichzüge. Jeder Pfeil ist ungefähr 4cm lang.

AUGENBEREICH

- Führen Sie federnde Bewegungen aus
- Verwenden Sie immer Stufe eins um den Augenbereich

Behandlungstipps

1. Sie sollten versuchen den Hautzustand des Kunden zu verstehen und verstehen, wie die Haut reagieren könnte, bevor Sie zu übermütig werden. Oft wollen Therapeuten ihre Kunden bei der ersten Behandlung so sehr beeindrucken, dass Sie zu viel Druck einsetzen und die Zone zu aggressiv bearbeiten. Dies führt dazu, dass die Haut sensibilisiert wird. Wenn Haut mit zu viel Druck bearbeitet wird, können rote Streifen sichtbar werden. Dies erfolgt aufgrund ehrgeiziger Therapeuten, die die Haut der Kunden nicht verstehen. Es ist notwendig, dass Therapeuten die Gleitbewegung über die Haut in einer sanften und kontrollierten Weise ausführen.

2. In der ersten Behandlung sollten Sie immer einen leichten Druck beibehalten und im Verlauf der Sitzungen langsam mit höheren Stufen und aggressiveren Behandlungen fortschreiten. Dadurch gewöhnt sich die Haut des Kunden an die Behandlung und der Kunde wird verstehen was vorgeht. Ein Kunde, der mit roten Streifen oder roter, empfindlicher Haut nach Hause geht wird ein unzufriedener Kunde sein, der höchstwahrscheinlich die nächsten Behandlungsabläufe absagen wird, da der Therapeut versäumt hat die Behandlung zu erläutern oder sie nicht richtig durchgeführt hat.

3. Übrigens: Benutzen Sie immer leichtes Vakuum an schwarzer und asiatischer Haut, wobei Stufe zwei nicht überschritten werden darf an Hauttyp V und VI der Fitzpatrick Skala.

4. Das Geheimnis des Behandlungserfolgs liegt am Druck der Streichzüge. Leichte, schnelle Streichzüge sollten für ein sanftes Peeling ausgeführt werden (federnd um das Auge herum), langsame Streichzüge sollten an Problemzonen angewandt werden. Bereiche, die von einem geringen Anteil Teleangiektasie (beschädigte Kapillaren) betroffen sind, sollten mit sanften und schnellen Streichzügen bearbeitet werden. Die Streichzüge sollten nicht länger sein als 4cm.

LEKTION 6 - LERNERGEBNISSE

- Gesundheits- und Sicherheitsprobleme bezüglich der Behandlung und die Instandhaltung des Geräts verstehen.

- fähig sein Kundenberichte sorgfältig zu aktualisieren

NOTWENDIGE MASCHINENAUFRECHTERHALTUNG

- Nach jeder Behandlung – schalten Sie das System aus und ziehen Sie den Stecker von der Stromquelle und aus dem Gehäuse.

- Beseitigen Sie das Kristallfläschchen und klopfen Sie das Handset auf Ihrer Handfläche ab, um jegliche Kristallüberreste zu entfernen. Jedes Mal wenn Sie ein Kristall-Fläschchen wechseln, schütteln Sie überschüssige Kristalle aus, die sich im inneren der Röhre ansammeln könnten. Dies garantiert, dass der Innenraum des Handsets zu jeder Zeit völlig freigehalten wird.

- Beseitigen Sie den Aufsatz und entsorgen Sie diesen.

- Entleeren Sie den Entsorgungsbehälter nach JEDER Behandlung, schrauben Sie den Entsorgungsbehälter vom Deckel ab; entleeren Sie die benutzten Kristalle vorsichtig und entsorgen Sie diese vernünftig.

- Stellen Sie sicher, dass der Entsorgungsbehälter gefahrlos und fest ersetzt wird und, dass er nicht überkreuzt angeschlossen ist

- Räumen Sie alle Schläuche und Zubehör in den Koffer und vergewissern Sie sich, dass alles sauber ist und bereit steht für die nächste Anwendung

WICHTIG:

Der Filterbehälter aus Plastik MUSS nach mindestens 80 Behandlungen ausgetauscht werden. Das Versäumnis einen neuen Behälter zu befestigen, führt dazu, dass die Vakuumleistung sinkt. Dies wiederum kann dazu führen, dass die Kristalle vom Papierfilter direkt in die Pumpe gesaugt werden, was das Gerät schwer beschädigen kann, und die Garantie erlischt.

Deutsch

INDICE

SkinBase™

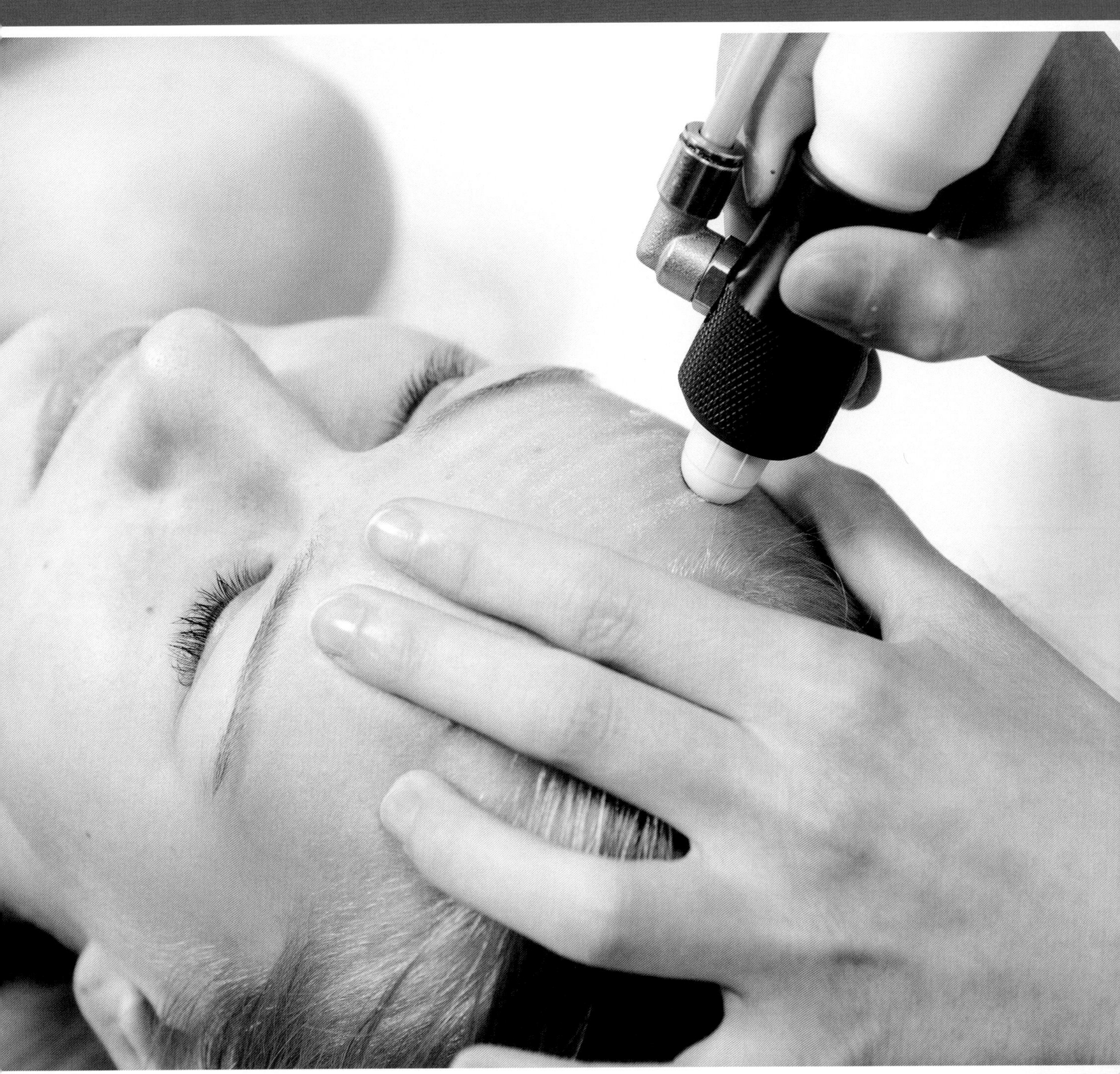

Microdermabrasion Utbildningsmanual

INNEHÅLL SIDA

UTBILDNING FÖR SKINBASE MICRODERMABRASION

Den här tvådagarskursen har utformats för att passa både nybörjare och erfarna utförare av microdermabrasion. Kursen täcker områden som Arbetsmiljö och säkerhet, Hudproblem och Hudsjukdomar, och ger också utbildning i att sköta apparaten så att dina kunder kan få en säker och trygg behandling i din verksamhet.

SkinBase MDPro är ett professionellt system för microdermabrasion, som tagits fram i Storbritannien. Med hjälp av terapeuter med flerårig erfarenhet av alternativa apparater på marknaden har vi tillverkat ett system som visar utmärkta resultat med hög kvalitet och erkänd pålitlighet.

Svenska

LEKTION 1 – UTBILDNINGSMÅL:

- Efter den här lektionen kommer du att vara medveten om och förstå ditt ansvar enligt arbetsmiljölagen och kunna handla därefter.
- Du kommer att kunna känna igen olika hudproblem och hudsjukdomar och förstå hur de kontraindikerar en viss behandling.
- Du kommer att få grundläggande kännedom om ansiktets och halsens anatomi och fysiologi.

ARBETSPLATSMILJÖ

Det här avsnittet handlar om ditt ansvar för dig själv, dina anställda (om du har några) och dina kunder beträffande arbetsmiljö. Det är viktigt att du känner till ditt ansvar och att du när så behövs ser till att nödvändiga åtgärder vidtas. Om du känner till vilka bestämmelser som gäller för arbetsmiljön kan du utföra behandlingarna på ett säkert sätt och uppträda professionellt och rutinerat på arbetet.

I arbetsmiljölagen fastslås vilka minimumstandarder för arbetsmiljön som gäller på arbetsplatsen. När du arbetar inom servicesektorn måste du enligt lagen tillhandahålla en säker och hygienisk miljö.

FÖR ATT UNDVIKA RISKER PÅ ARBETSPLATSEN SKA DU:

- Känna till vad lagen kräver av dig när det gäller att säkerställa att arbetsmiljölagen följs
- Se till att du själv uppträder enligt arbetsmiljölagens krav och följer de bestämmelser som gäller för arbetsplatser
- Följa gällande arbetsplatsrutiner för din arbetsfunktion och tillverkarnas anvisningar för en säker resursanvändning
- Att omedelbart rapportera eller åtgärda förhållanden som kan utgöra en risk på arbetsplatsen
- Ha beredskap för första hjälpen i fall av olyckshändelse eller sjukdom
- Ha en utrymningsplan och se till att alla anställda känner till vad den innebär
- Minimera risk för spridande av smitta och infektioner genom att hålla en hög hygienstandard

Elsäkerhet

Bestämmelserna gäller installation, underhåll och användning av elektrisk utrustning på arbetsplatsen. Elektriska utrustningar måste kontrolleras regelbundet av utbildad elektriker för att de ska uppfylla arbetsmiljökraven. Du ska föra register över de kontrollerna. Du måste vara medveten om de risker som elektriska utrustningar, exponerade ledningar, trasiga kontakter och överbelastade vägguttag kan medföra.

Det ligger visserligen på arbetsgivaren att se till att all utrustning är säker att använda, men de anställda har också ansvar att alltid kontrollera att utrustningen är säker innan de börjar arbeta med den och att aldrig använda den om den är trasig.

POTENTIELLA EL-RISKER

- Exponerade ledningar i kablar
- Trasiga kontakter eller vägguttag
- Överbelastade vägguttag

Första hjälpen

Även om du har vidtagit alla åtgärder för att se till att arbetsplatsen är så säker som möjligt, kan det ske olyckor. Se till att du har beredskap för första hjälpen och att alla vet hur de ska agera i fall av olycka, sjukdom eller annan nödsituation.

Alla arbetsplatser måste ha en första hjälpenlåda och en person som utsetts att kontrollera att den är komplett. Du ska ha en rapportbok, där du för in anteckningar om alla olyckor och incidenter.

DU SKA VETA:

Var rapportboken finns
Vem som är ansvarig för att kontrollera att första hjälpenlådan är komplett
Vem du ska informera vid olycka, sjukdomsfall eller annan nödsituation.

Avfallshantering

Avfall ska läggas i en soptunna med lock och isatt plastpåse, stark nog att inte rivas sönder. Soptunnan ska regelbundet rengöras med desinfekteringsmedel, varvid skyddshandskar ska bäras.

Hygien på arbetsplatsen

Det är viktigt att utrustningen steriliseras mellan kunderna, så att skadliga bakterier, svampar och virus som kan förorsaka infektion förstörs. God hygien på arbetsplatsen förhindrar korsinfektion och sekundärinfektion.

Korsinfektion är när mikroorganismer överförs genom fysisk kontakt personer emellan eller genom kontakt med ett infekterat instrument som inte har disinfekterats.

Sekundärinfektion kan utvecklas som resultat av en skada som kunden fått under behandlingen, eller om kunder redan har ett öppet sår, där bakterier kan komma in genom huden och förorsaka infektion.

Personlig hygien

En god hygien är av högsta vikt. Du ska tvätta händerna regelbundet och före och efter varje kund. Långt hår ska knytas bakåt, och du ska undvika att vidröra ansiktet. Om du har sår eller skrapmärken på händerna måste du sätta på ett rent plåster och byta det före och efter varje kund.

HUDÅKOMMOR OCH HUDSJUKDOMMAR

En kund som har en smittsam sjukdom bör inte genomgå skönhetsbehandling. Människor med vissa hudåkommor, även om de inte är smittsamma, bör inte heller behandlas av en skönhetsterapeut, eftersom behandlingen kan leda till en sekundärinfektion. Terapeuten måste kunna skilja mellan en frisk hud och en med en hudsjukdom eller hudåkomma.

VIKTIGT:

Om du är osäker eller inte kan identifiera en hudåkomma bör du inte behandla kunden, utan i stället råda honom eller henne att rådfråga sin läkare.

Vid vissa hudsjukdomar och hudåkommor är det olämpligt att genomföra en skönhetsbehandling. En sådan behandling skulle utsätta både terapeuten och andra kunder för risk för korsinfektion, och det är därför viktigt att du känner till de hudsjukdomar och hudåkommor som du kan komma i kontakt med.

Bakterieinfektioner

Bakterier kan finnas i stort antal på huden utan att orsaka någon skada. Men vissa typer av bakterier är skadliga för oss och kallas "patogena" bakterier. Patogena bakterier kan orsaka hudsjukdomar som är smittsamma, och du bör därför inte behandla en kund som konstateras ha följande bakteriella infektioner:

Impetigo, eller svinkoppor
Ytterst smittsamt och sprids lätt genom kontakt. Svinkoppor uppträder oftast på ansiktet, först kring näsa, mun och öron och kan sedan sprida sig till andra partier. Det börjar med röda kliande sår, som senare blir skorpiga och vätskande.

Konjunktivit, eller ögoninflammation
Ögoninflammation är inte alltid smittsamt, eftersom inflammationen kan ha orsakats av en allergisk reaktion eller av ett irriterande föremål. Men eftersom det skulle vara omöjligt för dig att avgöra det, bör du alltid behandla den som smittsam. Ögat är rött och inflammerat, ögonen kan också vara tåriga, och det kan komma var från ögonpartiet.

Hordoleum, eller vagel
Vagel är infektion av talgkörteln vid en ögonfransrot. Den orsakar en svullnad, som kan göra den omgivande vävnaden röd, och den angripna hårsäcken får oftast en liten klump fylld med var.

Furunkel eller spikböld
En spikböld orsakas av inflammation i hårsäcken, vilket får till följd en ansamling av var och död vävnad. Bölden är röd, varfylld, öm, varm och/eller smärtsam. En gul eller vit punkt kan ses mitt i när bölden är redo att tömmas.

Virusinfektioner

Viruspartiklarna är så små, att de inte själva kan växa och föröka sig, och därför behöver de en "värdcell". Virus tar sig in i friska levande celler i kroppen, så de kan föröka sig. De kommer in i kroppen på olika sätt, genom inandningsluften, genom saliv och sexuell kontakt. Vårt immunsystem är utformat för att ta bekämpa de flesta virus, och vi klarar själva lätt av de flesta infektionerna. Kunder som lider av följande virusinfektioner bör inte behandlas med microdermabrasion.

Herpes simplex (munsår)

Herpes smittar genom nära kontakt med någon som redan är har utslag. De känns igen på en stickande känsla i huden, följd av sår som får skorpor. Vanligen sitter de på näsans och läpparnas slemhinnor, men de kan också förekomma på andra hudpartier.

Bältros (herpes zoster)

Bältros är en infektion av en nerv och det hudparti som nerven leder till. Viruset angriper vanligen bara en enda nerv, oftast på bröstkorgen, buken eller övre delen av ansiktet. Symptomen visar sig i hudpartiet som nerven försörjer, och de består av rodnad, blåsor och sårskorpor.

Svampinfektioner

Svamp är parasitiska mikroskopiska växter som livnär sig på hudavlagringar. Vissa svampinfektioner finns på hudens yta, medan andra ligger djupare in i hudvävnaden. Kunder med svampinfektioner bör inte behandlas, eftersom de här sjukdomarna är smittsamma och kan spridas.

Ringorm eller Revorm

Ringorm är en svampinfektion i huden och förekommer på bålen, armarna, benen och ansiktet. Utslagen uppträder som röda fjällande fläckar på huden som sprider sig utåt. De läks inifrån, så att det blir en ring.

Andra hudåkommor smittar inte, men de bör ändå behandlas med viss försiktighet och i vissa fall helt undvikas.

Talgkörtelåkommor

Talgkörtlarna är små körtlar som avsöndrar ett fett sekret (talg) i hårsäckarna för att hålla huden smidig. De finns i störst koncentration i ansiktet och i hårbotten. Problem med talgkörtlarna kan t.ex. vara akne, rosacea och milier. Talgkörtelsåkommor orsakas vanligen av en överproduktion av talg.

Milier

Milier är cystor fyllda med hornämne och förekommer oftast runt näsan och ögonen. De är små, hårda, vita eller bleka prickar. De är inte smittsamma och kan tas bort genom att man sticker hål i den överliggande huden med en steril nål och sedan släpper ut hornämnet.

Komedoner/Pormaskar

Pormaskar orsakas av en överproduktion av talg och keratinceller som samlas i hårsäcken. De förekommer i ansiktet och på övre ryggen och bröstet och är inte smittsamma.

Talgcystor eller fettkulor

Kulorna bildas i hårsäcken när talgen blir blockerad och byggs upp till en knöl. De är inte smittsamma.

Svenska

Seborré
Seborré orsakas av en ökad avsöndring av talg och uppträder oftast under puberteten som följd av hormonförändringar. Personer som lider av detta har förstorade hårsäckar och överproduktion av talg. Det är inte smittsamt, och det förekommer vanligen i ansiktet och i hårbottnen. Det kan också förekomma på ryggen och på bröstet.

Akne
En ökning av talgproduktionen till följd av en obalans i hormonsystemet under puberteten framkallar en överproduktion av talg. Det i sin tur orsakar stockning i hårsäcksmynningen, vilket resulterar i hudinflammationer, pormaskar, pustler och papler. Akne är inte smittsamt, och det förekommer främst i ansiktet, på näsan, hakan och pannan. Aktiv akne bör undvikas under behandling med microdermabrasion.

Rosacea
Rosacea orsakas av en kombination av överproduktion av talg och en kronisk inflammatorisk sjukdom. Huden blir grov, porerna förstoras, och kinder och näsa blir röda och inflammerade. Huden kan se lilaaktig ut på grund av dålig blodcirkulation. Rosacea ska inte behandlas med Microdermabrasion.

Pigmentering

Hyperpigmentering – Ökad pigmentering
Ökad pigmentproduktion kan orsakas av UV-strålning och uppträder oftast under graviditet. Eftersom östrogen anses stimulera melaninproduktionen är det troligt att leverfläckar också orsakas p-piller. Leverfläckar uppstår på händerna, underarmarna, övre delen av bröstet och i tinningarna och pannan.

Fräknar uppstår när huden utsatts för UV-strålning, vilket stimulerar melaninproduktionen. De finns på näsan och kinderna hos ljushyade personer, och de kan också förekomma på händer, armar, axlar och rygg.

Åldersfläckar eller lentigo är pigmentfläckar, större än fräknar, och uppkommer antingen i barndomen eller i medelåldern som följd av solning. De finns i ansiktet och på händer och axlar.

Hypopigmentering - förlust av pigment
Vitiligo är vita hudpartier som inte har något pigment och därför är helt vita.

Albinism är när personen inte har något som helst pigment och huden, håret och ögonen därför är helt utan färg. Huden är blekrosa, ögonen är också rosa och håret är vitt.

Erythem
Erytem är en hudrodnad som beror på en utvidgning av blodkärlen som kontrollerar kapillärnäten i hudpartier som drabbats av skada eller infektion.

Vaskulära födelsemärken
Vaskulära födelsemärken är hudpartier med pigmentering som orsakats av permanenta kapillärutvidgningar

-Kapillärutvidgningar är små röda kapillärer som framträder på försummade eller torra hudpartier, t.ex. på kinderna.
-Spindelfödelsemärken är vidgade blodkärl med vidgade kapillärer som sprider ut sig från dem.
-Smultronmärken är röda eller lilafärgade bulliga märken som framträder på huden vid födelsen.
-Portvinsmärke är större partier med utvidgade kapillärer.

Telangiektasi (Brustna kapillärer)
Alla former av brustna kapillärer kan förvärras genom vakuumbehandlingen som ingår i microdermabrasion. De här bristningarna är ganska vanliga i partiet runt näsa och haka. Antingen undviker man partiet helt, eller också utför man behandlingen på mycket låg nivå.

Keloider
Keloider är ärrvävnad med onormalt mycket kollagen. Huden reser sig och blir röd med åsar. Den här typen av ärrvävnad kan inte behandlas med microdermabrasion. Hudbristningar och ärr efter operationer kan dock behandlas, men ju äldre hudbristningarna och ärren ju svårre det är att förbättra dem. Färsk ärrvävnad bör dock inte behandlas innan all inflammation har försvunnit (vanligtvis 6 månader efter operationen).

Dermatit
Dermatit är en inflammation i huden orsakad av ett irriterande ämne eller allergen. Det finns flera typer av dermatit. Symptomen kan vara att huden rodnar, kliar, flagar, fjällar, fuktar sig eller svullnar och ibland till och med får blåsor, beroende på hur allvarlig inflammationen är.

Dermatit orsakad av en irriterande substans kan uppstå kort efter det att huden utsatts för stark irritation eller efter en längre period av upprepad kontakt med ett svagt irriterande ämne. Vanliga orsaker till dermatit av denna typ är tvål, schampo och rengöringsmedel, damm, olja och fett och upprepad långvarig kontakt med vatten.

Allergisk kontaktdermatit uppstår när den drabbade utvecklar en allergi mot en substans. Vanliga sådana substanser är hårfärgningsmedel, lim och livsmedel, t.ex. skaldjur.

Eksem
Det finns två former av eksem, atopiskt eksem och kontakteksem. Atopiskt eksem utvecklas oftast i barndomen, och många barn växer ifrån det. Kontakteksem drabbar ofta vuxna och orsakas av kontakt med en allergen, t.ex. nickel eller rengöringsmedel, tvål eller parfymer.

När man får eksem blir huden kliande, torr och flagig och ofta är den röd och gör ont. Ibland fuktar den sig och blöder. Partier som ofta blir drabbade är ansikte och hals och i synnerhet arm- och knäveck.

Psoriasis
Psoriasis är en kronisk autoimmun sjukdom som påverkar huden och lederna. Psoriasis orsakar fjällande hudpartier som kallas psoriasisplack. Det är inflammerade hudpartier med överproduktion av hud, som snart blir silvervitt på grund av det tjocka hudlagret.

ANATOMI OCH FYSIOLOGI

Det är viktigt att en terapeut som ska utföra behandlingar har en viss kännedom om anatomi och fysiologi.

HUVUDETS OCH HALSENS BEN

Ansiktet består av 14 ansiktsben, som visas i diagrammet nedan.

Ansiktets ben

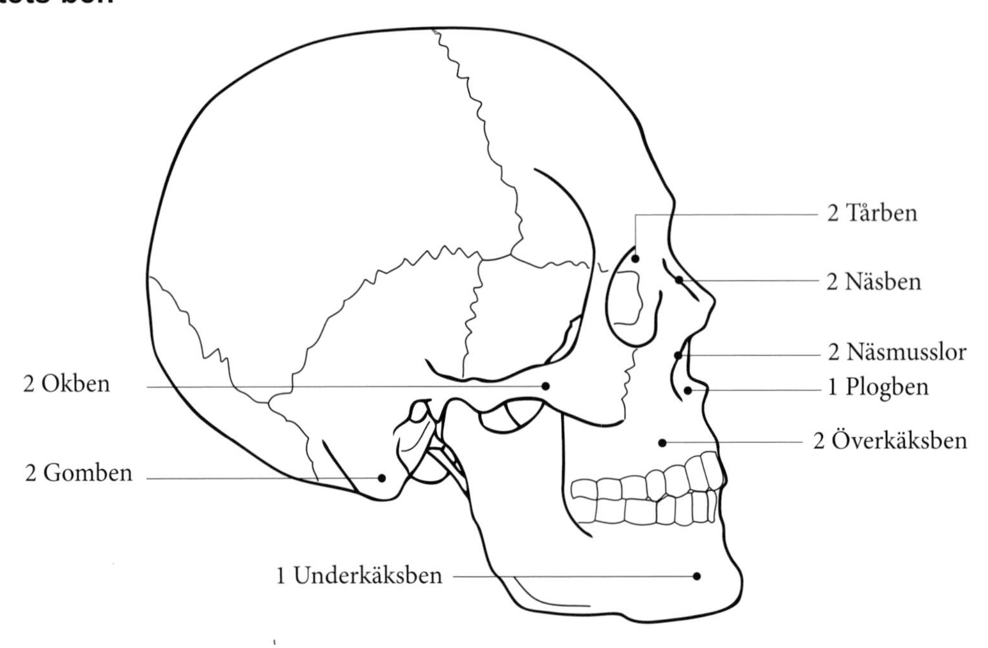

Ben	Beskrivning
Gomben	x 2 Utgör golv och vägg för näsa och tak för munnen
Näsben	x 2 Utgör näsryggen
Näsmusslor	x 2 Utgör näsans ytterväggar
Plogben	Utgör näsans mittenvägg
Tårben	x 2 Utgör ögonhålornas innerväggar
Överkäksben	x 2 Utgör tillsammans överkäken
Underkäksben	Utgör underkäken
Okben	x 2 Utgör kindbenen

Resten av skallen består av kraniebenen. Det finns 8 kranieben, som visas i diagrammet nedan.

Kranieben

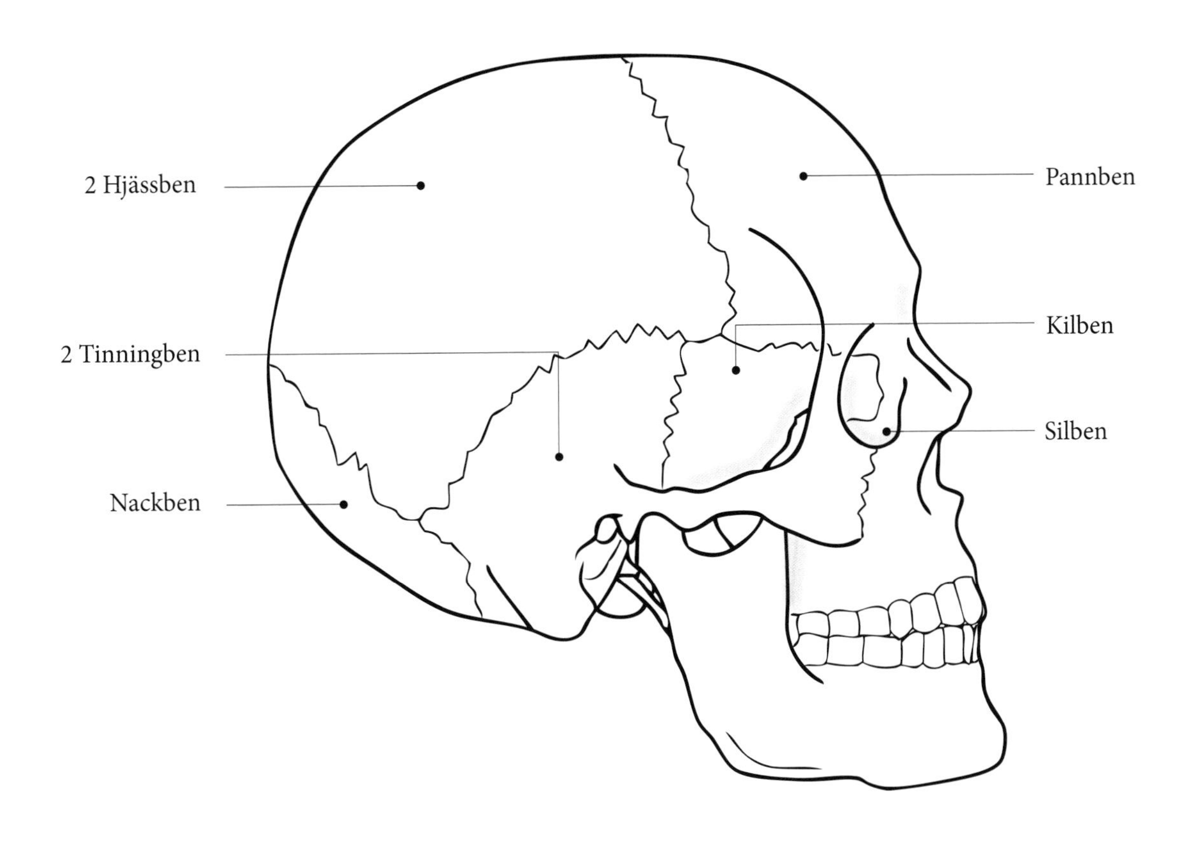

Ben	Beskrivning
Nackben	I bakre skallen, innehåller hål så att ryggmärg, nerver och blodkärl kan passera.
Hjässben	x 2 Sitter ihop och bildar hjässan
Pannben	Panna och övre del av ögonhålorna
Tinningben	x 2 Sidorna av huvudet
Silben	Bildar del av näshålorna
Kilben	Fladdermusformat ben som håller ihop alla kraniebenen

Hals, bröstkorg och skulderblad

Fram

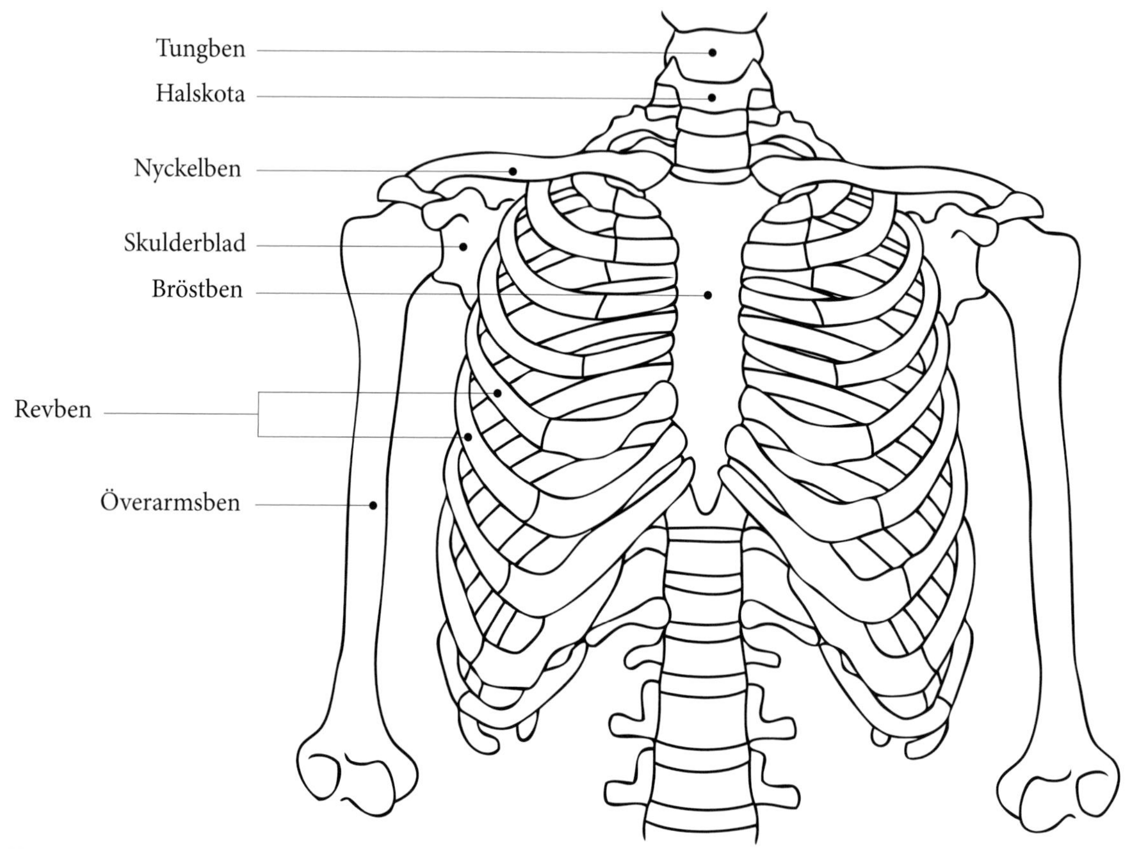

Bak

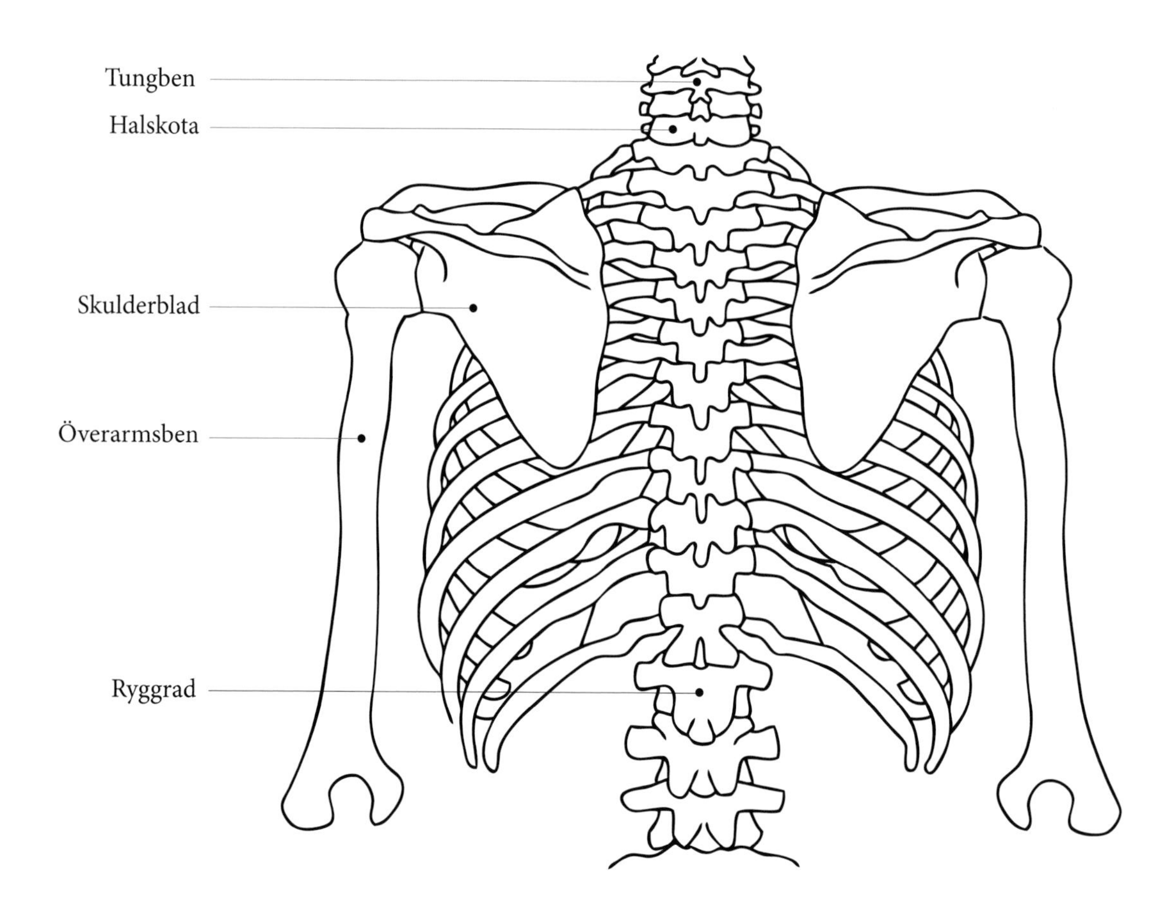

ANSIKTETS OCH HALSENS MUSKLER

Musklerna i ansiktet ansvarar för våra ansiktsuttryck. När vi blir äldre gör uttrycken som vi använder ofta rynkor på huden, och vi börjar visa yttre tecken på åldrande. Microdermabrasion tar bort döda celler från huden och göra så att de tunna linjerna och rynkorna inte framträder så tydligt.

Svenska

Ansiktets muskler

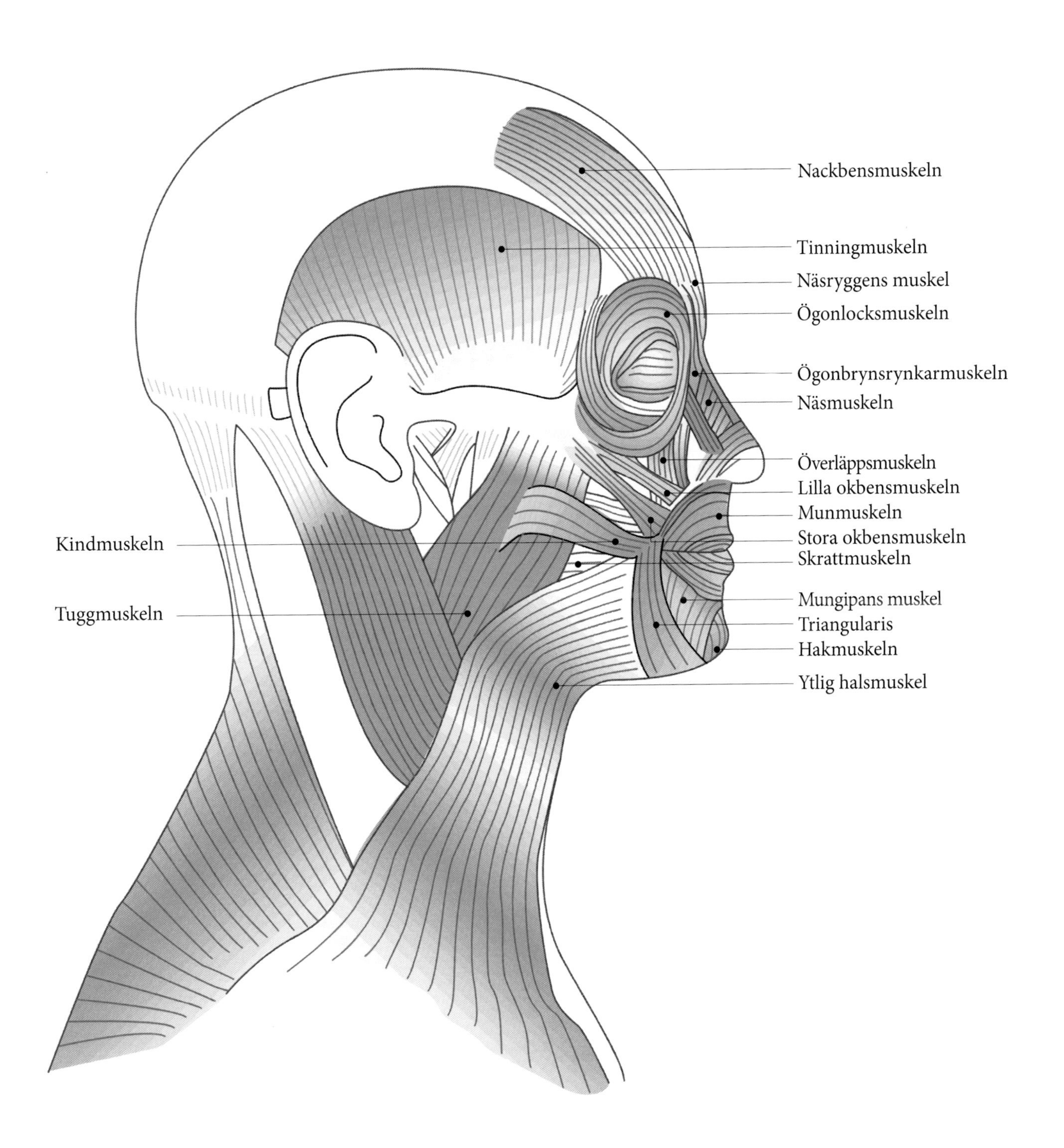

Svenska

Halsens Muskler

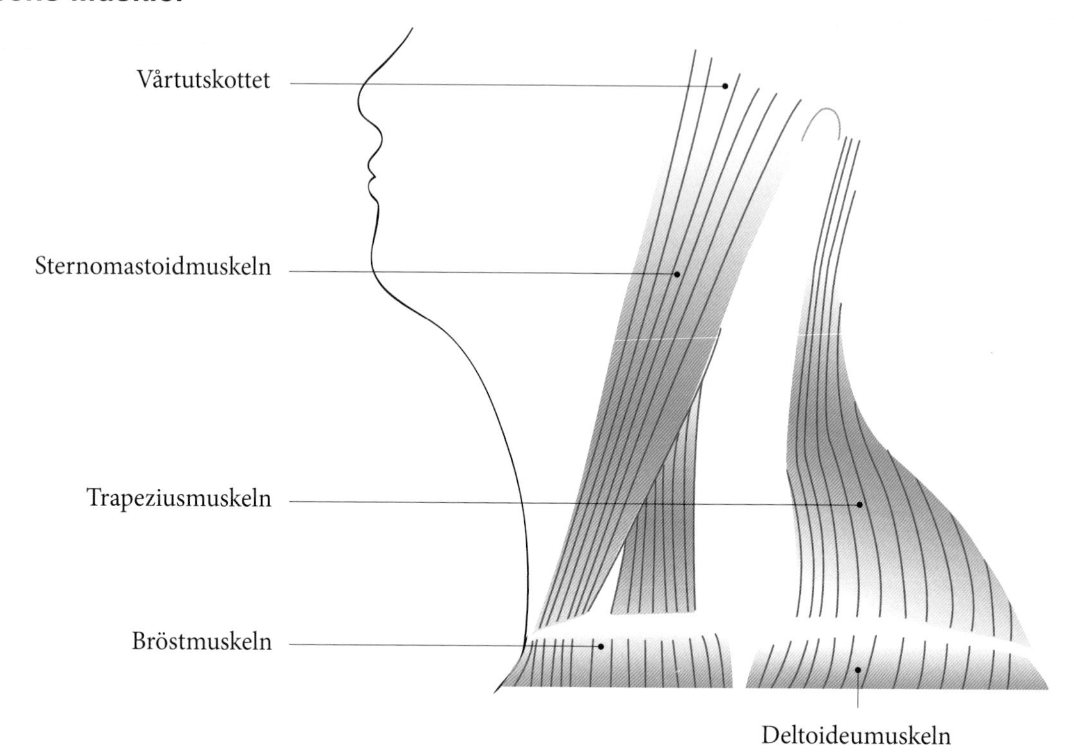

KRANIALNERVER

Nervsystemet är kroppens verktyg för att skicka meddelanden från hjärnan till andra delar av kroppen.

Nerverna i ansikte och hals, eller "kranialnerverna", kontrollerar musklerna i huvudet och halsen och förmedlar nervimpulser (känselinformation) från sinnesorganen till hjärnan.

De 5e, 7e and 11e kranialnerverna är de som vi ägnar oss åt när vi gör ansiktsbehandlingar.

5e Kranialnerven - "Trillingnerven"

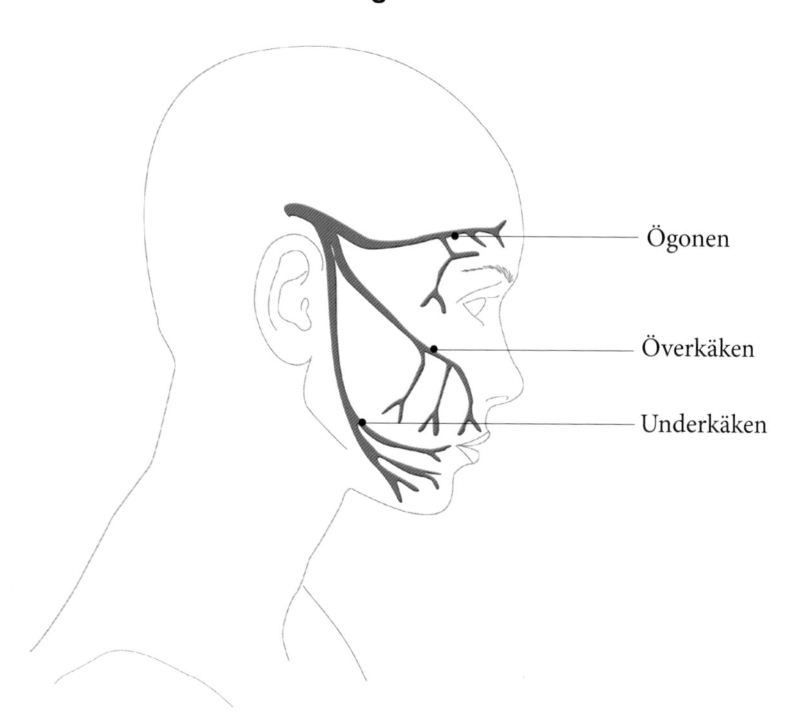

7e Kranialnerven – "Ansiktsnerven"

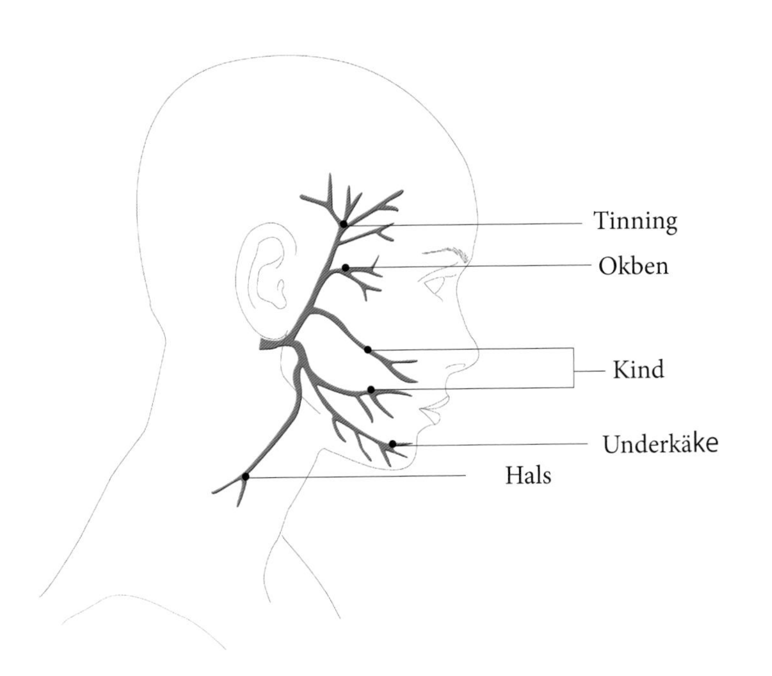

11e Kranialnerven - "Hjälpnerven"

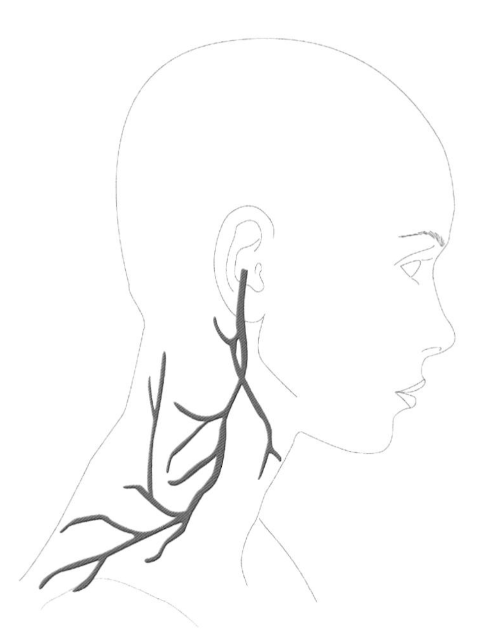

Nerv	Funktion	Nervgrenar	Skickar signaler till:
5e Trillingnerven	Styr tuggmusklerna	Till ögonmusklerna	Tårkörtlarna Pannans muskler Övre delen av kinderna
	Förmedlar känselinformation från ansiktet	Till överkäksmusklerna	Övre delen av käken
		Till underkäksmesklerna	Nedre delen av käken
7e Ansiktsnerven	Styr musklerna för ansiktisuttryck	Till tinningsmuskeln	Muskler runt ögonen
		Till okbensmuskeln	Muskler i pannan Ögonmuskler
		Till kindmuskeln	Överläppen Sidorna av näsan
		Till underkäksmuskeln	Underläppen Hakan
		Till halsmuskeln	Sidorna av halsen och hakan
11e Hjälpnerven	Rör hals och axlar		

LEKTION 2 - UTBILDNINGSMÅL:

- Grundläggande kännedom om hudens uppbyggnad och funktion
- Du kommer att kunna känna igen olika hudtyper
- Goda kunskaper i microdermabrasionens teori
- Du kommer att kunna identifiera problempartier som kan behandlas med microdermabrasion
- Förstå hur en serie microdermbrasionbehandlingar fungerar

HUDEN

Huden är kroppens största organ. Huden skyddar oss från den omgivande miljön på många olika sätt.

- Förhindrar att skadliga ämnen tas upp av kroppen
- Hjälper till att reglera kroppstemperaturen
- Fungerar som barriär mot infektioner
- Melanin i huden skyddar oss från skadlig påverkan från UV-strålning
- Ger ett vattentätt skyddstäcke som skyddar oss från uttorkning
- Fungerar som energireserv i form av lagrat fett

Hudens uppbyggnad

Huden består av två väl avskilda lager; överhuden och läderhuden. Mellan dem ligger basalmembranet, som håller ihop de två lagren. Nedanför dessa lager finns underhuden, ett fettlager som skyddar, stötdämpar, isolerar och lagrar extra energi för kroppen.

Överhuden

Överhuden är det övre lagret i huden. Den består av fem lager. De olika lagren i överhuden kan kännas igen på cellernas form och funktion. Den dominerande celltypen i överhuden är keratinocyten, som producerar proteinet keratin, eller hornämne.

Cellförnyelsen sker under en period av omkring fyra veckor. Cellerna förs uppåt från nedre lagret av överhuden (tillväxtlagret) till det övre lagret (hornlagret), och ändrar samtidigt form och struktur. Den övre delen av överhuden dör och stöts bort från huden. Det kallas avstötning eller "deskamation". Det är det lagret som avlägsnas i microdermabrasionsbehandlingen, och det är också det lagret som hjälper till att reflektera UV-strålningen bort från huden, vilket gör det extra viktigt att kunderna använder solskyddsfaktor efter microdermabrasionsbehandlingen.

Överhuden

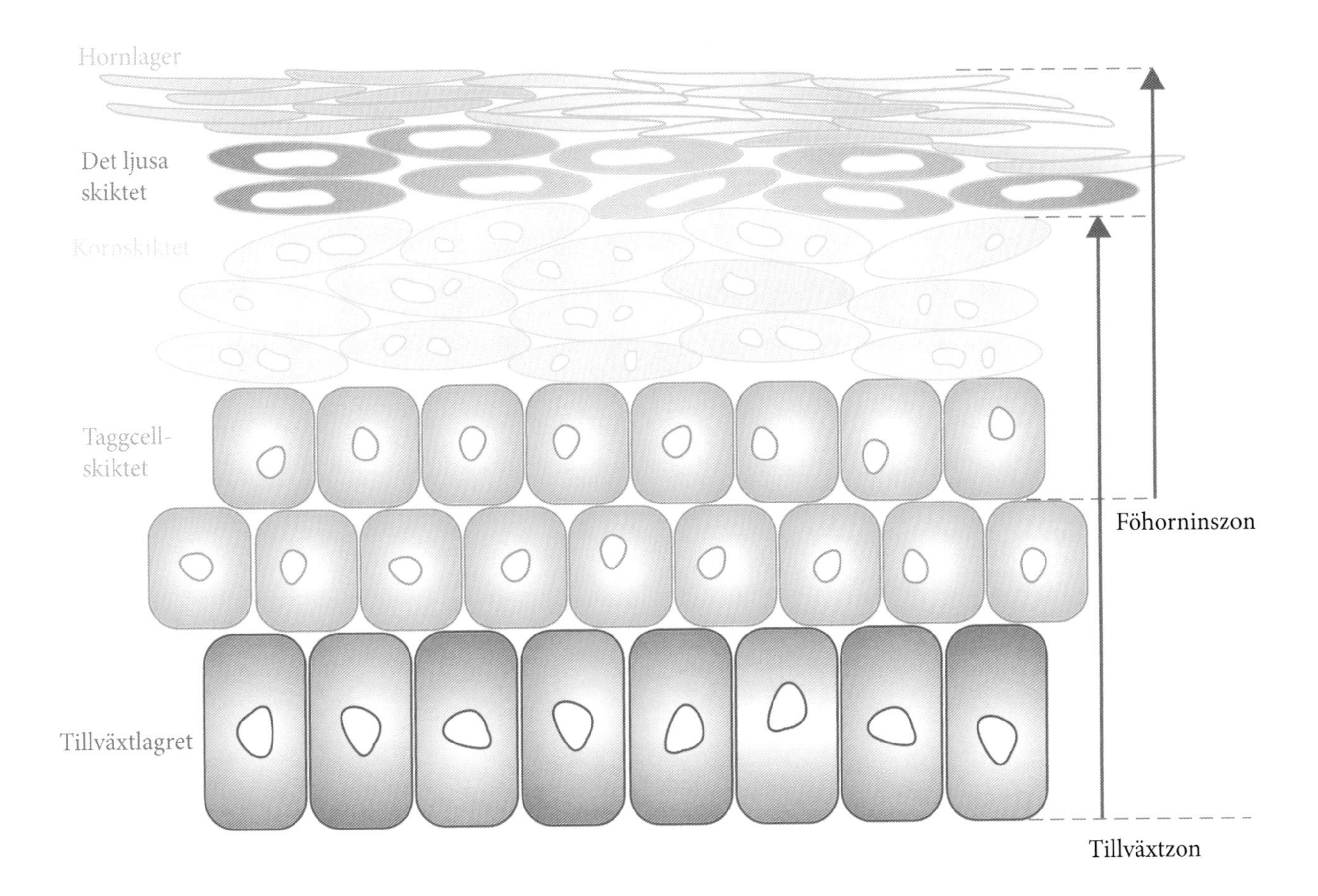

Svenska

Överhudens fem lager

1. Stratum Corneum eller 'Hornlagret'

Hornlagret är överhudens yttersta lager och består av flera lager hopplattade, i huvudsak döda överlappande celler. De cellerna hjälper till att reflektera UV-strålningen.

Mycket mörk hud, som har utvecklas för att stå emot stark UV-strålning, har ett tjockare hornlager än ljus hud. Det tar omkring tre veckor för hudcellerna att komma upp från tillväxtlagret till hornlagret. Cellerna avstöts sedan i en process som kallas deskamation.

2. Stratum Lucidum eller 'Det ljusa skiktet'

Det ljusa skiktet finns bara i tjockare partier av överhuden, t.ex. i handflatorna och fotsulorna.

3. Stratum Granulosum eller 'Kornskiktet'

I kornskiktet börjar cellerna dö. De här cellerna innehåller något som ser ut som korn och som orsakas av att cellerna håller på att brytas upp. De kornen kallas keratohyalinkorn och omvandlas senare till keratin (=hornämne).

4. Stratum Spinosum eller 'Taggcellsskiktet'

Taggcellsskiktet består av celler som har en taggig yta (därav namnet) som förbinder dem med omgivande celler. Det är i det här lagret som förhorningen börjar.

5. Stratum Germinativum eller 'Tillväxtlagret'

Pelarformade celler ansvarar för produktion av nya hudceller. Cellerna delar sig och vandrar upp i de högre lagren. De återstående cellerna delar sig och fyller ut mellanrummen. Den här celldelningen kallas mitos. Överhudens tillväxtzon innehåller två andra viktiga celler, Langerhans celler och melanocyter. Langerhans celler absorberar och oskadliggör främmande materia som kommer in i huden. De rör sig ut från överhuden och ner i läderhuden och fortsätter in i lymfsystemet, kroppens "avfallssystem" Melanocytceller ansvarar för produktionen av melanin i huden. De skyddar andra hudceller från skadlig påverkan från UV-strålning. Melaninet bestämmer vår hudfärg - ju mer melanin vi har, desto mörkare är huden.

Svenska

Läderhuden

Läderhuden är lagret nedanför överhuden och svarar för styrkan och elasticiteten i huden. Den innehåller också många specialiserade celler och strukturer, t.ex. nerver, blodkärl, körtlar och hårsäckar. Läderhuden består av två skikt, det papillära och det retikulära skiktet. Det övre skiktet, det papillära, innehåller ett tunt lager av kollagenfibrer. Det retikulära skiktet nedanför består av täta kollagenfibrer som ligger parallellt med hudens yta.

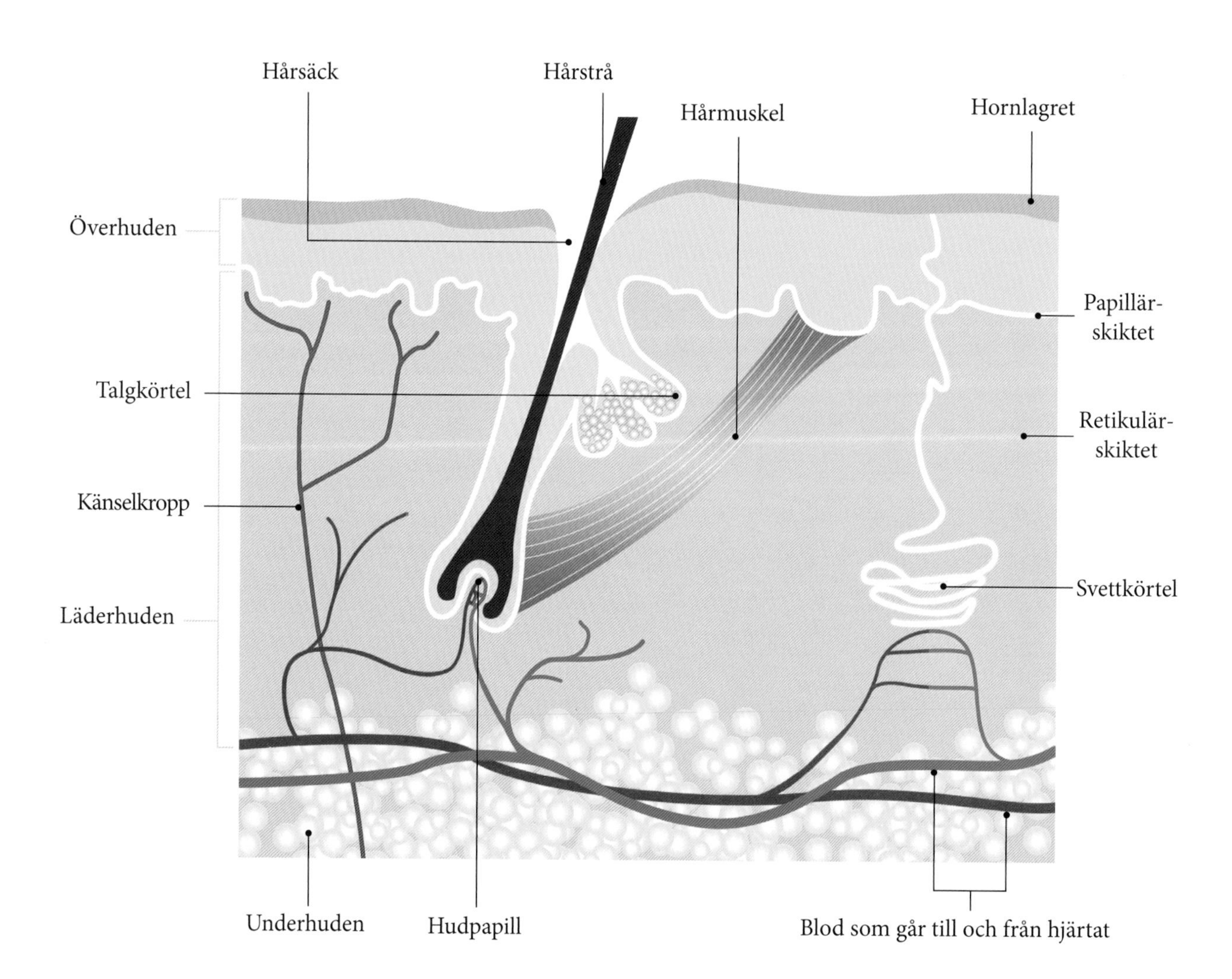

Retikulära skiktet

Retikulära skiktet består av två sorters protein: elastinfibrer, som ger huden dess elasticitet, och kollagenfibrer, som ger den dess styrka. De här fibrerna omsluts av en geléliknande substans som kallas grundsubstans. Elastinfibrerna och kollagenfibrerna bildar ett starkt nätverk som ger oss ett ungt utseende.

När vi åldras börjar de här fibrerna att bli hårdare och falla sönder. Nätverket börjar brytas ner, och huden förlorar sin elasticitet och visar tecken på åldrande. Blodtillförseln till huden blir sämre, näringsämnena når inte upp till ytan, och huden blir färglös. Fettlagret under huden blir tunnare, vi får hårdare ansiktsdrag och benstrukturen blir mer framträdande. Det retikulära skiktet är viktigt för hudens hälsa och utseende, och därför är det viktigt att vi sköter det och förhindrar ålderstecknen.

Blodflödet

Blodet cirkulerar genom kroppen till alla cellerna och för med sig viktiga näringsämnen och energi, t.ex. syre, glykos och andra råmaterial som är viktiga för kroppens hälsa, skötsel och tillväxt.

Vakuumfunktionen i microdermabrasionsbehandlingen hjälper stimuleringen av mikrocirkulationen nära hudens yta. Det ger en ökad blodtillförsel till det partiet, vilket främjar kollagen- och elastinproduktionen i huden och även cellförnyelsen (hudregenerering), så att vävnaderna repareras och resultatet blir en slätare och fräschare hud.

Det här diagrammet visar hur blodet flyter genom cellerna. Först tillförs näring och syre, och därefter avlägsnas avfallsprodukterna, så som koldioxid.

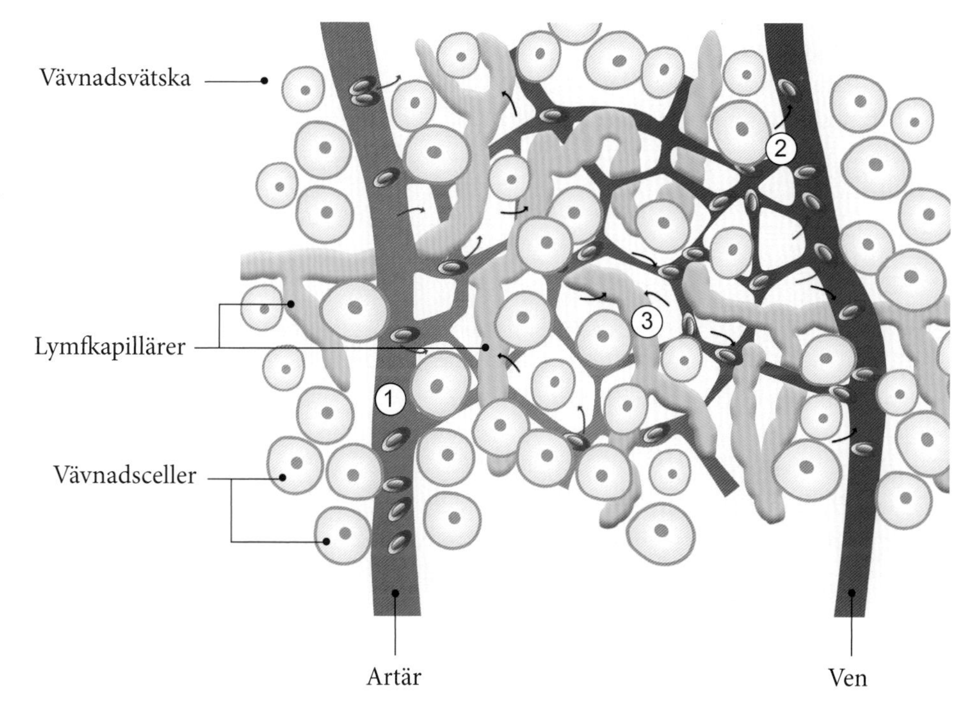

① Blodet är under högt tryck när det flyter genom kapillärnätet och pressar ut vätska i vävnaden. Vätskan, som nu kallas vävnadsvätska, för med sig nyttiga substanser, t.ex. syre och näring som är nödvändiga för cellerna. Blodceller och stora proteiner stannar kvar i kapillärerna.

② När blodet har lämnat sitt syre, reverserar trycket och en del av vätskan som innehåller avfallsprodukter strömmar tillbaka in i kapillärerna för att föras bort.

③ Överflödig vätska, avfallsprodukter och stora molekyler, t.ex. proteiner som inte kunde komma in i blodet igen, tas upp av lymfkapillärerna och förs till lymfnoderna, där de tas om hand och sedan förs tillbaka in i blodbanan närmare hjärtat.

Blodströmmen genom huden

Normal kroppstemperatur är 37°c. Kroppen försöker hålla den temperaturen. Om kroppstemperaturen stiger, går blodet närmare huden för att avge värme. När kroppstemperaturen faller, dras kapillärerna ihop, och blodet passerar genom "växlingsblodkärl" som ligger djupare i läderhuden, för att på så sätt minska värmeförlusten genom huden.

Vasodilation inträder när du är:
Varm - Blodet passerar nära ytan, och värme avges

Vasokonstriktion inträder när du är:
Kall - Blodet passerar genom "växlingsblodkärl" bort från ytan , och värme hålls kvar

Hudtyper

Det finns sex stora hudtyper, men en persons ansiktshud kan variera under olika faser i livet, beroende på sjukdom eller hormonell obalans.

Torra hudtyper

Torr hud orsakas av underaktiva eller inaktiva talgkörtlar som inte producerar tillräckligt med fett för att hålla huden naturligt fuktad. Huden blir glanslös, och den känns torr och kliande, ibland känslig för beröring. Torr hud måste återfuktas från insidan (genom att man dricker vatten) och från utsidan med feta fuktgivande krämer eller salvor.

Feta hudtyper

Fet hud orsakas av talgkörtlar som producerar för mycket talg, vilket gör att huden ser glansig ut, med stora öppna porer. Feta hudtyper utvecklar ofta pormaskar och finnar. Trots de här olägenheterna ser fet hy oftast yngre ut och håller sig smidig längre än andra hudtyper. Fet hud mår mycket bra av microdermabrasion, med en efterbehandling av en lätt återfuktare.

Känsliga hudtyper

Känsliga hudtyper kan vara torra, normala eller feta och kännetecknas av att de lätt blir irriterade. Känsliga hudtyper reagerar ofta negativt på olika miljöfaktorer och kräver oftast specialbehandling för att hållas i god kondition. Känslig hud har mycket stor behållning av naturliga hudvårdsprodukter och behandlingar.

Normala hudtyper

Normal hud producerar lagom med talg, och huden är i balans. Normal hud är smidig, väl fuktbalanserad och har frisk färg. En normal hud är något att vara tacksam för, men den måste skötas. Den mår mycket bra av regelbunden rengöring, toning och återfuktning.

Blandade hudtyper

Blandad hud är den vanligaste hudtypen. Den känns oftast igen på en fet T-formad zon som täcker panna, näsa och haka, medan huden runt kinder, ögon och mun är normal till torr. Personer med blandad hudtyp bör låta huden ses över regelbundet och använda olika produkter på olika partier i ansiktet.

Mogna hudtyper

Äldre hudtyper har följande kännetecken: Huden blir torr när talgkörtlarna blir mindre aktiva. Huden förlorar sin elasticitet och det uppstår fina linjer och rynkor. Huden verkar tunnare och får små brustna blodkärl, särskilt på kinderna och runt näsan. Ansiktets konturer blir slappa när muskeltoningen minskar. Den underliggande benstrukturen framträder tydligare när fettlagret under huden tunnas ur. Blodcirkulationen försämras, vilket försvårar näringstillförseln i huden, och huden blir glanslös. Den försämrade ämnesomsättningen gör att slaggprodukter inte förs bort så snabbt, huden ser ofta "påsig" ut. Äldre hud måste återfuktas genom att man dricker vatten regelbundet och använder närande fuktkrämer.

Hudfärgstyper

Färgen på människans hud kan variera från mörkbrun till nästan färglös pigmentering, som på grund av blodet i huden ser närmast rosa ut. Européer har i allmänhet ljusare hud, hår och ögon än andra grupper, även om detta inte alltid stämmer. Av praktiska skäl kan man räkna med sex typer enligt Fitzpatrickskalan (1975). Hudfärgerna har listats från ljusaste till mörkare.

Fitzpatrickskalan

HUDTYP	OCKSÅ KALLAD	REAKTION PÅ SOLNING	HÅR-OCH ÖGONFÄRG
I	Mycket ljus	Blir ofta röd sällan brun	Har ofta fräknar, rödhårig eller blond, blå eller gröna ögon
II	Ljus eller ljushyad	Blir ofta röd	Har ofta ljust hår, blå eller gröna ögon
III	Mellanljus eller mörk hud	Blir ibland röd, oftast brun	Har oftast brunt hår och mörka ögon
IV	Mellanmörk/oliv	Blir ibland röd, oftast brun	Har ofta mörkbrunt hår och bruna ögon
V	Mörk eller brun hudtyp	Naturligt brun hud	Har ofta mörkbrunt hår och mörkbruna ögon
VI	Mycket mörk, hudtyp	Naturaligt svart-brun hud	Har oftast svart eller brunt hår och svarta eller bruna ögon

MICRODERMABRASION - VAD ÄR DET?

Microdermabrasion är ett säkert, kontrollerat system av intensiv exfoliering som föryngrar huden med hjälp av ultrafina kristaller. Kristallerna verkar som en lätt slipning av huden och avlägsnar döda celler, lager för lager. Kristallernas oregelbundna form gör det lättare att arbeta på svåråtkomliga partier utan att skada huden. Behandlingen är progressiv, vilket betyder att kunden hela tiden ser resultat vartefter som behandlingen pågår.

Graden av överhudsslipning kan varieras genom att kristallernas hastighet ändras när munstycket förs över huden. När hornlagret avlägsnas känns huden genast slätare och friskare, och nybildningen av ny hud och kollagen stimuleras. Under behandlingsserien märker man hur huden får en ny lyster och känns ung igen.

Genom vakuumfunktionen drivs använda kristaller och döda hudceller bort, och samtidigt stimuleras blodcirkulationen, och blodflödet till partiet ökar. Produktionen av kollagen och elastin stimuleras, vilket gör huden fastare och ungdomligare.

Microdermabrasion kan användas på alla hudtyper på alla partier på kroppen och ansiktet. SkinBase rekommenderar en serie på 8 behandlingar, vanligen utförd var 7 – 10 dag. Personer med ärr efter akne kan behöva fler behandlingar, och vi rekommenderar 1 behandling varje månad efter behandlingsseriens slut för att upprätthålla resultaten. Efter behandlingen kan huden kännas stram och bli något röd. Därför är det viktigt att kunderna använder en bra fuktkräm. Eventuella bieffekter är milda och försvinner 24 timmar efter behandlingen.

Vilka är fördelarna att använda microdermabrasion framför andra behandlingsmetoder?

Obehaget som kan kännas under en microdermabrasionsbehandling är mycket litet, och patienten kan fortsätta med sin dag som normalt efteråt. Kristallmicrodermabrasion använder en helt neutral och steril substans med ingen risk för allergisk reaktion.

- Eliminerar möjliga negativa reaktioner som ofta är förknippade med kemiska lösningar.
- Kunden kan återvända till sitt normala liv omedelbart efter behandlingen. Det blir t.ex. ingen onormal rodnad i huden.
- Alla hudfärger och hudtyper kan behandlas på ett säkert sätt.
- Omedelbara synliga resultat, redan efter den första behandlingen, vilket gör kunden motiverad.
- Bidrar till att motverka tidiga tecken på åldrande och ger en allmän föryngring av huden.
- Vakuumverkan ger en förbättrad elasticitet och muskeltoning av huden och stimulerar också fibroblasternas kollagenproduktion.
- Gör så att hudprodukter lättare tas upp av huden efter behandlingen.
- Perfekt för oren hy med öppna porer och pormaskar och hud som ofta drabbas av akne.
- Varierbar intensitet med djupare exfoliering av förtjockad skadad hud och ärrbildningar, t.ex. efter akne.
- Bidrar framgångsrikt med att avlägsna oönskade pigmenteringsmärken.
- Perfekt för solskadad hud.
- Exfoliering av hela kroppen fungerar som cellulitbehandling, eftersom behandlingens vakuumverkan ger lymfdränering.

Finns det några risker förknippade med microdermabrasion?

Olämpligt användande eller ohygieniska förhållanden utgör en risk när man utför microdermabrasionsbehandling, och det är därför som vi insisterar på god hygien på arbetsplatsen. MDPro använder engångsmunstycken och utesluter på så sätt riskerna för korsinfektion mellan kunderna, eftersom munstycket är den enda komponenten som kommer i kontakt med huden under behandlingen.

KRISTALLERNA

Kristallerna är gjorda av aluminiumoxid, ett mineral som förekommer naturligt i naturen. De är sterila och icke giftiga och inga negativa hudreaktioner har rapporterats, men som säkerhetsåtgärd rekommenderar vi trots detta en hudallergitest innan behandlingen påbörjas.

Aluminiumoxid räknas som låg hälsorisk om det inandas, och branschstandarden klassificerar eventuell inandning av ämnet som irriterande damm. Inandning av vilket fint partikeldamm som helst, t.ex. konstgjort nageldamm, kan efter långa perioder av exponering orsaka irritation och hosta. Aluminiumoxid innehåller ingen fri kiselsyra, vilket betyder att det inte medför några respiratoriska risker att inandas det.

Kristallkänslighet - Hud Test

Det är viktigt att först utföra ett hudtest för att kontrollera att kunden inte är känslig för kristallerna som används. Det är mycket ovanligt att kunden är känslig för kristallerna som används, men man bör i alla fall före behandlingen utföra ett hudtest på insidan av underarmen. Om partiet blir irritabelt eller svullet ska behandlingen inte påbörjas. Om kunden får röda märken på huden efter behandlingen beror det vanligen på att terapeuten har tryckt för hårt.

VILKA HUDÅKOMMOR KAN MICRODERMABRASION ANVÄNDAS FÖR ATT BEHANDLA?

Alla kan dra nytta av en microdermabrasionsbehandling. Behandlingen förbättrar hudens allmänna utseende och ger huden en frisk lyster och får den att se yngre ut. Microdermabrasion är också mycket effektivt för att behandla ett antal hudproblem. Det kan användas i ansiktet och på kroppen och är t.ex. en utmärkt behandling mot ärrbildning efter akne på ryggen.

Akne och ärrbildning

Microdermabrasion fungerar genom att avlägsna det översta lagret av döda hudceller från hudytan, vilket gör metoden särskilt effektiv som aknebehandling. När de döda hudcellerna försvinner från hudytan blir porerna frilagda och risken för att nya finnar ska utvecklas blir mindre.

Fina linjer och rynkor
Åldrande hud

Microdermabrasionens vakuumsfunktion stimulerar kollagenproduktionen i huden. När vi blir äldre börjar produktionen av elastin och kollagen avta. Kombinationen av kollagenstimulering och ökad hud-förnyelse förbättrar hudytans och slätar ut fina linjer och rynkor.

Torr och uttorkad hud
Ojämn hudton

Normalt förnyar huden sig själv ungefär var 28:e dag. Genom att avlägsna de döda cellerna från de övre hudlagren påskyndar microdermabrasion den naturliga hudförnyelsen och visar upp en ny, fräsch hud med strålande lyster.

Celluliter, "apelsinhud"

Microdermabrasion kan inte bota celluliter, men det stimulerar cirkulationen och förbättra blodtillförseln på partiet. För att förbättra utseendet på cellulithud bör man dricka mycket vatten och motionera regelbundet.

Hudbristningar
Pigmenteringar och fläckar

Microdermabrasion kan radikalt förbättra utseendet på pigmenteringar och hudbristningar. Microdermabrasion stimulerar det behandlade partiet att producera mer kollagen och påskynda förnyelseprocessen, förbättra hudens kondition och göra så att hudbristningar och missfärgningar av huden inte framträder så tydligt.

Hudbristningar bör behandlas medan de fortfarande är röda. Har de blivit silvriga i färgen kan microdermabrasionsbehandlingen inte ta bort hudbristningarna helt, men en regelbunden behandling kan förbättra de behandlade partierna och göra bristningarna mindre framträdande. Ärrvävnad bör inte behandlas förrän all inflammation har försvunnit från hudpartiet (förslagsvis 6 månader efter operationen).

Regelbunden behandling med microdermabrasion gör så att hudbristningarna ser bättre ut. Tack vare en utjämnande effekt med den omgivande ärrvävnaden och en minskning av den problematiska pigmenteringen, som ju ofta gör bristningarna mer synliga.

Hyperpigmentering och orsakerna därtill (Melasma)

De vanligaste orsakerna är användande av p-piller eller hormontillskott, graviditet eller interaktion med viss medicinering. Alltför långvarig eller intensiv solning inverkar också, liksom inflammation eller skada i huden. Vissa kemikalier som finns i parfymer kan också orsaka pigmentering. Regelbunden microdermabrasionsbehandling visar sig vara mycket välgörande för solskadad hud och bidrar till att avlägsna oönskade pigmenteringsfläckar.

En serie SkinBase microdermabrasionsbehandlingar kan ge välgörande resultat för behandling av pigmenteringsfläckar. Kunderna bör informeras om att det kan behövas en serie av 10-15 behandlingar. Det är också viktigt att kunden rekommenderas att alltid använda solskyddsfaktor.

Observera att microdermabrasionsbehandling inte kan hjälpa kunder med hudåkomman vitiligo.

Melasma och kloasma (mörkfärgning av huden på grund av hormonväxlingar) kan förbättras med microdermabrasionsbehandling. Den hjälper det instängda pigmentet att röra sig upp genom hudlagren för att sedan avstötas på vanligt sätt. Emellertid krävs det ofta många behandlingar för att förbättra det aktuella hudpartiet.

HUR EN BEHANDLINGSSERIE FUNGERAR

Microdermabrasion är en mer progressiv behandling än en aggressiv. Hudlagren avlägsnas sakta och säkert under en serie behandlingar. I en serie utförs behandlingen var 7:e eller var 10:e dag. Det betyder att hornlagret som togs bort under förra behandlingen inte har haft tid att byggas upp igen, och kunden har också blivit tåligare mot behandlingen. Därför kan intensiteten i behandlingen ökas för att komma ner djupare i överhudens lager och framgångsrikt avlägsna ärr efter akne, lyfta pigmentering och släta ut fina linjer.

Vanligtvis brukar en kund välja en serie med 6 behandlingar som utförs med 7-10 dagars mellanrum för maximal effekt. Efter avslutad behandling kan kunden fortsätta med en underhållsbehandling varje månad för att uppehålla resultatet av behandlingen.

Kunder som har tuffare hud kan behöva flerA veckors behandling en normalt, men en kur på 15-20 behandlingar är maximalt tillåtet. Därefter måste kunden fortsätta på en underhållsbehandling med en behandling per 4-6 veckor.

LEKTION 3 - UTBILDNINGSMÅL:

- Du kommer att kunna utföra en fullständig kundkonsultation inför en behandling.
- Du kommer att känna till vilka kontraindikationer mot microdermabrasionsbehandling det finns.
- Du kommer att förstå vilken eftervård som krävs och vilka möjliga reaktioner på behandlingen som kan infinna sig.

KUNDKONSULTATION

1. Kontrollera kundens lämplighet för behandling med hjälp av listan på kontraindikationer.

2. Kontrollera om kunden har några allergier som t.ex. nickelallergier.

3. Genomföra en hudanalys och känna igen hudpartier som bör undvikas under behandlingen, t.ex. mindre kontraindikationer som telangiektasier (spruckna kapillärer).

4. Känna igen hudpartier som kräver särskild uppmärksamhet, som ärr efter akne eller pigmentering, öppna porer eller ojämn hudfärg.

5. Föreslå en behandlingsplan och se till att du förklarar kostnad och tidsåtgång och hur ofta behandlingarna i serien ska göras.

6. Förklara för kunden vad behandlingen går ut på och hur deN känns.

7. Förklara för kunden hur huden kan komma att reagera. Även om reaktionerna är obetydliga, måste du se till att kunden inser att det kan finnas en viss känslighet.

8. Diskutera med kunden om hur eftervården kan se ut, så att de är medvetna om vad de ska göra efter behandlingen för att sköta om sin hud.

9. Det är viktigt att kunden förstår att det är nödvändigt att följa råden hemma mellan behandlingarna och att han eller hon vet vad som krävs för att få resultat, dvs. att en korrekt användning av solskyddsmedel är av största vikt för att undvika framtida pigmenteringsproblem.

10. FYLL ALLTID I ETT KUNDKORT:
Det garanterar att kundens specifika behov särskilt uppmärksammas. Förklara kontraindikationer mot en viss behandling och be kunden skriva under registreringskortet.

Föräldrar eller vårdnadshavare <u>måste</u> skriva under konsultationskort om kunden är under 18 år.

KONTRAINDIKATIONER MOT MICRODERMABRASIONBEHANDLING

ALLVARLIGA KONTRAINDIKATIONER - Utför inte behandling på kunder med följande:

Graviditet
Ökade hormonvärden vid graviditet kan påverka huden vilket kan orsaka hyperpigmentering. Därför rekomenderar vi inte microdermabrasion vid graviditet eftersom hudens tillstånd kan förvärras. Rådge kunder att använda solskyddsfaktor när de vistas utomhus för att undvika att hyperpimentering uppstår.

Cancer
Vi rekommenderar att du aldrig behandlar en kunder som har cancer. De måste ha nått remisison sedan 6 månader tillbaka. Microdermabrasion stimulerar blod flödet och lymfatisk dränering.

Akne, grad 4
Kunder med den här graden av akne borde inte undergå Microdermabrasionbehandling. OM huden är väldigt blockerad med finnar kan en behandling irritera huden och sprida baketerier.

Roaccutan
Roaccutan tunnar ut huden, om kunden tar emot Roaccutan-behandling för akne, borde du låta det gå 6 månader efter Roaccutan-behandlingen innan en microdermabrasion behandling startas.

Autoimmuna sjukdommar
Begrepp som används till att beskriva ett antal sjukdommar då kroppen attackerar sina egna celler och vävnader. Du borde undvika att behandla en kund som lider an en autimmun sjukdom. Exempel på autoimmuna sjukdommar är Multipel Skleros (MS), HIV, Reumatoid Atrit och GBS.

Diabetes.
Diabetes kan påverka nerver och cirkulationen och huden kan ta mycket längre tid på sig än normalt att läka. Kunderna måste ha skriftlig tillåtelse från sin läkare innan en behandling kan utföras.

Impetigo (Svinkoppor)
Det här är en smittbar sjukdom. Utför inte microdermabrasionbehandling.

Rosacea
Rosacea ska inte behandlas med microdermabrasion.

MINDRE ALLVARLIGA KONTRAINDIKATIONER
- utför behandling med försiktighet och undvik angripna områden.

Ögoninfektioner t.ex. Vagel, Cystor och Konjuktivit.
Hudsjukdommar t.ex. Seborroisk Dermatit och Munherpes
Psoriasis
Telangiektasi (brustna kapillärer)
Keloidärr
Utbuktande Födelsemärken, Vårtor, Hudflikar
Sår, Blåmärken, Skadad hud.

Om du är osäker eller har svårt att identifiera hudsymptom ska du inte utföra behandling. Be kunden att rådfråga sin läkare.

Svenska

ATT TÄNKA PÅ INNAN EN BEHANDLING

Vi rekommenderar att våra kunder följer följande råd innan en microdermabrasionsbehandling

Botox/Hudfyllningar

Låt det gå 14 dagar efter botox eller annan rynkbehandling innan microdermabrasion påbörjas. Gäller även påfyllningar. Detta är nödvändigt för att fyllningarna ska kunna lägga sig och läka.

Män

Män bör raka sig kvällen innan en behandling om behandlingen är följande förmiddag, eller på morgonen om behandlinegn är samma dag på eftermiddagen.

Laser och IPL-behandlingar

En serie laser eller IPL - behandlingar ska inte pågå samtidigt som en SkinBase microdermabrasion behandling. Låt det gå minst 2 veckor efter avslutad laser eller IPL-behandling innan en microdermabrasion behandling påbörjas.

Dermaroller

Låt det gå 2 veckor mellan en Dermaroller och en Microdermabrasion-behandling

RÅD FÖR EFTERVÅRD

Vi rekommenderar att våra kunder följer följande råd efter att en microdermabrasionsbehandling

12 första timmarna efter behandlingen:

Ingen täckande make up

24 första timmarna efter behandlingen:

Undvik simning i simmbasänger och saltvatten.
Ingen vaxning av ansiktet. Ingen "brun-utan-sol"

48 första timmarna efter behandlingen

Inget bastubad.
Sola inte solarium och undvik solen.
Ingen 'Botox', kollagen injektioner eller andra dermala fyllningar.

72 första timmarna efter behandlingen

Använd inte anti-ageing krämer eller krämer innehållande AHA, glykolsyror eller retinol efter en microdermabrasionsbehandling. Den nyslipade huden är känslig för alla produkter som stryks på, och alla exfolianter som används efter en behandling kan irritera huden.

Under hela behandlingsserien

Solskyddsfaktor 15 (eller högre) måste användas och huden bör inte utsättas för UV ljus. Regelbunden insmörjning är absolut nödvändigt för att återge fukt och förhindra att huden blir torr och flagnar.

Produkter måste vara av pH 4.5 och 7

Hud produkter som innehåller en hög dos av botaniska och eteriska oljor ska inte användas efter en microdermabrasion eftersom en del ingredienser i behandlingen kan framkalla en allergisk reaktion. Om detta skulle inträffa finns det en risk att både kunden och terapeuten tror att de är allergiska mot behandlingen, när det egentligen är hudprodukterna som användes efter behandlingen. Det är viktigt för att använda produkter som återställer fuktbalansen och förhindrar att huden blir torr och flagnar.

LEKTION 4 - UTBILDNINGSMÅL:

- Du kommer att kunna identifiera delar av microdermabrasion maskinen och dess funktioner.
- Du kommer att kunna montera upp utrustningen och kontrollera att den fungerar som den ska.
- Du kommer att kunna välja rätt behandling till kundens hudtyp

MONTERING AV SKINBASE MDPRO-SYSTEM

1. Kontrollera alltid att avfallsburken är tömd på använda kristaller innan en behandling påbörjas.
2. Kontrollera att handtaget är anslutet till avfallsburken genom den gråa slangen och ordentligt intryckt i båda ändarna.
3. Sätt på ett rent munstycke och en ny kristallpatron på handtaget och skruva fast den ordentligt.
4. Anslut sedan elkabeln i vägguttaget och starta apparaten på panelen. Om du använder en PAYG maksin bör du följa instruktionerna på insidan av den maskinen.

REGULERING AV BEHANDLINGSNIVÅ

Se till att en kristallpatron är ansluten till handtaget. Sätt pekfingret över hålet på munstycket, vrid regulatorn tills du får önskat tryck för ansiktsbehandlingen.
Se till att du förstår de olika trycknivåerna innan du påbörjar en microdermabrasionsbehandling.

OBS! METALLHÖLJET FÅR INTE UNDER NÅGRA SOM HELST OMSTÄNDIGHETER SKRUVAS AV OCH AVLÄGSNAS UTAN ATT ELKABELN HAR DRAGITS UR VÄGGUTTAGET.

BEHANDLINGSNIVÅER

Följande beskrivningar ger riktlinjer för hur du väljer lämplig behandlingsnivå för din kund.

NIVÅ ETT -0,3 spärren
Den lägsta nivån bör användas av nyutbildade terapeuter, innan de är vana vid hur lätta de ska vara på handen. Den här nivån ger en mild allmän slipning och bör alltid användas för kundens första behandling. Använd alltid den här nivån när du utför behandling runt ögonen (fjäderlätta drag)

Svenska

NIVÅ ETT -0,3 spärren

- Nyutbildade terapefter
- Första behandlingen
- Området runt ögonen

NIVÅ TVÅ -0,4 spärren
Den andra nivån bör väljas gradvis vid arbete på ärr efter akne eller tjockare hud. Inte högre än denna nivå för hudtyper V och VI på fitzpatrickskalan

NIVÅ TVÅ -0,4 spärren

- Tuffare områden
- Inte högre en denna nivå för hudtyper V och VI på Fitzpatrick skalan.

NIVÅ TRE -0,5 spärren
Den tredje nivån får bara användas på kunder vid slutet av behandlingsserien när huden är tåligare. Används bara som fokusering på ärr efter akne, pigmentering, linjer och rynkor. Inte som grundsipning av hela ansiktet. Kan användas för exfoliering av hela kroppen, hudbristningar och celluliter.

NIVÅ TRE -0,5 spärren

- Slutet av behandlingen när huden är tåligare.
- Slipning av kroppen
- Tuffare områden
- Aldrig för hudtyper V och VI på Fitzpatrickskalan

NIVÅ FYRA -0,6 spärren
Använd bara på kroppen. Ska aldrig användas på ansiktet.

LEKTION 5 - UNDERVISNINGSMÅL:

- Visa att du kan sköta apparaten och utföra behandlingen säkert och effektivt under den rekommenderade behandlingstiden
- Visa att du kan arbeta inom rimliga tidsbegränsningar som finns i branschen

BEHANDLINGSMETOD

1. Be kunden lägga sig i en halvliggande ställning
2. Se till att kundens hår inte ligger i ansiktet. Använd gärna pannband.
3. Tvätta kundens hud grundligt – måste använda en rengöringsgel
4. Huden måste vara helt torr
5. Spänn ut huden mellan tumme och långfinger
6. Håll handtaget som om det var en penna och för det försiktigt i svepande drag i ansiktspartiet (se bild på nästa sida)
7. GRUND: Genomför en lätt grundslipning på hela ansiktspartiet och halsen
8. FOKUSERING: När du har gjort en lätt grundslipning kan du gå tillbaka och fokusera på de partier som behöver mer uppmärksamhet, t.ex. ärr efter akne, pigmentfläckar, linjer och rynkor
9. När behandlingen är slutförd ska du torka bort alla eventuella rester av kristaller som ligger på huden. Använd fuktade bomullstussar/svampar (kallt vatten)
10. Stryk på en lätt toner/ansiktsvatten som passar känslig hud.
11. Fuktgivande ansiktsmask är valfritt
12. Lägg på en fuktgivande produkt för känslig hud.
13. Lägg på en solskyddsprodukt, minst faktor 15

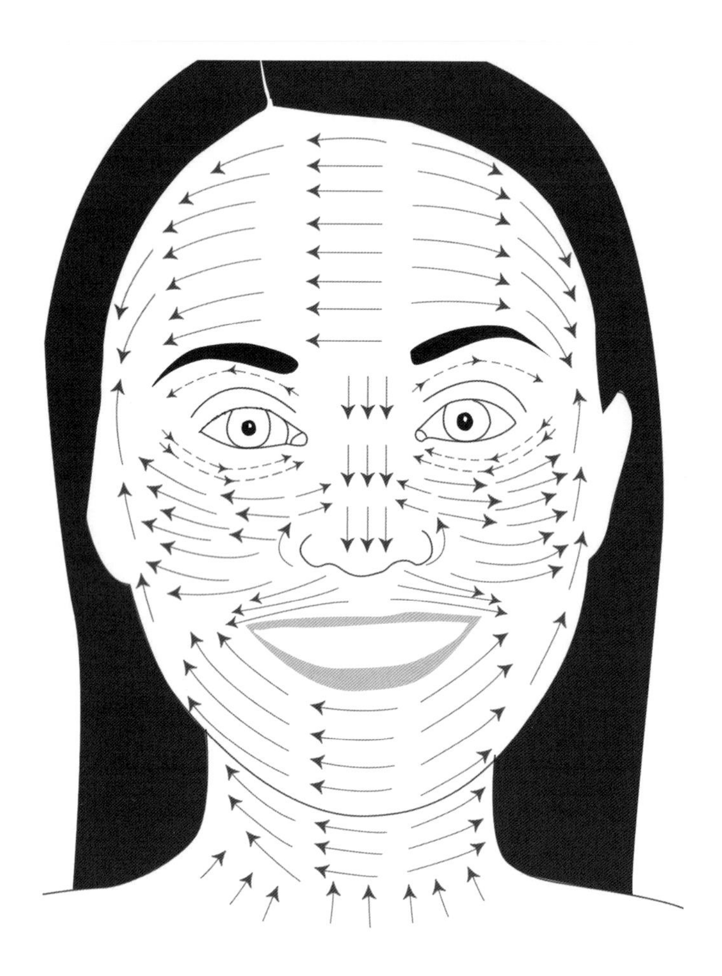

Bilden visar i vilken riktning du ska arbeta i när du behandlar ansiktet.

De streckade linjerna runt det ömtåliga ögat ska symbolisera snabba lätta drag. Varje pil (drag) är 4cm långt.

ÖGON OMRÅDET

- Fjäderlätta drag
- Använd alltid nivå 1 för ögonpartiet
- Behandla inte huden i ögonhålan. Håll dig på benet.

Behandlingstips

1. Du ska alltid försöka förstå och anpassa dig efter kundens hud och hur den reagerar innan du prövar för äventyrliga saker. Det händer ofta att terapeuter vill imponera på kunder så mycket vid den första behandlingen att de använder för mycket tryck och arbetar för aggressivt. Det gör att kundens hud blir för känslig, och om huden har hanterats med för mycket tryck kan det uppstå röda ränder och märken. Det är för att terapeuten har varit för ivrig och inte förstått kundens hud. Det är viktigt att terapeuten behärskar svepningsrörelsen och för handtaget över huden på ett lätt och kontrollerat sätt.

2. Gör alltid behandlingen på nivå 1 under första tillfället och gå sedan vidare mer aggressivt vartefter som behandlingsserien framskrider. På så sätt blir kundens hud tåligare mot behandlingen och kunden förstår vad som händer. En kund som går hem med röda ränder eller röd känslig hud kommer att vara en mycket missnöjd kund, som troligen avbokar sin nästa behandling på grund av att terapeuten inte har informerat tillräckligt eller inte har utfört behandlingen på ett korrekt sätt.

3. OBS: Var försiktig med hudtyperna V och VI på fitzpatrickskalan och använd aldrig mer än nivå 2 på dessa hudtyper då du annars kan osaka pigmentering.

4. Hemligheten med en lyckad behandling är hur snabbt man gör rörelserna. Snabba lätta drag bör användas för skonsam exfoliering (fjäderlätta runt ögonen), långsammare drag när man inriktar behandlingen på problempartier. Partier som uppvisar mindre telangiektasier (brustna kapillärer) bör behandlas mycket varsamt genom lätta snabba drag över partiet. Dragen bör aldrig vara längre än 4 cm och du ska aldrig trycka handtaget mot huden.

LEKTION 6 – UNDERVISNINGSMÅL:

- Du kommer att få en förståelse för hygien och säkerhet rörande skönhetsbehandling och skötsel av utrustningen.
- Du kommer kunna uppdatera kundregisterkort

Svenska

VIKTIG DAGLIG SKÖTSEL

- Efter varje behandling – stäng av utrustningen och dra ur elkabeln ur vägguttaget och höljet
- Ta bort kristallpatronen och slå handtaget lätt i handflatan för att ta bort eventuella kvarvarande kristaller i innerkanalen. Varje gång du byter kristallpatron måste du skaka ut alla överflödiga kristaller som kan finnas i handtagets innerkanal. På så sätt ser du till att handtaget är rent hela tiden
- Ta bort och kassera munstycket
- Skruva bort avfallsbehållaren från locket
- Töm avfallsbehållaren efter VARJE behandling. Töm ut de använda kristallerna och gör dig av med dem på korrekt sätt. Skaka locket mot avfallsbehållarens kant för att lossa kristaller och hudavfall från filtret.
- Se till att avfallsbehållaren sätts tillbaka fast och säkert. Kontrollera att locket på behållaren är riktigt fastsatt (om den inte är det minskar vakuumkraften)
- Sätt tillbaka alla slangar och tillbehör ordentligt i höljet och se till att allt är rent inför nästa användning

VIKTIGT:

Avfallsbehållaren MÅSTE bytas efter 80 behandlingar. Om man inte sätter in en ny behållare efter var 80:e behandling kommer vakuumeffekten att sjunka och kristaller kan dras in från pappersfiltret i behållaren direkt in i pumpen i enheten, vilket allvarligt kan skada din apparat och göra garantin ogiltig.

INDEX

SkinBase™

Manuale d'istruzione

Italiano

INDICE PAGINA

SISTEMA DI MICRODERMOABRASIONE SKINBASE : MANUALE DI ISTRUZIONE

Questo manuale d'istruzione è stato organizzato in modo da garantire al cliente di aver tutte le informazioni necessarie per il trattamento di microdermoabrasione. È comunque necessario che il tirocinante sia già sufficientemente qualificato nella professione estetica e/o abbia una significativa esperienza lavorativa.

Il corso comprende di capitoli essenziali quali: la salute e sicurezza nel luogo del lavoro, i disturbi e le malattie della pelle, ed inoltre è comprensivo di tutte le informazioni necessarie per l'utilizzo dell'apparecchio, così da garantire all'utilizzatore tutta la sicurezza necessaria per il trattamento dei clienti nel corso della propria attività professionale.

SkinBase MDPro è un sistema professionale per la microdermoabrasione, progettato e costruito nel Regno Unito da un'azienda che vanta una notevole esperienza presso centri di medicina estetica. Ciò ha consentito una lunga sperimentazione sul campo che ci ha aiutati a progettare un sistema dalle prestazioni eccezionali, di altissima qualità e di indiscussa attendibilità.

SESSIONE 1 - RISULTATI DI APPRENDIMENTO

- Al termine di questa sessione avrete la preparazione necessaria e capirete quali saranno le vostre responsabilità riguardo le norme di sanità e sicurezza sul lavoro.
- Sarete capaci di riconoscere i differenti disturbi e le differenti malattie della pelle e le relative controindicazioni al trattamento.
- Migliorerete la vostra conoscenza di base in anatomia e fisiologia relativamente al viso ed al collo.

SALUTE E SICUREZZA NEI LUOGHI DI LAVORO

La sessione affronta tutte le problematiche relative alle responsabilità del titolare, degli eventuali dipendenti e degli stessi clienti in merito alla salute, alla sicurezza e al benessere sul posto di lavoro. È di vitale importanza avere consapevolezza delle proprie responsabilità e applicare le stesse con la massima professionalità. La conoscenza delle problematiche legate alla salute e sicurezza aiuteranno a garantire trattamenti sicuri, dimostrando nel contempo professionalità ed attitudine al lavoro.

Le norme relative a sanità e sicurezza che concernono gli istituti di bellezza riguardano i requisiti di base e le garanzie di benessere sul posto di lavoro. Chi opera in una società di servizi è legalmente obbligato a garantire sicurezza ed igiene secondo le norme legislative.

Per evitare potenziali pericoli e rischi sul posto di lavoro è necessario:

- Conoscere le proprie responsabilità legali in merito all'attuazione di quanto necessario per garantire salute e sicurezza sul posto di lavoro.
- Garantire che la presenza al lavoro sia in linea con i requisiti legislativi in tema di sanità e sicurezza e con le procedure interne dell'azienda.
- Attenersi alle procedure interne stabilite per il luogo di lavoro, sia relativamente al ruolo del lavoratore che ai criteri di lavorazione, al fine di garantire sempre le condizioni di sicurezza per le risorse umane impiegate.
- Segnalare immediatamente eventuali rischi che potrebbero creare un pericolo per il posto di lavoro.
- Avere il necessario per un pronto soccorso sul posto di lavoro in caso di incidenti o malori.
- Ridurre al minimo le possibilità di diffusione di infezioni e malattie, mantenendo costantemente elevati livelli di igiene.

Norme Relative All' Uso Di Energia Elettrica Nei Luoghi Di Lavoro

Le norme riguardano l'installazione, la manutenzione e l'uso di apparecchi elettrici sul posto di lavoro. Gli apparecchi elettrici devono essere regolarmente controllati da un elettricista qualificato per essere sicuri che siano conformi alle norme di salute e sicurezza. I controlli vanno sempre registrati. Inoltre è necessario essere sempre consapevoli dei potenziali pericoli associati agli apparecchi elettrici: fili elettrici scoperti, spine rotte o prese sovraccariche.

Nonostante sia responsabilità dell'addetto, assicurarsi che lo strumento sia in condizioni di sicurezza, è anche di sua responsabilità il controllo continuo dello stesso, prima dell'uso e la certezza che lo stesso non venga mai usato in caso di evidenti problemi.

Potenziali Pericoli Legati All' Elettricità:

- Fili elettrici scoperti
- Spine danneggiate
- Prese sovraccariche

Pronto Soccorso

Anche nel caso siano state prese tutte le precauzioni per garantire la sicurezza sul posto di lavoro, si possono verificare incidenti. È pertanto necessario avere una procedura di pronto soccorso sul posto di lavoro nota a tutti gli operatori, che sapranno come comportarsi nell'eventualità di un incidente, di un malore o di un'emergenza.

Ogni luogo di lavoro deve essere dotato di un armadietto di pronto soccorso e di una figura interna responsabile della manutenzione dello stesso. Ogni infortunio sul lavoro va registrato sistematicamente su un apposito registro.

TUTTI I LAVORATORI DEVONO SAPERE:

Dov'è collocato il registro di pronto soccorso;
Chi è il responsabile della manutenzione dell'armadietto di pronto soccorso;
Chi si deve informare nel caso di incidente, malore o emergenza.

Eliminazione Del Materiale Monouso

Il materiale monouso da eliminare va collocato in un contenitore rivestito da un sacchetto di politene resistente agli strappi. Il contenitore va regolarmente igienizzato con disinfettante usando guanti protettivi.

Norme Igieniche Sul Posto Di Lavoro

La sterilizzazione dell'apparecchio, tra un cliente e l'altro, è essenziale per distruggere batteri nocivi, funghi e virus che potrebbero causare infezioni. Norme igieniche adeguate sul posto di lavoro prevengono infezioni incrociate e secondarie.

Le infezioni incrociate si verificano quando microrganismi sono trasferiti attraverso il contatto o per contatto con ugelli infetti che non sono stati sterilizzati.

Le infezioni secondarie possono essere provocate da eventuali ferite provocate al cliente durante il trattamento o se il cliente ha già una escoriazione sulla pelle; in tal caso i batteri possono penetrare causando l'infezione.

Igiene Personale

Un alto standard di igiene personale è essenziale. Occorre lavarsi le mani regolarmente prima e dopo il trattamento di ciascun cliente. I capelli lunghi vanno raccolti. Evitare di toccarsi il viso. Coprire eventuali tagli o abrasioni sulle mani con una benda pulita.

DISTURBI E MALATTIE DELLA PELLE

I trattamenti di bellezza sono controindicati nei soggetti affetti da malattie infettive contagiose. Soggetti con alcune forme di disturbi della pelle, anche se non contagiose, non dovrebbero essere trattati dal terapista, in quanto i trattamenti potrebbero provocare infezioni secondarie. Il terapista deve essere in grado di distinguere la differenza fra una pelle sana o malata.

IMPORTANTE :

Nel caso in cui non si sia certi o in grado di identificare le condizioni della pelle, non si deve procedere al trattamento del cliente, suggerendo allo stesso di informare il proprio medico di fiducia.

Il trattamento di bellezza è controindicato in alcuni casi da disturbi o malattie della pelle. L'eventuale trattamento potrebbe esporre il terapista ed altri clienti al rischio di infezioni incrociate, perciò è di vitale importanza essere a conoscenza di tutti i casi di disturbi e malattie della pelle con cui si può entrare in contatto.

Infezione Batteriche

Nonostante sulla pelle si annidino un gran numero di bateri, questi ultimi possono anche non causare malattie. Comunque, alcuni tipi di batteri sono dannosi per la nostra salute e questi sono noti come "patogeni". I batteri patogeni possono causare malattie della pelle rendendole infettive, perciò un cliente non va mai trattato se risulta sofferente delle seguenti infezioni batteriche:

Impetigine
Estremamente infettiva e facilmente trasmettibile per contatto. L'impetigine di solito si manifesta prima sul volto intorno al naso, la bocca e le orecchie e può diffondersi in altre parti del corpo. Inizialmente caratterizzata da rossore e irritazione, si manifesta con pustole che progressivamente si trasformano in croste umide.

Congiuntivite
La congiuntivite non è sempre infettiva e può essere causata da una reazione allergica o essere il risultato di una irritazione. Comunque, stante la difficoltà di determinare se è una forma infettiva o meno, dovrebbe essere sempre considerata come infettiva. L'occhio appare rosso e infiammato: gli occhi potrebbero essere anche lacrimosi o secernere pus.

Orzaiolo
Gli orzaioli sono infezioni della ghiandola sebacea alla radice delle ciglia. Ciò causa un gonfiore che rende la parte rossa ed il follicolo infetto è caratterizzato da un piccolo grumo pieno di pus.

Vescica/Foruncolo
La vescica o il foruncolo è causata dalla infiammazione dei follicoli dei peli con il risultato di un accumulo di pus e la morte dei tessuti. Le vesciche sono rosse, piene di pus, morbide, calde e/o dolorose. Un puntino giallo o bianco al centro del gonfiore è evidente quando la vescica è pronta per prosciugarsi.

Infezioni Virali

Le particelle di un virus sono così piccole che non possono crescere e riprodursi da sole, ma hanno bisogno di una cellula "ospite". Pertanto i virus invadono le cellule sane e viventi del corpo al fine di riprodursi. Essi penetrano nel nostro corpo in ogni modo possibile - attraverso inalazione, saliva e rapporti sessuali. Il nostro sistema immunitario è organizzato per fronteggiare la maggior parte dei virus e cosicché da distruggere la maggior parte delle infezioni. I clienti affetti dalle seguenti forme virali, non dovrebbero ricevere trattamenti di microdermoabrasione:

Herpes Simplex
L'herpes simplex viene trasmesso attraverso il contatto ravvicinato con qualcuno che ne è affetto. È caratterizzato da una sensazione di prurito sulla pelle, seguita da ulcere. Comunemente presenti sulle membrane della mucosa del naso e delle labbra, le infezioni da herpes simplex possono presentarsi anche in altre parti del corpo.

Herpes Zoster (Fuoco di S. Antonio)
L'herpes Zoster è un'infezione del nervo e della parte servita dal nervo. Il virus di solito colpisce un nervo, comunemente nel torace, nell'addome e nella parte superiore del viso. I sintomi si manifestano sulla parte della pelle interessata dal nervo, causando arrossamento e vescicole.

Infezioni Da Funghi

I funghi sono organismi parassitari e microscopici che si nutrono da prodotti di scarto della pelle. Alcune infezioni da funghi si trovano sulla superficie della pelle e altre in tessuti più profondi della pelle. I clienti con infezioni micotiche non dovrebbero essere trattati in quanto queste malattie sono infettive e possono essere trasmesse.

Tinea Corporis/Tricofizia Del Corpo

La tinea corporis è un infezione da fungo della pelle che si evidenzia sul torace, sugli arti e sul volto. Ha l'aspetto a scaglie, con chiazze rosse sulla pelle che si allargano. Le chiazze si cicatrizzano dal centro lasciando un anello sulla pelle.

Altri disturbi della pelle non sono infettivi, comunque in tali casi i trattamenti dovrebbero essere effettuati con qualche precauzione ed in alcuni casi non effettuati affatto.

Disturbi Delle Ghiandole Sebacee

Le ghiandole sebacee sono piccole ghiandole che secernono una sostanza oleosa, chiamata sebo, nel follicolo dei peli, per lubrificare la pelle. Tali ghiandole sono numerose sulla faccia e sul cuoio capelluto. I disturbi delle ghiandole sebacee includono l'acne, la rosacea e la milia. Tali disordini sono generalmente causati da una sovrapproduzione di sebo.

Grani Di Milio

Sono una manifestazione benigna, dovuta a cisti di cheratina che appaiono di solito sul naso e sugli occhi. Sono in apparenza piccoli, duri, bianchi o giallo pallido. Non sono infettivi e possono essere rimossi usando un ago sterile per forare la pelle sovrastante ed eliminare la cheratina.

Comedoni/Punti Neri

Provocati da un eccesso di sebo e cellule di cheratina che ostruiscono il follicolo dei peli, si manifestano sul viso, sulla parte superiore del dorso e sul torace. Non sono infettivi.

Seborrea

Provocata da una eccessiva produzione di sebo, di solito si manifesta durante la pubertà a causa dei cambiamenti ormonali. Chi ne è affetto avrà follicoli dilatati e sebo eccessivo. Non è infettiva e di solito si manifesta sulla faccia e sul cuoio capelluto. Può anche interessare il dorso ed il torace.

Cisti Sebacee

Si formano nel follicolo dei peli quando il sebo resta bloccato ed assume una forma indefinita.

Acne Vulgaris

Scompensi ormonali in pubertà causano un aumento di produzione del sebo. Ciò a sua volta provoca congestione nei condotti sebacei con il risultato di infiammazione della pelle, comedoni, pustole e papule. Essa non è infettiva e si manifesta generalmente su volto, naso, mento e fronte. In alcuni casi è riscontrabile sul torace e sul dorso. Nella fase attiva dell'acne sarebbe opportuno evitare trattamenti di microdermoabrasione.

Rosacea
Provocata dalla combinazione di una eccessiva secrezione di sebo ed infiammazione cronica, rende la pelle ruvida, i pori dilatati e le guance ed il naso diventano rossi ed infiammati. La pelle può apparire di colore violaceo, causa la scarsa circolazione del sangue. I casi di rosacea non possono essere sottoposti a trattamenti di microdermoabrasione.

Pigmentazione

Iperpigmentazione: aumento della pigmentazione

Cloasma: l'incremento della produzione di pigmenti può essere causato da raggi UV. Spesso si verifica durante la gravidanza, perché gli estrogeni sono deputati alla stimolazione di produzione di melanina, ma può anche essere provocato dall'assunzione di pillole contraccettive. Esso si manifesta sulle mani, sugli avambracci, alla parte superiore del torace, sulle tempie e sulla fronte.

Efelidi (lentiggini): provocate da esposizione ai raggi UV che stimolano la produzione di melanina. Si manifestano sul naso e sulle guance di persone di pelle chiara. Talvolta sono presenti su mani, braccia, spalle e dorso.

Lentigo: chiazze di iperpigmentazione più ampie delle lentiggini, si manifestano in età infantile o nella mezza età e sono causate da esposizione ai raggi solari; si riscontrano sul volto, sulle mani e sulle spalle.

Ipopigmentazione: priva di pigmentazione

Vitiligine: chiazze della pelle in assenza di pigmentazione, così da apparire completamente bianche.

Albinismo: pelle priva di pigmentazione, per cui la pelle, i capelli e gli occhi sono senza colore. La pelle appare molto pallida e rosa, anche gli occhi sono rosa ed i capelli bianchi.

Eritema
L'eritema è un arrossamento della pelle causato dalla dilatazione dei vasi sanguigni che con trovano la rete dei capillari nella zona della pelle affetta dal danno dell'infezione.

Nevi Vascolari
Sono aree di pigmentazione causate da una dilatazione permanente dei capillari del sangue.

Capillari dilatati - piccoli capillari rossi visibili nelle zone che sono o trascurate o secche come sulle guance.
Nevi a ragnatela - vasi sanguigni dilatati con capillari dilatati che si diffondono intorno ad essi.
Nevi dei piccoli vasi, "voglia di fragola": macchie rosse o porporine rialzate che si manifestano sulla pelle sin dalla nascita.
Nevi capillari: "macchia di vino", ampie zone di capillari dilatati.

Telangectasie (capillari rotti)
Si tratta di una manifestazione di capillari rotti che possono peggiorare con l'azione del vuoto della microdermoabrasione. Queste "vene filiformi" sono abbastanza comuni intorno al naso e sulle guance. Le aree della pelle interessate non dovrebbero essere trattate o, in alternativa, il trattamento dovrebbe essere effettuato ad un livello di potenza molto basso.

Cheloidi

Sono tessuti cicatriziali per un eccesso di deposito di collagene. La pelle è apparentemente sollevata, rossa e con sporgenze. Questo tipo di tessuto cicatriziale non può essere trattato con la microdermoabrasione. Smagliature e cicatrici post operatorie possono comunque essere sottoposte a trattamento. Il tessuto cicatrizzato non dovrebbe essere trattato sino a che l'infiammazione è completamente scomparsa, per esempio 6 mesi dopo l'intervento.

Dermatite

È un'infiammazione della pelle causata da un'irritazione o una sostanza allergica. Ci sono diversi tipi di dermatiti. I sintomi possono includere una pelle rossa, senso di prurito, squame, incrostazioni, trasudazione, gonfiore e possibilità di pustole a seconda della gravità del caso.

La dermatite irritativa da contatto può essere causata dal breve contatto con un forte irritante o da un'esposizione prolungata e ripetuta per un lungo periodo ad una sostanza debolmente irritante. Le cause comuni di tale tipo di dermatite sono: saponi, shampoo e detergenti, polvere, oli e grassi, ripetuto e prolungato contatto con l'acqua.

La dermatite allergica da contatto si manifesta quando chi ne è colpito sviluppa una reazione allergica ad una sostanza. Le cause più comuni sono coloranti per capelli, sostanze adesive e cibi come i frutti di mare.

Eczema

Ci sono due diversi tipi di eczema: l'atopico e l'eczema da contatto.

L'eczema atopico si tende a sviluppare nell'età infantile e molti bambini ne sono affetti.

L'eczema da contatto di solito colpisce gli adulti ed è causato da contatto con una sostanza allergica come il nichel o alcuni detergenti, saponi e profumi.

In caso di eczema la pelle dà prurito, diventa secca e a scaglie ed è spesso rossa e dolorante. Qualche volta è umida e sanguinante. Le parti comunemente colpite sono il volto, il collo e le pieghe interne della pelle del gomito e dietro le ginocchia.

Psoriasi

È una malattia autoimmune cronica che colpisce la pelle e le giunture. La psoriasi provoca chiazze squamose della pelle chiamate placche della psoriasi, che sono parti di pelle infiammata con una eccessiva produzione di cellule cutanee che rapidamente assumono un colore bianco argenteo dovuto alla crescita.

ANATOMIA E FISIOLOGIA

È importante che un terapista in grado di effettuare trattamenti abbia una conoscenza di base di anatomia e fisiologia.

OSSA DELLA TESTA E DEL COLLO

La testa è composta da 14 ossa identificate come segue:

Ossa Facciali

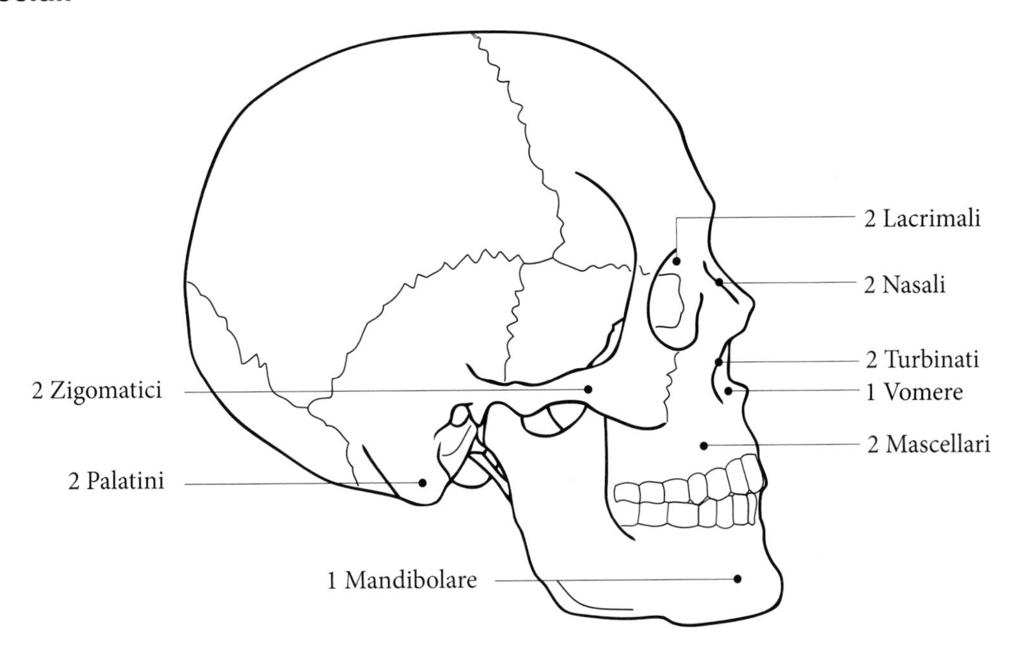

Italiano

Ossa	
Palatino x 2	Formano la parte inferiore e superiore del naso e la parte superiore della bocca
Nasale x 2	Formano il ponte del naso
Turbinato x 2	Formano le pareti esterne del naso
Vomere	Parete che divide in due il naso
Lacrimale x 2	Parti interne delle cavità degli occhi
Mascellare x 2	Sono incernierate per formare la parte superiore della mascella
Mandibolare	Rappresenta la parte più bassa della mascella
Zigomatico x 2	Ossa delle guance

Il resto del cranio è formato dalle ossa craniche, otto in totale, come evidenziato dal seguente schema:

Ossa Craniche

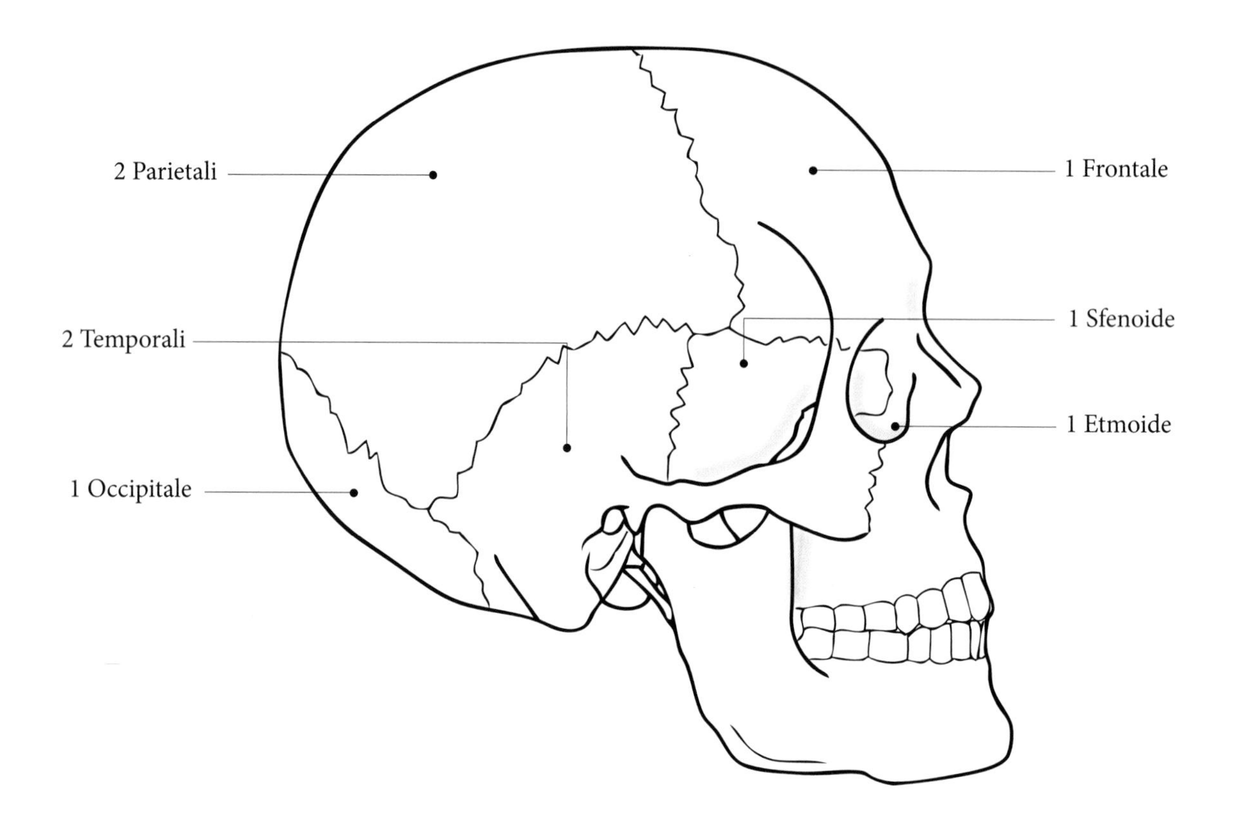

Italiano

Ossa	
Occipitale	Collocato sul retro del cranio, ha un foro un buco attraverso il quale passano il midollo spinale, i nervi e i vasi sanguigni
Parietale x 2	Incernierati per formare la calotta cranica
Frontale	Fronte e cavità superiore degli occhi
Temporale x 2	Le parti laterali della testa
Etmoide	Forma parte della cavità nasale
Sfenoide	Osso a forma di pipistrello che tiene insieme tutte le ossa del cranio

Ossa Di Collo, Torace E Spalle

Fronte

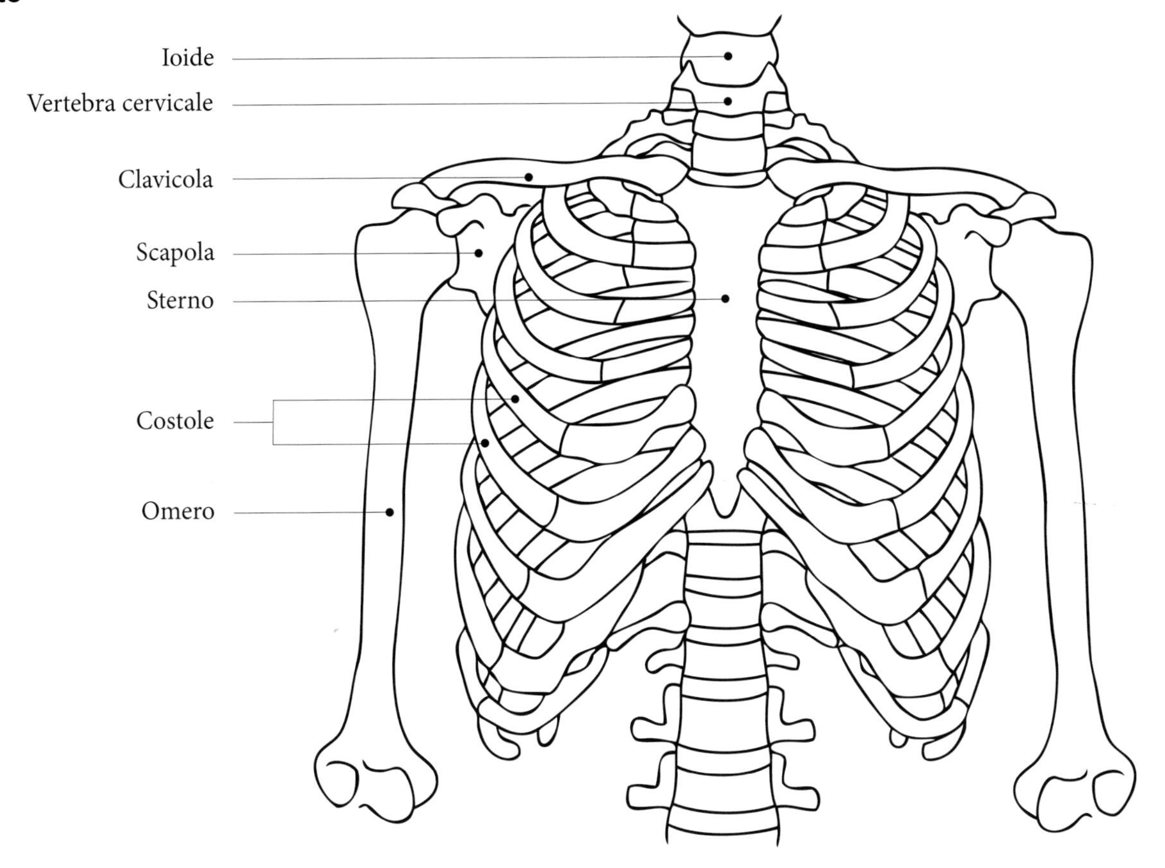

Retro

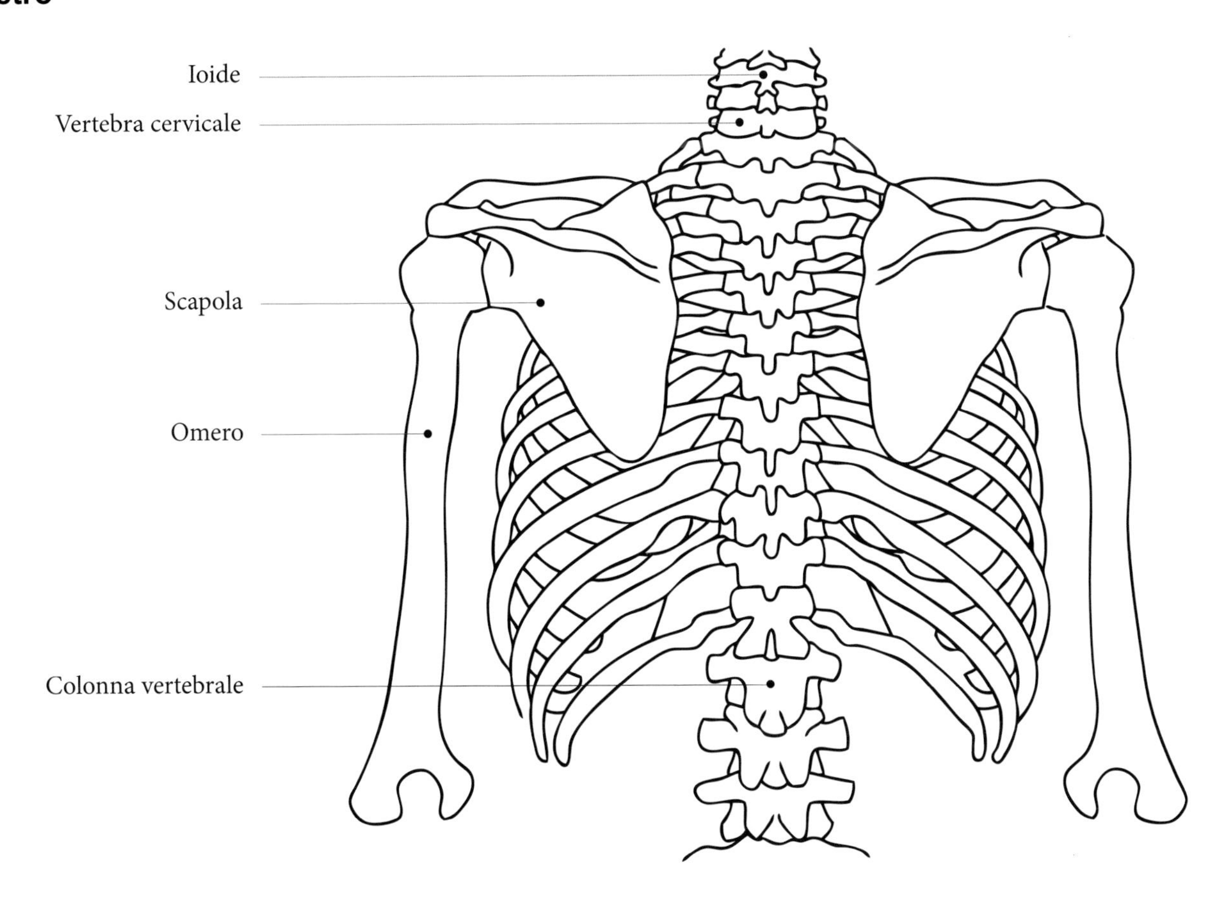

Italiano

MUSCOLI DELLA TESTA E DEL COLLO

I muscoli del volto e del collo sono responsabili delle nostre espressioni facciali. Con il passare degli anni le espressioni che usiamo quotidianamente producono linee sulla pelle rendendo evidenti i segni dell'età. La microdermoabrasione rimuove le cellule morte dall'epidermide migliorando l'aspetto di queste linee sottili e delle rughe.

Muscoli Facciali

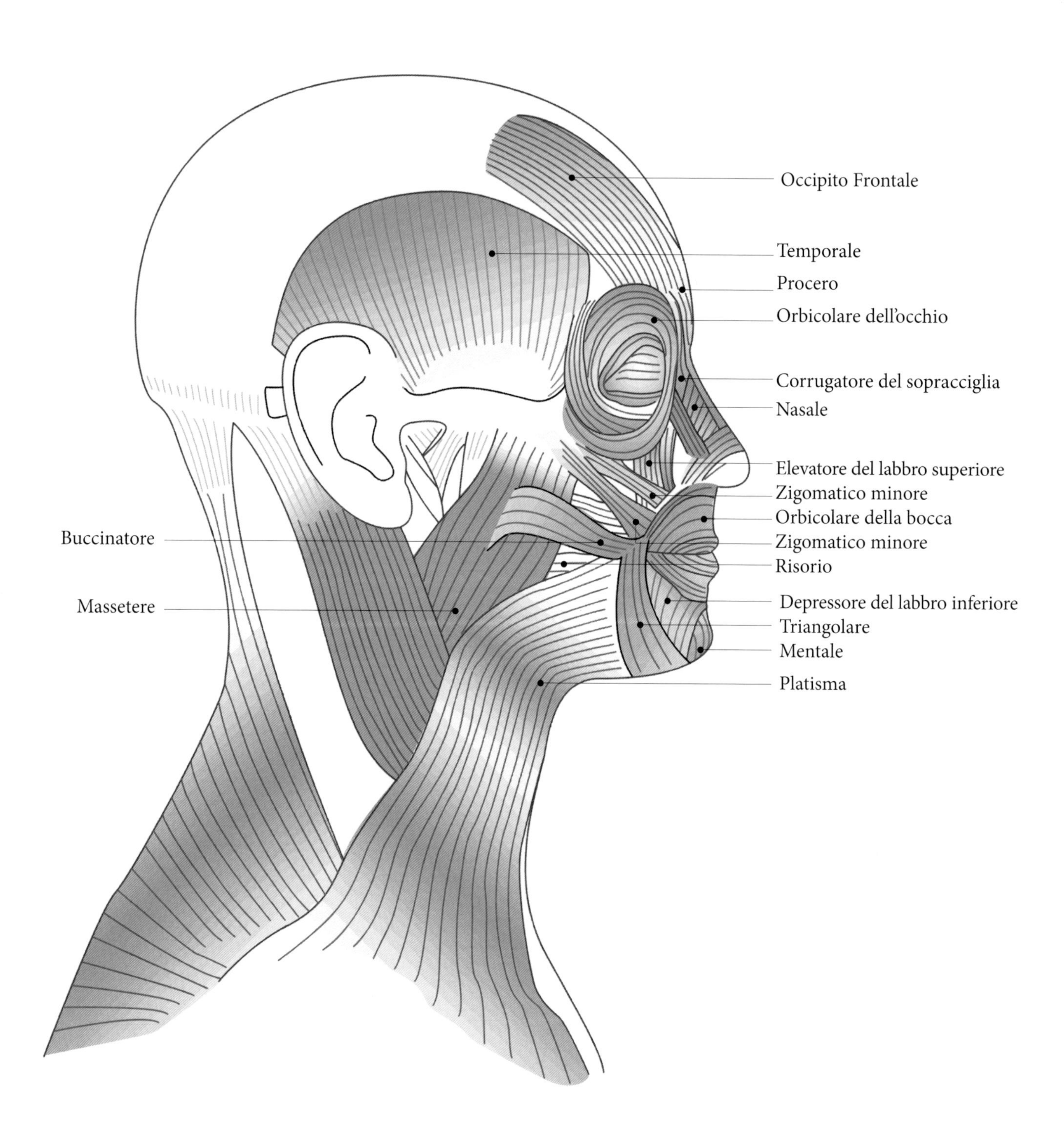

Muscoli Del Collo

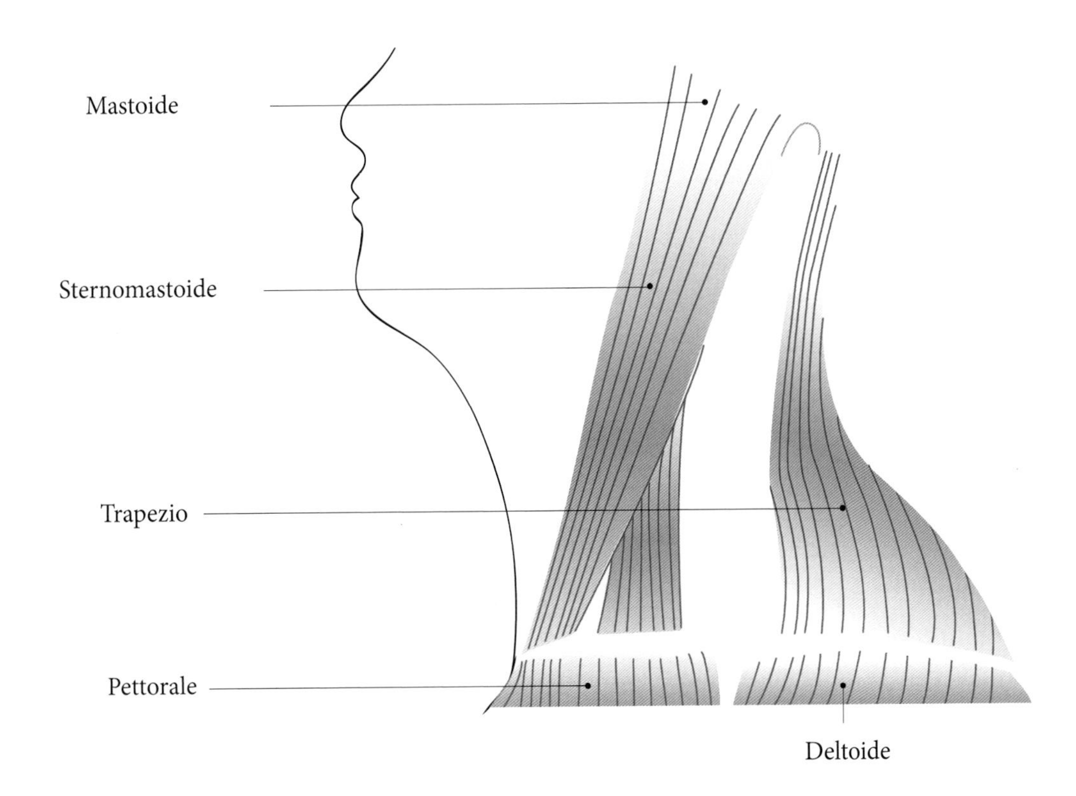

Italiano

NERVI DEL CRANIO

Il sistema nervoso è il metodo con cui vengono inviate tutte le informazioni dal cervello a tutte le altre parti del corpo. I nervi della faccia e del collo, detti nervi cranici, controllano i muscoli del volto e del collo e trasferiscono gli impulsi nervosi (informazioni sensoriali) dagli organi sensoriali al cervello. Il 5°, 7° ed 11°nervo cranico sono quelli che il terapista deve considerare quando effettua un trattamento facciale.

5º Nervo Cranico - Trigemino

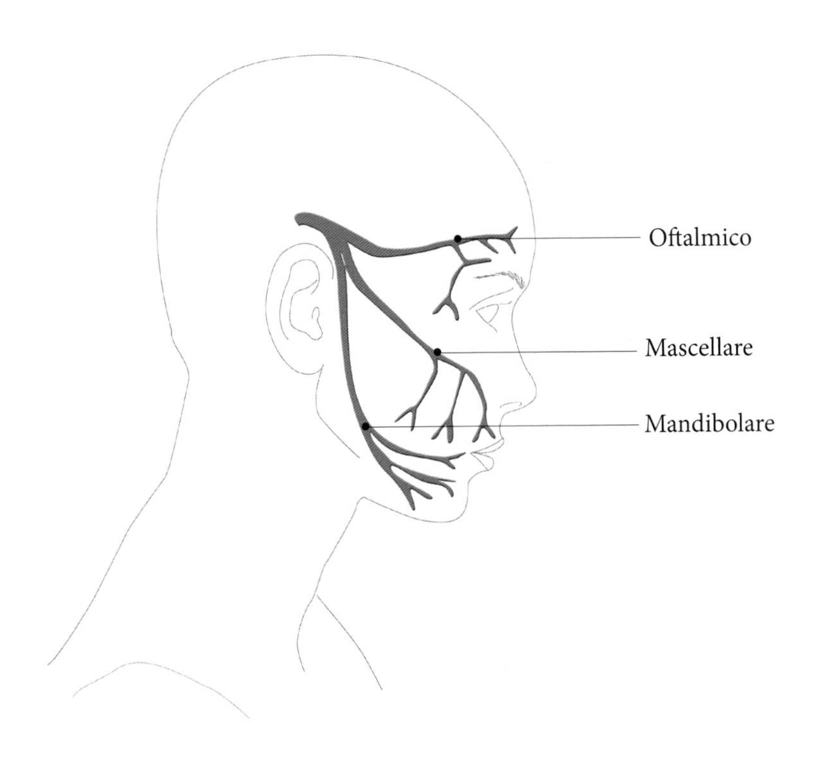

7°Nervo Cranico - 'Facciale'

11° Nervo Cranico - 'Accessorio'

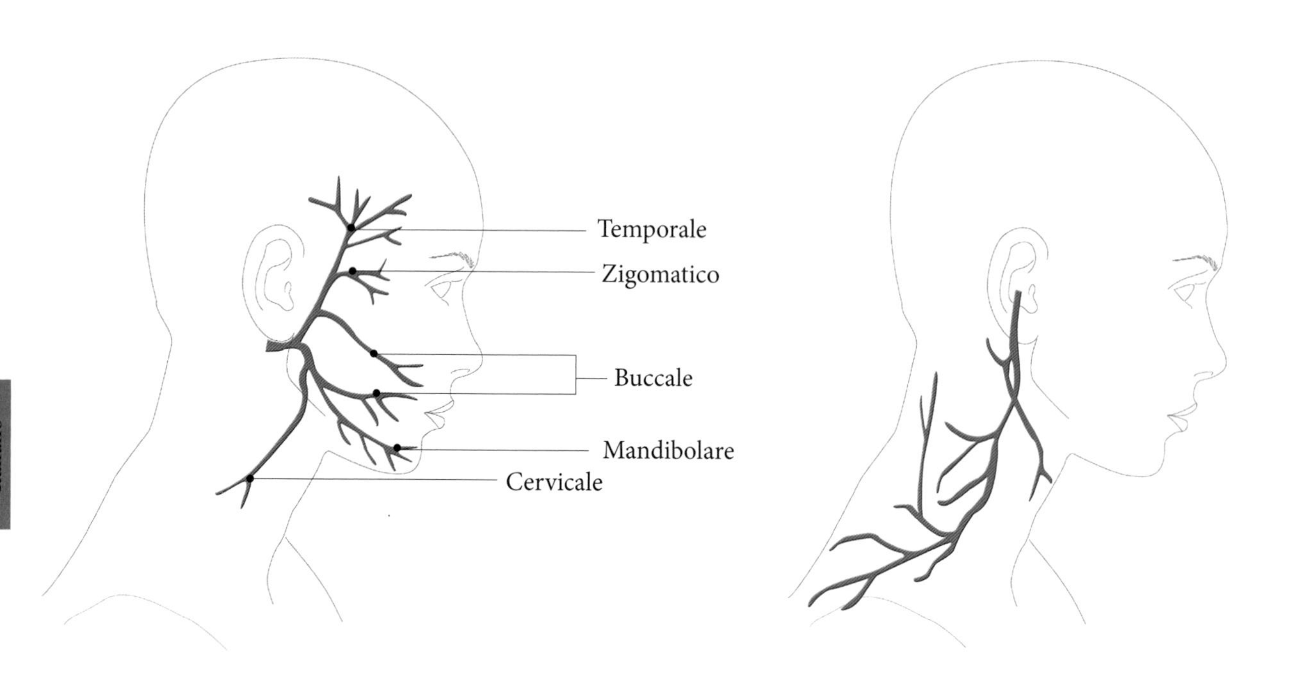

Nervo	Funzione	Branche Nervose	Manda Messaggi a
5° trigemino	Controlla i muscoli per la masticazione	Oftalmico	Ghiandole lacrimali della pelle della fronte. Parte superiore delle guance
	Passa le informazioni sensoriali dalla faccia	Mascellare	Muscolo superiore della mascella
		Mandibolare	Muscolo inferiore della mascella, denti, muscoli per la masticazione
7° facciale	Controlla i muscoli usati per le espressioni facciali	Temporale	Muscoli intorno agli occhi Muscoli della fronte
		Zigomatico	Muscoli degli occhi
		Buccale	Labbro superiore, lati del naso
		Mandibolare	Labbro inferiore, mento
		Cervicale	Lato del collo e del mento
11° accessorio	Muove il collo e le spalle		

SESSIONE 2 - RISULTATI DI APPRENDIMENTO

- Conoscenza di base della struttura e della funzione della pelle
- Identificazione dei differenti tipi di pelle
- Buona conoscenza della teoria della microdermoabrasione
- Identificazione delle parti della pelle che possono essere trattate con la microdermoabrasione
- Conoscenza del funzionamento di un ciclo di trattamenti di microdermoabrasione

LA PELLE

La pelle è l'organo più esteso del corpo umano. La pelle utilizza diverse funzioni per proteggerci dagli agenti esterni.

- Previene l'assorbimento di sostanze dannose
- Aiuta a regolare la temperatura corporea
- Agisce da barriera contro le infezioni
- Tramite la melanina, ci protegge dagli effetti dannosi dei raggi UV
- Crea un rivestimento impermeabile che impedisce la disidratazione
- Crea una riserva energetica sotto forma di riserva di grasso

La Struttura Della Pelle

La pelle è composta di due distinti strati: l'epidermide ed il derma. Tra loro c'è una membrana di base che tiene insieme i due strati. Al di sotto di questi strati c'è lo strato sottocutaneo, uno strato di grasso che protegge, ammortizza, isola e conserva energia aggiuntiva per il corpo.

L'Epidermide

L'epidermide è lo strato più esterno della pelle ed è a sua volta composto di cinque strati. Ciascuno strato dell'epidermide può essere riconosciuto dalla forma e dalla funzione delle sue cellule. Il tipo di cellule tipico dell'epidermide è il cheratinocito che produce la proteina chiamata cheratina.

Il rinnovamento cellulare avviene approssimativamente ogni quattro settimane. Le cellule passano dallo strato inferiore dell'epidermide (strato basale) a quello superiore (strato corneo) cambiando forma e struttura durante il passaggio. Lo strato superiore dell'epidermide è quello le cui cellule muoiono e che è caratterizzato dalla "desquamazione" della pelle. È questo lo strato che viene rimosso dalla microdermoabrasione ed è anche lo strato capace di riflettere i raggi UV, e per tale motivo è importante che i clienti usino sempre una crema protettiva dopo il trattamento di microdermoabrasione.

L'Epidermide

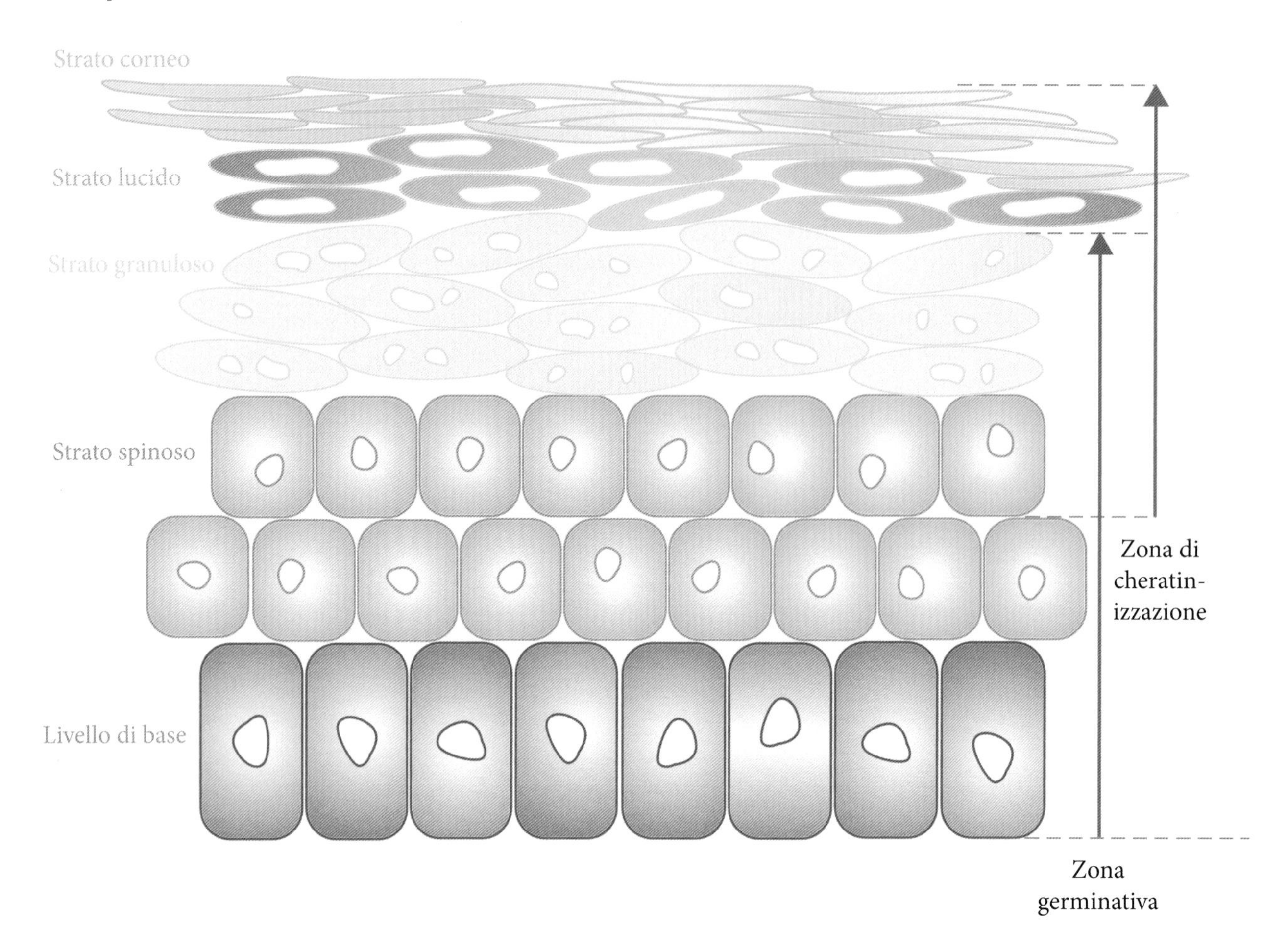

I Cinque Strati Dell'Epidermide

1. Stratum Corneum (strato corneo)

È lo strato più esterno dell'epidermide, fatto a sua volta di diversi strati di cellule appiattite, per lo più morte e sovrapposte. Queste cellule aiutano a riflettere i raggi UV. La pelle scura che si sviluppa con l'esposizione ai raggi UV ha uno strato corneo più spesso di quello della pelle caucasica o bianca. Ci vogliono circa tre settimane perché le cellule dell'epidermide raggiungano lo strato corneo dallo strato germinativo. A quel punto le cellule sono rimosse e tale processo si chiama desquamazione.

2. Stratum Lucidum (strato lucido)

Tale strato si trova soltanto nelle parti più dure della pelle come il palmo della mano o la pianta del piede.

3. Stratum Granulosum (strato granuloso)

In questo strato le cellule cominciano a morire. Le cellule sembrano dei granuli a causa della rottura dei nuclei. Questi granuli sono conosciuti come granuli di cheratina.

4. Stratum Spinosum (strato spinoso)

Lo strato spinoso è fatto di cellule dalla superficie appuntita (di qui il nome) per unirsi alle cellule circostanti. È questo lo strato in cui inizia la sintesi della cheratina.

5. Stratum Germinativum (strato basale)

Alcune cellule a forma di colonna sono responsabili della produzione di nuove cellule epidermiche. Le cellule si separano e passano agli strati superiori. Le restanti cellule si separano per riempire i vuoti. Questo processo di divisione cellulare è conosciuto come mitosi.

La zona germinativa dell'epidermide contiene anche due altre importanti tipi di cellule: Langerhans e Melanociti.

Le cellule di Langerhans assorbono e rimuovono i corpi estranei che penetrano la pelle. Passano dall'epidermide al derma, entrando poi nel sistema linfatico dell'individuo, sistema capace di eliminare le scorie prodotte dal corpo.

I melanociti sono responsabili alla produzione di melanina nella pelle. Proteggono le altre cellule dell'epidermide dagli effetti nocivi dei raggi UV. La melanina aiuta a determinare il colore della pelle, per cui una maggiore quantità di melanina ha come risultato una gradazione più scura della nostra pelle.

Il Derma

Italiano

Il derma è lo strato che si trova sotto l'epidermide ed è responsabile della resistenza ed elasticità della pelle. Contiene anche una certa quantità di cellule specializzate e strutturate inclusi i nervi, i vasi sanguigni, le ghiandole e i follicoli dei peli. Il derma è formato da due strati: il papillare ed il reticolare. Lo strato superiore detto papillare contiene una disposizione sottile di fibre di collagene. Lo strato reticolare sottostante è fatto di dense fibre di collagene situate parallelamente rispetto alla superficie della pelle.

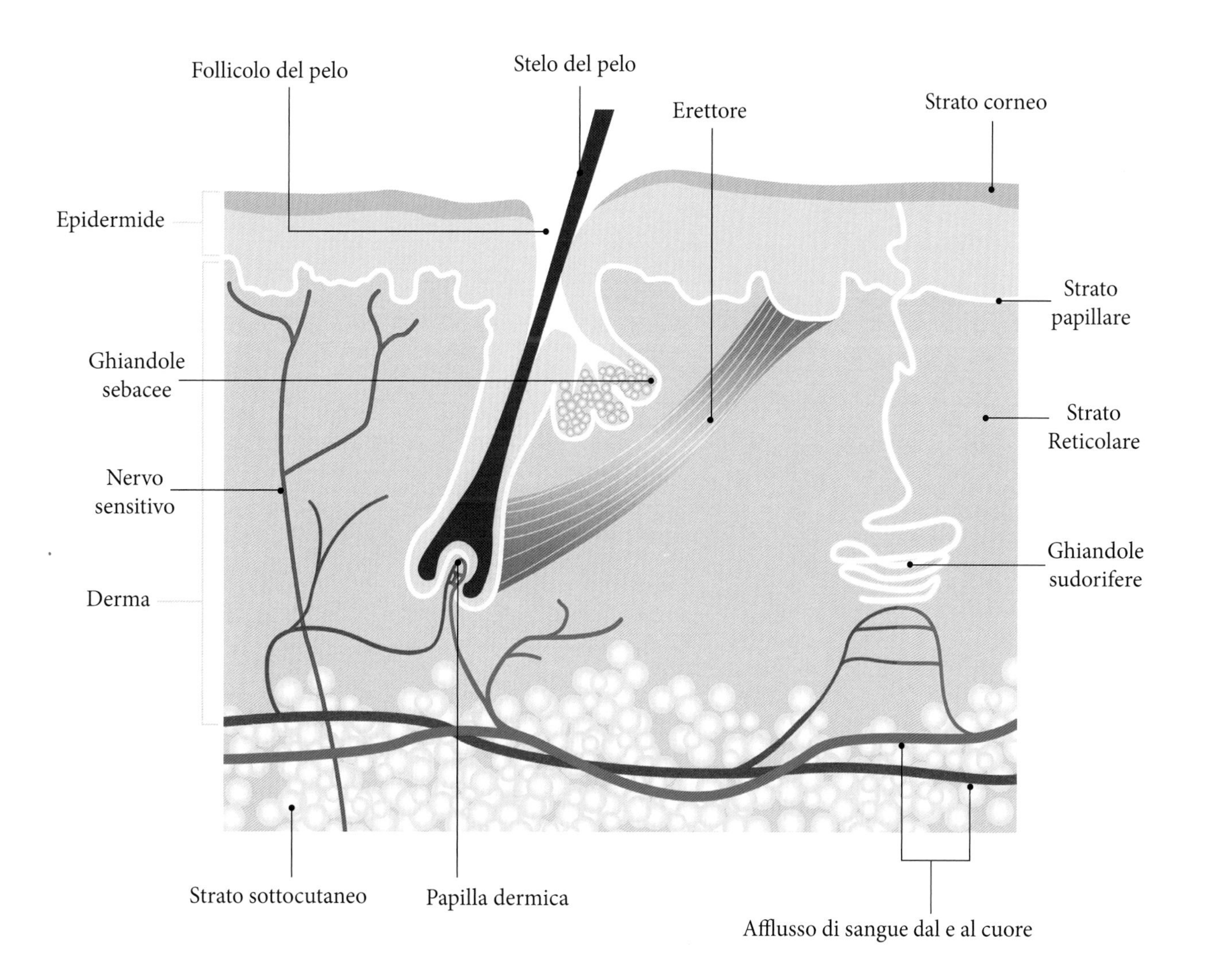

Lo Strato Reticolare

Lo strato reticolare è formato da due specie di proteine:le fibre di elastina che danno elasticità alla pelle e le fibre di collagene che danno forza alla pelle. Queste fibre sono tenute insieme in una sostanza gelatinosa. L' elastina e le fibre di collagene formano una rete resistente che danno un aspetto giovanile alla pelle.

Con l'età queste fibre cominciano ad indurirsi e a frammentarsi, così il reticolo inizia a dissolversi, la nostra pelle comincia a perdere elasticità e mette in mostra visibilmente i segni dell'età. La circolazione del sangue nella pelle diminuisce e così le sostanze nutritive non raggiungono la superficie, da cui un colorito della pelle più pallido. Lo strato oleoso al di sotto della pelle diventa più sottile, così da darci un aspetto "più tirato", dal momento che la nostra struttura ossea diviene più prominente. Lo strato reticolare è di vitale importanza per la salute e l'aspetto della nostra pelle; è pertanto essenziale prendersene cura per prevenire i segni dell'età.

Flusso Sanguigno

Il sangue circola nel corpo umano raggiungendo tutte le cellule e trasportando sostanze nutrienti, energia come l'ossigeno ed il glucosio ed altre materie prime essenziali per la salute, il mantenimento e la crescita della pelle.

L'azione del vuoto della microdermoabrasione stimola una microcircolazione sulla superficie della pelle. Ciò produce un aumento del flusso sanguigno nell'area trattata,che genera la produzione di collagene ed elastina nella pelle ed inoltre il rinnovo (rigenerazione della pelle), migliorando quindi la qualità dei tessuti e generando una pelle più levigata e fresca.

Il disegno mostra come il sangue fluisce attraverso le cellule. Prima di tutto trasportando sostanze nutrienti ed energia, poi rimuovendo prodotti di scarto come l'anidride carbonica.

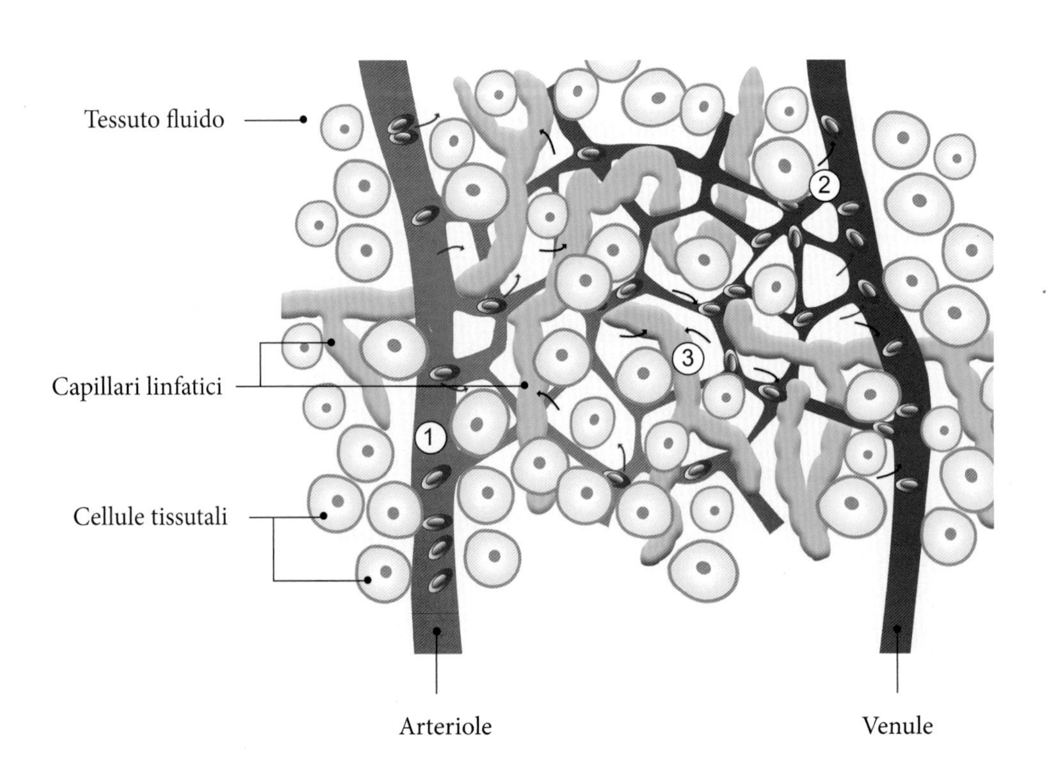

(1) Il sangue sotto l'effetto della pressione fluisce attraverso la rete dei capillari sfociando nel tessuto e diventando tessuto fluido. Questo fluido contiene sostanze utili, come l'ossigeno e nutrienti, essenziali per le cellule. Le cellule del sangue e le grandi proteine rimangono nei capillari.

(2) Appena il sangue diventa deossigenato, la pressione cambia e il fluido contenente sostanze di scarto rientra nei capillari e viene eliminato.

(3) Fluidi in eccesso, prodotti di scarto e grandi molecole come le proteine incapaci di rientrare nel sangue sono catturati dai capillari linfatici e portate ai linfonodi, dove il fluido viene scomposto e rientra nel sangue più vicino al cuore.

Flusso Del Sangue Attraverso La Pelle

La temperatura corporea normale è di 37°C. Il corpo si attiva per mantenere tale temperatura. Se la temperatura corporea comincia ad aumentare, il sangue passa nella pelle e libera parte del suo calore. Quando la temperatura del corpo scende, i capillari si restringono ed il sangue passa attraverso i vasi più profondi nel derma, riducendo la quantità di calore perso attraverso la pelle.

La vasodilatazione si verifica quando si ha caldo
- il sangue caldo passa vicino alla superficie e rilascia il calore.

La vasocostrizione si verifica quando si ha freddo - il flusso di sangue freddo attraversa i vasi più profondi e si allontana dalla superficie – trattenendo così il calore.

Tipi di Pelle

Esistono fondamentalmente sei tipi di pelle. La pelle del viso di un soggetto può cambiare diverse volte durante la vita, per malattie o scompensi ormonali.

Pelle Secca

La pelle secca è causata dalla scarsa o inattività delle ghiandole oleose non producendo sebo sufficiente per mantenere la pelle naturalmente idratata. Di solito ha una apparenza opaca ed è secca, affetta da prurito e qualche volta molto delicata. La pelle secca deve essere idratata regolarmente dall'interno (bevendo liquidi) e dall'esterno con creme e lozioni idratanti.

Tipi Di Pelle Grassa

La pelle grassa è causata da una sovrapproduzione di sebo da parte delle ghiandole, con il risultato che la pelle appare lucida e con pori dilatati. I tipi di pelle oleosa sono inclini a sviluppare comedoni (punti neri) ed acne. Ciononostante questo tipo di pelle oleosa conserva un aspetto giovanile e più elastico nel tempo, rispetto ad altri tipi di pelle. La pelle grassa trae grandi benefici dalla microdermoabrasione con l'applicazione di creme idratanti leggere.

Tipi Di Pelle Sensibile

Le pelli sensibili possono essere secche, normali o grasse e sono caratterizzate dalla loro delicatezza. La pelle sensibile reagisce di frequente negativamente alle condizioni ambientali e spesso richiede uno speciale trattamento per mantenere la migliore condizione. La pelle sensibile trae grandi benefici da prodotti naturali per la pelle e dai trattamenti.

Pelle Normale
La pelle normale produce sebo in quantità moderata e quindi è in una situazione di equilibrio ideale. La pelle normale appare di consistenza turgida, idratata ed in buona salute. Possederla è una grande fortuna, ma ciononostante è necessaria molta attenzione; la pelle normale trae beneficio da detersione regolare, tonificanti e creme idratanti.

Pelle Mista
La pelle mista è il più comune tipo di pelle. La pelle mista è frequentemente caratterizzata da una zona "T" grassa che copre la fronte, il naso e il mento, mentre la pelle nella zona delle guance, degli occhi e della bocca è normale o secca. Le persone con pelle mista dovrebbero controllare la loro pelle regolarmente ed usare differenti prodotti sulle diverse parti del viso.

Pelle Matura
La pelle matura ha le seguenti caratteristiche. Diventa secca non appena le ghiandole sebacee diventano meno attive. Perde elasticità, e quindi appaiono le prime linee fini e le prime rughe. La pelle appare più sottile con capillari rotti specie sulle guance e intorno al naso. I contorni del viso risultano meno definiti per la riduzione del tono muscolare. La struttura ossea sottostante diventa più evidente, dal momento che lo strato adiposo sotto la pelle diventa più sottile. La circolazione del sangue diventa scarsa e ciò interferisce con il nutrimento della pelle che appare pallida. A causa della diminuzione della velocità del metabolismo, i prodotti di scarto non sono più rimossi velocemente, e quindi, producono gonfiore della pelle. La pelle matura deve essere ben idratata bevendo acqua con regolarità ed usando creme idratanti nutritive.

Tonalità Della Pelle

La tonalità della pelle umana può variare dal marrone scuro a una pelle priva di pigmentazioni, quindi senza colore, che possono apparire rossastre per il sangue che circola sotto la pelle. Gli Europei hanno generalmente pelle, capelli ed occhi più chiari di altri gruppi etnici, sebbene possono esserci delle eccezioni. Per motivi di praticità sono stati identificati 6 tipi, secondo la scala Fitzpatrick (1975). I colori della pelle sono elencati nel senso dell'incremento di colore.

La Scala Fitzpatrick

Tipo	Comportamento	All'abbronzatura	Colore capelli e occhi
I	Molto chiara, anche chiamata Nordica	Spesso si scotta, raramente si abbronza	Tendenzialmente lentiggini, capelli biondi, occhi blu o verdi
II	Abbastanza chiara	Spesso si scotta	Tendenzialmente capelli chiari occhi blu o verdi
III	Mediamente chiara o scura di tipo razza bianca europea	Qualche volta si scotta, di solito si abbronza	Tendenzialmente capelli ed occhi scuri
IV	Mediamente scura detta mediterranea o olivastra	Qualche volta si scotta spesso si abbronza	Tendenzialmente ed occhi scuri
V	Scura di tipo bruno	Pelle normalmente di un colore bruno scuro	Spesso capelli e occhi neri
VI	Molto scura o di tipo nero	Pelle naturalmente di un colore bruno scuro	Di solito capelli e occhi neri

MICRODERMOABRASIONE: COS'È?

La microdermoabrasione è un sistema sicuro e controllato di esfoliazione intensiva attraverso l'utilizzo di cristalli puri, per il ringiovanimento della pelle. I cristalli effettuano una leggera azione abrasiva rimuovendo cellule morte. La forma irregolare dei cristalli permette di operare energicamente su tutte le parti senza danneggiare la pelle. I trattamenti sono progressivi e ciò vuol dire che i clienti potranno vedere buoni risultati durante il ciclo di trattamenti.

Il grado di abrasione può essere cambiato modificando la velocità del getto di spruzzo dei cristalli una volta a contatto con la pelle. La rimozione dello strato corneo ha come risultato immediato una sensazione di maggiore levigatezza e freschezza della pelle, provocando nel contempo la crescita di pelle nuova e collagene. Al termine di un ciclo di trattamento la pelle risulterà splendente e ringiovanita.

L'azione del vuoto da un lato elimina i cristalli usati e le cellule morte, dall'altro stimola la circolazione del sangue aumentandone il flusso nella parte trattata. Si stimola la produzione di collagene ed elastina con la conseguenza di generare una pelle più soda e dall'aspetto più giovanile.

La microdermoabrasione può essere applicata a tutti i tipi di pelle e su tutte le parti del corpo e del viso. SkinBase raccomanda un ciclo di 8 trattamenti, con cadenza settimanale oppure ogni 10 giorni. Le persone affette da acne o che presentano cicatrici da acne potrebbero aver bisogno di un numero maggiore di trattamenti e si consiglia di effettuare un trattamento mensile di mantenimento dopo il termine del normale ciclo, con lo scopo di mantenere nel tempo i risultati ottenuti.

Dopo il trattamento la pelle potrebbe apparire tesa e manifestare un leggero rossore. Perciò è di fondamentale importanza che i clienti usino una buona crema idratante. Questi effetti di solito si verificano all'incirca 24 ore dopo il trattamento.

Quali Sono I Benefici Dell'Utilizzo Della Microdermoabrasione Rispetto Ad Altri Metodi Di Trattamento?

- Il disagio per il cliente durante il trattamento è minimo.
- I cristalli usati per la microdermoabrasione sono completamente inerti e sterili con rischio minimo alle reazioni allergiche spesso associate all'utilizzo di soluzioni chimiche.
- Il cliente può tornare alla sua quotidianità subito dopo il trattamento, per esempio non si verificano rossori eccessivi della pelle ecc.
- Si possono trattare con sicurezza tutti i tipi di pelle e di qualsiasi tonalità di colore.
- I risultati sono tangibili sin dal primo trattamento e ciò aiuta a mantenere il cliente motivato.
- Aiuta a trattare subito i segni dell'età e garantisce un completo ringiovanimento di pelli mature.
- L'azione del vuoto migliora l'elasticità ed il tono muscolare della pelle e stimola inoltre i fibroblasti a produrre collagene.
- Accresce la capacità di penetrazione dei prodotti consentiti dopo il trattamento.
- È ideale per pelli congestionate con pori dilatati, comedoni ed acne.
- Permette un controllo variabile della profondità di esfoliazione per pelli ispessite e deformate e con cicatrici da acne.
- L'esfoliazione totale del corpo offre anche un trattamento anti-cellulite dal momento che l'azione aspirante del trattamento favorisce il drenaggio linfatico.

Quali Sono I Rischi Associati Alla Microdermoabrasione?

Un uso improprio del sistema o l'uso in condizioni non igieniche può comportare dei rischi. Si sottolinea quindi l'importanza di un buon livello di igiene sul luogo di lavoro. Il sistema MDPro usa beccucci monouso eliminando in tal modo ogni eventuale rischio di contaminazione incrociata tra clienti, essendo l'unico componente a contatto con la pelle durante il trattamento.

I CRISTALLI

I cristalli sono di ossido di alluminio, un minerale naturale, sterile, non tossico e con un rischio minimo che si verifichino effetti collaterali. Si raccomanda comunque sempre l'esecuzione di un test per eventuali allergie, prima di effettuare il trattamento, come misura precauzionale.

L'ossido di alluminio è considerato un minerale a basso rischio per la salute in caso di inalazione. Gli standard industriali trattano le inalazioni di questo tipo solo come polvere fastidiosa. L'inalazione di qualsiasi particella sottile di polvere, per esempio polvere di unghie artificiali, può causare irritazione e tosse per esposizioni prolungate. L'ossido di alluminio non contiene silice libera e ciò significa nessun rischio di inalazione.

Italiano

Sensibilità ai Cristalli

È importante eseguire il patch test sulla pelle per verificare l'eventuale sensibilità dei clienti ai cristalli usati per il trattamento. È abbastanza raro che un cliente sia sensibile ai cristalli usati per il trattamento, comunque un test sulla pelle dovrebbe essere effettuato sul retro dell'avambraccio prima del trattamento. Se la parte diventa irritata o gonfia è bene non procedere al trattamento. Se il cliente sviluppa macchie rosse sulla pelle dopo il trattamento, ciò è normalmente dovuto a una maggiore pressione usata dal terapista.

QUALI SONO LE CONDIZIONI CHE POSSONO ESSERE TRATTATE CON LA MICRODERMOABRASIONE?

Tutti possono beneficiare del trattamento di microdermoabrasione, che migliora l'aspetto della pelle rendendola splendente e più giovanile. La microdermoabrasione è anche estremamente efficace per una serie di problemi della pelle. Può essere usata sul volto e sul corpo, per esempio, con buoni risultati per cicatrici da acne sulla schiena.

Acne E Cicatrici D'Acne

La microdermoabrasione rinnova gli strati superiori delle cellule morte dalla superficie della pelle rendendosi particolarmente efficace nel trattamento dell'acne. Libera la superficie della pelle dalle cellule morte e libera dalle ostruzioni i pori con il risultato di ridurre la possibilità di ulteriore sviluppo di nuovi inestetismi.

Linee Sottili E Rughe
Pelle Invecchiata

L'azione del vuoto nei trattamenti di microdermoabrasione stimola la produzione di collagene sulla pelle. Con l'età la produzione di elastina e di collagene comincia a diminuire. L'uso combinato di stimolazione del collagene e rinnovamento della pelle migliora la qualità della superficie della pelle distendendo le linee sottili e le rughe.

Pelle Secca E Disidratata
Tono Irregolare Della Pelle
Normalmente la pelle si rinnova ogni 28 giorni. Rimuovendo le cellule morte dallo strato superiore della pelle, la microdermoabrasione aumenta la velocità di rinnovamento della stessa rendendo la pelle più fresca e donandole splendore.

Cellulite Effetto "Buccia D'arancia"
La microdermoabrasione non può curare la cellulite, comunque stimola la circolazione, migliorando il flusso sanguigno nell'area trattata. Per migliorare l'aspetto della cellulite le clienti dovrebbero bere molta acqua e fare regolarmente esercizi fisici.

Smagliature, Pigmentazione Ed Imperfezioni
La microdermoabrasione può migliorare di molto l'aspetto di pigmentazione e smagliature. Il trattamento di microdermoabrasione stimola le parti trattate affinché producano più collagene e accelera il processo di rinnovamento della pelle, migliorando le condizioni della stessa e diminuendo la visibilità delle smagliature e lo scolorimento della pelle.

Il trattamento di microdermoabrasione non può eliminare le smagliature, comunque un regolare trattamento può migliorare le parti trattate rendendo le lesioni meno visibili. I tessuti cicatriziali non dovrebbero essere trattati fino a quando l'infiammazione non cessa del tutto sulla parte da trattare (6 mesi dopo gli interventi chirurgici).

Trattamenti regolari di microdermoabrasione migliorano l'aspetto delle smagliature creando un effetto di uniformità sui tessuti circostanti la cicatrice, e riducendo eventuali problemi di pigmentazione che spesso rendono le smagliature più evidenti.

Iperpigmentazione (Melasma) e Le Cause
Le più comuni cause sono l'uso di contraccettivi, o terapie per scompensi ormonali, gravidanza o interazioni con alcuni farmaci. L'esposizione ripetuta o prolungata ai raggi del sole può essere anche causa di questo problema della pelle. Alcune sostanze chimiche, come quelle contenute nei profumi, possono far insorgere macchie di pigmentazione. Un trattamento regolare di microdermoabrasione apporta benefici significativi alla pelle danneggiata dai raggi del sole ed aiuta a eliminare le irregolarità di pigmentazione indesiderate.

Un ciclo di trattamenti SkinBase può dare ottimi risultati per le irregolarità di pigmentazione. I clienti devono sapere che potrebbe essere necessario un ciclo di 10-15 trattamenti. È anche imperativo che i clienti sappiano di dover usare sempre creme solari. Tenete presente che il trattamento di microdermoabrasione **non** può curare persone affette da vitiligine.

Il melasma e il cloasma (imbrunimento della pelle dovuto a cambiamenti ormonali) possono essere trattati con esito positivo. Il trattamento facilita l'eliminazione del pigmento attraverso lo strato epidermico. Per migliorare le aree affette possono comunque essere necessari molti trattamenti.

DEFINIZIONE DEI CICLI DI TRATTAMENTO

La microdermoabrasione è un trattamento progressivo piuttosto che aggressivo. Gli strati epidermici sono rimossi delicatamente e con sicurezza durante un ciclo di trattamento. Un ciclo di trattamento può avere una cadenza di 7 -10 giorni; in questo modo lo strato corneo rimosso in precedenza non ha la possibilità di ricostituirsi ed anche la tolleranza del cliente al trattamento aumenta. Perciò, ad ogni trattamento successivo, l'intensità dello stesso può aumentare al fin di raggiungere le parti più profonde dello strato dell'epidermide e di rimuovere con successo le cicatrici dell'acne, trattare le zone a pigmentazione irregolare e levigare le linee sottili. Un ciclo di 15-20 trattamenti con cadenza settimanale è considerato il massimo possibile.

SESSIONE 3 - RISULTATI DI APPRENDIMENTO

- Capacità di effettuare un consulto al cliente prima del trattamento.
- Conoscenza delle controindicazioni al trattamento di microdermoabrasione.
- Conoscenza degli interventi richiesti dopo il trattamento e le possibili reazioni al trattamento.

CONSULTO AL CLIENTE

1. Verificare l'idoneità al trattamento facendo riferimento alla lista delle controindicazioni.

2. Verificare che il cliente non abbia allergie come per esempio quella ai metalli, altrimenti potrebbe essere più sensibile al trattamento.

3. Effettuare un analisi localizzata eliminando le parti su cui evitare il trattamento. Ad esempio controindicazioni minori come le telangectasie (capillari rotti).

4. Localizzare le parti che richiedono speciale attenzione, come le cicatrici d'acne o la pigmentazione, i pori aperti o le parti con tono della pelle irregolare.

5. Suggerire un programma di trattamento spiegando nei dettagli i costi, la durata, la frequenza richiesta.

6. Spiegare al cliente in che cosa consiste il trattamento e le reazioni che avvertirà.

7. Spiegare al cliente le possibili reazioni della pelle. Nonostante il rischio di reazione sia molto basso, assicurarsi che i clienti siano consapevoli delle cure che la loro pelle dovrà seguire dopo il trattamento.

8. Discutere con il cliente la fase post-trattamento, accertandosi che lo stesso sia consapevole di come dovrà curare la pelle dopo il trattamento.

9. È di vitale importanza che il cliente segua un regime di vita corretto tra un trattamento e l'altro e che si impegni per raggiungere i risultati, per esempio usando una crema solare con un certo fattore di protezione per evitare problemi di pigmentazione.

10. COMPILARE SEMPRE UNA SCHEDA CLIENTE

Ciò permette di seguire meglio il cliente evidenziando necessità. Spiegare le controindicazioni al trattamento e chiedere al cliente di firmare la propria scheda.

Per i clienti di età inferiore a 16 anni è richiesta la firma dei genitori/tutori (che devono avere età superiore a 18 anni).

CONTROINDICAZIONI AL TRATTAMENTO DI MICRODERMOABRASIONE

Controindicazioni Maggiori - Non procedere al trattamento

Gravidanza

Durante la gravidanza, un aumento di ormoni può avere delle ripercussioni sulla pelle, provocando l'insorgenza di pigmentazioni. Per questa ragione consigliamo di non sottoporsi a trattamenti di microdermoabrasione dal momento che la pelle può avere reazioni avverse, potendo in alcuni casi peggiorarne le condizioni. Un valido consiglio per le clienti è quello di utilizzare una buona protezione solare per prevenire l'insorgenza di pigmentazioni.

Cancro

È consigliabile non sottoporre al trattamento clienti malati di cancro, infatti, dovrebbero essere in remissione per almeno 6 mesi prima di cominciare un ciclo di trattamenti. La microdermoabrasione stimola la circolazione sanguigna e il drenaggio linfatico.

Acne IV grado

I clienti affetti da acne al IV grado non dovrebbero sottoporsi a trattamenti di microdermoabrasione. Se la pelle è molto congestionata con pustole e papule, il trattamento potrebbe irritare la pelle e diffondere il batterio.

Roaccutan

Il Roaccutan provoca un assottigliamento della pelle, quindi se il cliente è sottoposto a trattamenti a base di Roaccutan per curare l'acne, è necessario procedere a trattamenti di microdermoabrasione solo dopo 6 mesi dall'interruzione al farmaco.

Malattia auto-immune

Il termine viene utilizzato per descrivere numerose malattie che attaccano le cellule e i tessuti dell'organismo. È consigliabile non sottoporre al trattamento di microdermoabrasione il cliente affetto da una malattia auto-immune.

Diabete

Il diabete colpisce i nervi e la circolazione, di conseguenza, la pelle avrà tempi di guarigione più lunghi del solito. Prima di sottoporsi a trattamenti di microdermoabrasione, i clienti affetti da diabete dovrebbero presentare un permesso scritto del loro medico curante.

Impetigine

Non procedere al trattamento in caso di clienti affetti da impetigine, un'infezione contagiosa della pelle.

Rosacea

I casi di rosacea non possono essere sottoposti a trattamenti di microdermoabrasione.

Controindicazioni Minori - Procedere con cautela al trattamento ed evitate le zone affette dalle seguenti patologie:

- Infezione agli occhi: Congiuntivite, Orzaioli/Hordolea, Cisti
- Disturbi della pelle, Acne in fase attiva, Seborroica Dermatite, Herpes Facciale, Eczema, Psoriasi
- Cicatrici Cheloidi
- Capillari Rotti
- Moli Sollevati, Verruche, Acrochordon
- Tagli, Contusioni, Abrasioni

Se non siete sicure o non riuscite ad identificare una delle patologie sopra elencate è opportuno non sottoporre il cliente al trattamento e consigliargli di consultare il loro medico curante.

CONSIGLI PRE-TRATTAMENTO

È necessario che il cliente si attenga ai consigli proposti di seguito prima di iniziare il ciclo di trattamenti:

Botox/Filler

Fare trascorrere almeno 14 giorni prima di sottoporsi a un trattamento di microdermoabrasione o altre iniezioni, in modo da permettere al botox/filler di assestarsi.

Uomini

Gli uomini dovrebbero rasarsi la sera prima del trattamento se il trattamento viene fatto al mattino, altrimenti al mattino se il trattamento è previsto nel pomeriggio.

Trattamenti Laser

Un ciclo di trattamenti laser non porterebbero i giusti risultati se si effettua anche un ciclo di trattamenti di microdermoabrasione SkinBase. Fare trascorrere almeno 2 settimane dalla fine dei trattamenti laser prima di iniziare quelli di microdermoabrasione.

Derma Rollers

Non usarli per 2 settimane prima del trattamenti di microdermoabrasione.

CONSIGLI POST-TRATTAMENTO

È necessario che il cliente si attenga ai consigli proposti di seguito dopo il trattamento di microdermoabrasine:

Per 12 ore:

Evitare il trucco pesante.

Per 24 ore:

Non fare nuoto. Non fare cerette a caldo al viso.

Per 48 ore:

Non sottoporsi a sauna o lettino solare. Evitare l'esposizione a luce U.V. Non sottoporsi ad iniezioni di botulino e ad infiltrazioni sottocutanee.

Per 72 ore:

Non usare AHA, sostanze glicoliche e retinolo, in quanto la nuova pelle irritata è ricettiva ad ogni prodotto applicato e quindi l'uso di qualsiasi esfoliante può irritare la pelle.

Sempre durante un ciclo di trattamenti:

Applicare una crema protettiva contro il sole con almeno SPF 15.
Applicare regolarmente creme idratanti per tenere idratata la pelle ed evitare che si secchi e spelli.

I prodotti usati devono avere un pH compreso tra 4,5 e 7,0

L'uso di prodotti per la cura della pelle che contengono un'alta percentuale di componenti botanici ed oli essenziali è inopportuno dopo il trattamento di microdermoabrasione, in quanto alcuni componenti possono causare una reazione allergica. Se ciò dovesse accadere si creerebbe un danno reale sia per il cliente che per il terapista ed il cliente potrebbe pensare che sia stato il trattamento a provocare la reazione allergica, mentre in realtà ciò è stato causato da alcuni ingredienti del cosmetico usato. È importante anche usare prodotti tali da garantire una idratazione alla pelle, evitando quindi che la stessa si secchi e si spelli.

SESSIONE 4 - RISULTATI DI APPRENDIMENTO

- Conoscenza dei componenti e delle funzioni dell'apparecchio di microdermoabrasione.
- Conoscenza delle modalità di avviamento e di controllo dell'apparecchio.
- Capacità di selezionare il trattamento opportuno per ciascun tipo di cliente.

Italiano

MESSA IN FUNZIONE DELL'APPARECCHIO SKINBASE MDPRO

1. Aprire il coperchio ed estrarre:
   - il cavo elettrico
   - il manipolo completo con tubo
   - il contenitore vuoto completo di connettore a scatto.
2. Quindi collegare il connettore a scatto, accertandosi che sia completamente inserito e che il dis positivo di bloccaggio sia in posizione corretta. Se non è ben fissato si creerà una diminuzione della pressione del vuoto.
3. Accertarsi che il manipolo sia collegata al contenitore (dove vanno i cristalli usati) tramite il tubo argentato e fermamente connessa ad entrambe le estremità.
4. Fissare una boccetta di cristalli al manipolo ed avvitare saldamente.
5. Infine inserire un nuovo beccuccio blu al manipolo.
6. Ora collegare il cavo elettrico, accendere l'interruttore e il pannello.
7. Mettendo il dito indice sul foro del beccuccio blu (importante), ruotare la valvola di regolazione sino a raggiungere la pressione desiderata per il trattamento. Accertarsi di aver ben compreso il sistema dei livelli di pressione prima di procedere al trattamento di microdermoabrasione.

ATTENZIONE: in nessun caso il rivestimento metallico deve essere svitato e rimosso prima di averlo completamente disconnesso dal cavo di alimentazione.

LIVELLI DI TRATTAMENTO

Con le seguenti note descrittive si forniscono le linee guida per selezionare il livello corretto di trattamento per ogni cliente.

PRIMO LIVELLO - 0,3 bar

Questo livello va usato dai terapisti con poca esperienza, sino a quando acquisiranno una maggiore confidenza con il trattamento.

Questo livello permette un' esfoliazione leggera e va selezionato anche per i clienti al primo trattamento.

Questo livello va sempre selezionato per trattare la zona del contorno occhi.

SECONDO LIVELLO - 0,4 bar

Questo livello dovrà essere selezionato gradualmente su una pelle affetta da acne.

Non usare un livello più alto di questo per tipi di pelle V e VI della scala Fitzpatrick

TERZO LIVELLO - 0,5 bar

Questo livello va usato solo per clienti prossimi alla fine del ciclo di trattamenti quando la pelle è più tollerante.

Si usa per curare cicatrici da acne, pigmentazione, linee sottili, rughe and anche per trattamenti sul corpo per curare le smagliature e il cellulite.

Non usare su pelli nere/asiatiche.

QUARTO LIVELLO - 0.6 bar

Da utilizzare solo per trattamenti corpo. **Non deve mai essere usato sul viso**.

SESSIONE 5 - RISULTATI DI APPRENDIMENTO

- Capacità di utilizzare l'apparecchio e intervenire in modo sicuro ed efficace per tutta la durata del trattamento.
- Capacità di operare entro limiti di tempo accettabili nel settore estetico.

METODO DI TRATTAMENTO

1. Posizionare il cliente in posizione semi-reclinata.
2. Assicurarsi che i capelli del cliente siano accolti in modo che non tocchino il volto.
3. Pulire accuratamente la pelle del cliente. Si deve usare un detergente in gel (non in crema).
4. La pelle deve essere completamente asciutta.
5. Distendere la pelle con il pollice ed il medio.
6. Tenere il manipolo come se fosse una penna, muoverlo delicatamente sulla zona del viso (vedi immagine nella pagina seguente).
7. Effettuare una esfoliazione delicata sull'intera superficie del viso e del collo.
8. Completata l'esfoliazione in modo delicato ritornare sulle parti che necessitano di maggiore attenzione come le cicatrici d'acne, la pigmentazione, le lesioni da trazione, le linee fini e le rughe.
9. A trattamento completato, pulire ogni residuo di cristalli e di pelle, usando un tampone di cotone umido (acqua fredda).
10. Tonificare usando un tonico delicato.
11. L'eventuale maschera è facoltativa.
12. Idratare.
13. Applicare una lozione o crema SPF 15.

IN QUALI DIREZIONI EFFETTUARE IL TRATTAMENTO

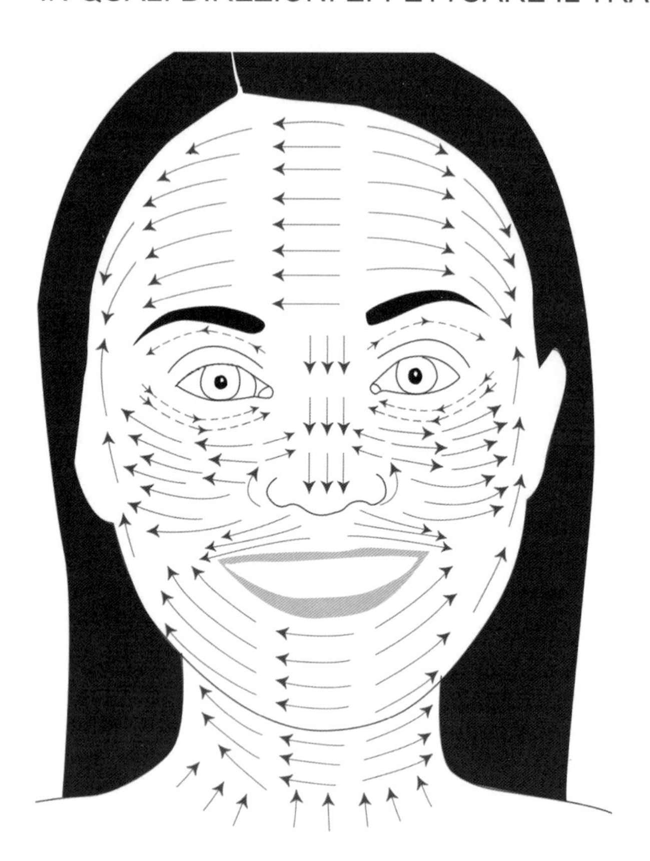

Il disegno mostra le direzioni con cui effettuare i trattamenti sul volto.

Ogni freccia copre una distanza di circa 4 cm.

Le linee tratteggiate intorno alla zona delicata degli occhi indicano tratti veloci e leggeri. Usare sempre il livello 1 intorno agli occhi.

Italiano

Scelta Del Corretto Livello Di Pressione

1. Per non correre rischi è necessario conoscere bene il tipo di pelle del cliente e le eventuali reazioni. Purtroppo assai spesso i terapisti vogliono impressionare favorevolmente il cliente al primo trattamento e pertanto utilizzano un livello di pressione molto alto, operando in modo molto aggressivo. Il risultato è che la pelle del cliente diventa sensibile e se la stessa è stata tirata con molta pressione si noteranno con evidenza delle striature rosse. Questo è dovuto all'errato intervento del terapista ed alla mancata conoscenza della pelle del cliente. È di fondamentale importanza che il terapista maneggi il manipolo con delicatezza e in maniera controllata quando effettua il trattamento.

2. Durante la prima seduta effettuare un trattamento leggero, solo dopo il primo trattamento procedere lentamente verso un trattamento più deciso seguendo il percorso del ciclo.

In questo modo la pelle del cliente si abitua al trattamento ed il cliente stesso si rende conto dei risultati. Un cliente che torna a casa con striature rosse o pelle sensibilizzata e arrossata sarà deluso e probabilmente penserà di cancellare il ciclo di trattamenti perché il terapista ha sbagliato nel fornire spiegazioni o nell'effettuare il trattamento.

3. N.B. Usare sempre una pressione leggera su pelle asiatica o nera, non più alta del livello 2 per tipi di pelle V e VI della scala Fitzpatrick.

4. Il segreto di un buon trattamento dipende dalla pressione applicata. Per una leggera esfoliazione fare passaggi leggeri e veloci (leggerissimi intorno agli occhi) e passaggi più lenti sulle parti problematiche. I movimenti del manipolo non devono mai superare i 4 cm.

SESSIONE 6 - RISULTATI DI APPRENDIMENTO

- Buona conoscenza delle problematiche relative alla salute e sicurezza nel trattamento e uso dell'apparecchio.
- Aggiornamento accurato delle schede clienti.

MANUTENZIONE DELL'APPARECCHIO

- Dopo ogni trattamento spegnere l'apparecchio e togliere la spina dalla presa di corrente e dall'apparecchio.
- Rimuovere la boccetta di cristalli e scuotere il manipolo nel palmo della mano al fine di rimuovere ogni residuo di cristalli dal suo interno. Ogni volta che si sostituisce una boccetta di critalli, agitare il manipolo per rimuovere eventuali tracce di cristalli che potrebbero rimanere all'interno. Ciò garantisce che la parte interna del manipolo resti sempre pulita.
- Togliere ed eliminare il beccuccio blu.
- Svuotare il contenitore (dove vanno i cristalli usati) dopo **OGNI** trattamento, svitare il contenitore dal coperchio e svuotarlo, eliminando con cura e in modo appropriato i cristalli usati.
- Avvitare di nuovo il coperchio al contenitore. Controllare che il coperchio del contenitore sia avvitato correttamente (in caso contrario si avrebbe una diminuzione della potenza del vuoto.)
- Riavvolgere con ordine tutti i tubi e i dispositivi di connessione nella valigetta e assicurarsi che tutto sia pulito e pronto per l'uso successivo.

Italiano

IMPORTANTE: QUANDO CAMBIARE IL CONTENITORE E IL MANIPOLO

Contenitore

Il contenitore monouso deve essere sostituito dopo ogni 80 trattamenti. In caso contrario potrebbe inibire l'azione aspirante durante il trattamento ed i cristalli possono essere risucchiati dal filtro di carta direttamente nel contenitore e nella pompa, con la possibilità di danneggiare l'apparecchio. In tal caso la garanzia non è più valida.

Manipolo

Il manipolo dovrà essere cambiato immediatamente quando vengono utilizzate 7 boccette di cristalli a trattamento. L'ossido di alluminio è un composto abrasivo che viene rilasciato gradualmente dalla bocchetta del manipolo. La velocità di fuoriuscita dei cristalli può variare a secondo dell'intensità e dal numero di trattamenti effettuati.

INDICE

SkinBase™

Manuel de formation de microdermabrasion

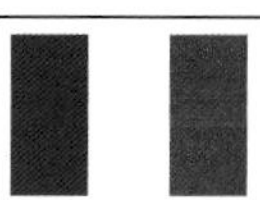

Français

TABLES DES MATIÈRES PAGE

FORMATION MICRODERMABRASION SKINBASE

SkinBase MDPro est un système de microdermabrasion conçu et fabriqué au Royaume-Uni. Nous avons travaillé en collaboration avec des spécialistes de la beauté possédant des années d'expérience dans l'utilisation de produits alternatifs sur le marché, qui nous ont aidés à mettre au point un système aux performances exceptionnelles, d'excellente qualité et extrêmement fiable.

SESSION 1 – RÉSULTATS DE L'APPRENTISSAGE:

- A la fin de cette session, vous connaitrez et comprendrez vos responsabilités dans le cadre de la loi sur la santé et la sécurité au travail (1974) et vous saurez comment les appliquer.
- Vous saurez reconnaitre les différentes affections et maladies cutanées et leurs contre-indications dans le traitement.
- Vous acquerrez des connaissances de base sur l'anatomie et la physiologie du visage et du cou

SANTÉ ET SÉCURITÉ AU TRAVAIL

Cette section couvre vos responsabilités envers vous-même, vos employés (le cas échéant) et vos clients concernant la santé, la sécurité et le bien-être sur le lieu de travail. Il est important que vous connaissiez parfaitement ces responsabilités et que vous les appliquiez dans la mesure du possible. La connaissance des problèmes liés à la santé et à la sécurité vous permettra d'effectuer les traitements sans danger et traduira une attitude professionnelle au travail.

La loi de 1974 sur la santé et la sécurité au travail établit les normes minimum de santé, de sécurité et de bien-être exigées sur le lieu de travail. Lorsque vous travaillez dans une industrie tertiaire, vous avez l'obligation légale de garantir un environnement sûr et hygiénique.

POUR ÉVITER LES DANGERS ET LES RISQUES POTENTIELS SUR LE LIEU DE TRAVAIL VOUS DEVEZ:

- Connaître vos responsabilités légales relatives à l'application des règles de santé et de sécurité au travail
- Vous assurer que votre présentation personnelle au travail répond aux conditions de santé et de sécurité et aux conditions législatives conformément aux règles relatives au lieu de travail
- Suivre les règles relatives au lieu de travail s'appliquant à votre fonction et les instructions du fabricant pour garantir une utilisation sûre des ressources
- Signaler immédiatement ou remédier aux risques qui peuvent représenter un danger sur le lieu de travail
- Disposer de matériel de premier secours en cas d'accident ou de maladie
- Disposer d'une procédure d'évacuation en cas d'incendie et s'assurer que tous les employés savent comment appliquer cette procédure
- Réduire le risque de propagation des infections ou des maladies en maintenant un excellent niveau d'hygiène

Règlements de 1989 sur l'électricité au travail

Ces règlements couvrent l'installation, l'entretien et l'utilisation de matériel électrique sur le lieu de travail. Le matériel électrique doit être testé régulièrement par un électricien qualifié pour vérifier qu'il est conforme aux normes de santé et de sécurité. Vous devez conserver un enregistrement de ces contrôles. Vous devez également connaître les dangers potentiels liés au matériel électrique, aux fils exposés, aux prises fissurées et aux prises surchargées.

Bien que la vérification de la sécurité de tout le matériel soit la responsabilité de l'employeur, l'employé a aussi l'obligation de toujours vérifier que le matériel est sûr avant de l'utiliser et ne doit jamais l'utiliser s'il est défectueux.

Risques électriques potentiels

- Fils exposés dans les flexibles
- Fiches fissurées ou prises cassées
- Prises surchargées

Français

Premier secours

Même si vous avez pris toutes les précautions pour faire en sorte que le lieu de travail soit aussi sûr que possible, des accidents peuvent se produire. Mettez en place une procédure de premier secours et veillez à ce que tout le monde sur le lieu de travail sache comment se comporter en cas d'accident, de maladie ou d'urgence.

Chaque lieu de travail doit être doté d'une trousse de premier secours et une personne désignée doit être responsable de l'entretien de cette trousse. Conservez un enregistrement des éventuelles blessures dans un registre des accidents.

SACHEZ:

où se trouve le manuel de premier secours
qui est responsable de l'entretien de la trousse de premier secours
qui informer en cas d'accident/maladie/urgence

Elimination des déchets

Les déchets doivent être éliminés dans une poubelle fermée contenant un sac à ordures en polythène suffisamment solide pour résister aux déchirures. La poubelle doit être régulièrement aseptisée avec du désinfectant, en portant des gants de protection.

Hygiène sur le lieu de travail

La stérilisation du matériel entre deux clients est indispensable pour détruire les bactéries, champignons et virus nocifs qui peuvent provoquer des infections. Une bonne hygiène sur le lieu de travail permet d'éviter les infections croisées et les infections secondaires.

Les infections croisées se produisent lorsque des microorganismes sont transmis par contact personnel ou par contact avec une buse infectée qui n'a pas été stérilisée.

Les infections secondaires peuvent se produire à la suite d'une blessure du client pendant le traitement, ou si le client a déjà une plaie ouverte. Les bactéries peuvent alors pénétrer dans la peau et causer l'infection.

Hygiène personnelle

Un excellent niveau d'hygiène personnelle est indispensable. Vous devez vous laver les mains régulièrement, avant et après chaque client. Les cheveux longs doivent être attachés, et vous devez éviter de vous toucher le visage. Couvrez les éventuelles coupures ou abrasions sur vos mains avec un pansement propre.

AFFECTIONS ET MALADIES CUTANÉES

Les maladies infectieuses contagieuses sont une contre-indication au traitement esthétique. Les personnes souffrant de certaines affections cutanées, même si elles ne sont pas contagieuses, ne doivent pas être traitées par le thérapeute, car le traitement peut entraîner une infection secondaire. Le thérapeute doit être capable de distinguer une peau en bonne santé d'une peau présentant une affection ou une maladie cutanée.

IMPORTANT:

Si vous avez des doutes ou si vous ne pouvez pas identifier le problème d'une peau, vous ne devez pas traiter le client et lui conseiller de consulter son médecin.

Certaines affections et maladies cutanées représentent des contre-indications à certains traitements esthétiques: le traitement pourrait exposer le thérapeute et d'autres clients à des risques d'infection croisée; il est donc impératif que vous vous familiarisiez avec les affections et maladies cutanées avec lesquelles vous pourriez être en contact.

Infections bactériennes

Les bactéries peuvent être présentes en grandes quantités sur la peau sans causer aucun dommage. Cependant, certains types de bactéries sont nocifs et sont considérés comme 'pathogènes'. Les bactéries pathogènes peuvent provoquer des maladies cutanées qui sont infectieuses. Par conséquent un client ne doit pas être traité s'il souffre des infections bactériennes suivantes:

Impétigo

Extrêmement infectieux et à propagation rapide par contact. L'impétigo apparait généralement sur le visage, d'abord autour du nez, de la bouche et des oreilles, et peut s'étendre à d'autres zones. Des vésicules apparaissent: elles sont rouges et démangent au début, puis des croûtes se forment et les plaies suintent.

Conjonctivite

La conjonctivite n'est pas toujours infectieuse et peut être causée par une réaction allergique ou par un irritant. Cependant, comme il est impossible de le savoir, la conjonctivite doit toujours être traitée comme infectieuse. L'oeil est rouge et enflammé; les yeux peuvent aussi pleurer ou du pus peut en sortir.

Orgelet/Hordoleum

L'orgelet est une infection de la glande sébacée située à la racine des cils. Il se traduit par un gonflement qui peut provoquer des rougeurs de la paupière. Le follicule concerné présente une petite masse remplie de pus.

Furoncle

Un furoncle est causé par l'inflammation des follicules pileux, et se traduit par une accumulation de pus et de tissus morts. Les furoncles sont des masses rouges remplies de pus qui sont tendres, chaudes et/ou douloureuses. On peut observer un point jaune ou blanc au centre de la masse lorsque le furoncle est prêt à se vider.

Infections virales

Les particules d'un virus sont si petites qu'elles ne peuvent pas se développer et se reproduire seules et ont besoin d'une cellule 'hôte'. Les virus envahissent les cellules saines du corps pour se reproduire. Ils pénètrent dans le corps de diverses manières, par inhalation, par la salive, lors de rapports sexuels Notre système immunitaire est conçu pour se défendre contre la plupart des virus et nous combattons naturellement la plupart des infections. Les clients souffrant des infections virales suivantes ne doivent pas recevoir de traitement de microdermabrasion.

Herpès Simplex (boutons de fièvre)

Les boutons de fièvre s'attrapent par contact rapproché avec quelqu'un qui a déjà des boutons de fièvre. Ils sont caractérisés par une sensation de picotement de la peau, suivie de plaies qui forment une croûte. Généralement situés sur les muqueuses du nez ou les lèvres, ils peuvent aussi apparaître sur d'autres parties de la peau.

Herpès Zoster (zona)

Le zona est une infection du nerf et de la zone desservie par le nerf. Le virus affecte généralement un nerf et apparait souvent sur le torse, l'abdomen ou la partie supérieure du visage. Les symptômes se manifestent dans la zone cutanée desservie par le nerf, et se traduisent par des rougeurs, des vésicules et des croûtes.

Infections fongiques

Les champignons sont des plantes parasites microscopiques qui se nourrissent des déchets de la peau. Certaines infections fongiques apparaissent à la surface de la peau, d'autres plus en profondeur dans le tissu cutané. Les clients souffrant d'infections fongiques ne doivent pas être traités car ces maladies sont infectieuses et peuvent se propager.

Tinea Corporis/Teigne

La teigne est une infection fongique de la peau qui concerne le tronc, les membres et le visage. Elle se manifeste sous forme de plaques rouges squameuses sur la peau qui s'étendent vers l'extérieur. Les plaques cicatrisent à partir du centre en laissant la trace d'un cercle. D'autres affections cutanées ne sont pas infectieuses, cependant elles doivent être traitées avec prudence et, dans certains cas, absolument évitées.

Affections des glandes sébacées

Français

Les glandes sébacées sont de petites glandes qui sécrètent une substance graisseuse appelée sébum dans le follicule pileux afin de lubrifier la peau. On les trouve en grande quantité sur le visage et le cuir chevelu. Les affections des glandes sébacées incluent l'acné, la rosacée et le milium. Les affections des glandes sébacées sont généralement causées par une surproduction de sébum.

Milium

Egalement appelé 'grains de milium' ou 'boules de graisse' il s'agit de kystes bénins remplis de kératine qui apparaissent généralement autour du nez et des yeux. Ces grains sont petits, blancs ou jaune pâle. Ils ne sont pas infectieux et peuvent être éliminés au moyen d'une aiguille stérile pour percer la peau qui les recouvre et libérer la kératine.

Comédons/Points noirs

Causés par un excès de sébum et par des cellules kératinisées qui obstruent le follicule pileux. Ils apparaissent sur le visage, le haut du dos et le torse et ne sont pas infectieux.

Séborrhée

Causée par une sécrétion excessive de sébum, elle se manifeste généralement pendant la puberté en raison des changements hormonaux. Les personnes qui en souffrent ont des follicules dilatés et un excès de sébum. Elle n'est pas infectieuse et apparait le plus souvent sur le visage et le cuir chevelu. Elle peut aussi concerner le dos et le torse.

Kystes sébacés

Ils se forment dans le follicule pileux lorsque le sébum reste emprisonné et une grosseur apparait. Ces kystes ne sont pas infectieux.

Acné vulgaris

Le déséquilibre hormonal qui a lieu à la puberté entraîne une augmentation de la production de sébum, qui provoque à son tour une congestion des conduits sébacés et une inflammation de la peau, des comédons, des pustules et des papules. Il n'est pas infectieux et se manifeste généralement sur le visage, le nez, le menton et le front. Il peut aussi apparaitre sur le torse et le dos. L'acné actif doit être évité pendant le traitement de microdermabrasion.

Rosacée
Causée par l'association d'une sécrétion excessive de sébum et une condition inflammatoire chronique, la peau devient rugueuse, les pores se dilatent et le nez devient rouge et enflammé. La peau peut avoir un aspect rougeâtre en raison de la circulation sanguine lente. La rosacée ne peut pas être traitée par microdermabrasion.

Pigmentation

Hyperpigmentation – Augmentation de la pigmentation

Chloasmes 'taches brunes' – augmentation de la production de pigments pouvant être causée par les rayons UV, apparaissant souvent pendant la grossesse. Les oestrogènes stimulent la production de mélanine et ce phénomène peut aussi se manifester lors de la prise de la pilule contraceptive. Les taches apparaissent sur les mains, les avant-bras, le décolleté, les tempes et le front.

Ephélides 'taches de rousseur' – causées par l'exposition aux rayons UV qui stimulent la production de mélanine. Présentes sur le nez et les joues des personnes à peau claire, elles peuvent aussi apparaître sur les mains, les bras, les épaules et le dos.

Lentigo – taches d'hyperpigmentation plus grandes que des taches de rousseur, apparaissant soit pendant l'enfance soit à l'âge mûr, dues à l'exposition au soleil. Présentes sur le visage, les mains et les épaules.

Hypopigmentation – Perte de pigmentation

Vitiligo – zones cutanées qui n'ont plus de pigments et qui apparaissent alors complètement blanches.

Albinisme – Absence totale de pigments. La peau, les cheveux et les yeux n'ont pas de couleur.
La peau est rose très pâle, les yeux sont roses et les cheveux sont blancs.

Erythème
L'érythème est un rougissement de la peau causé par la dilatation des vaisseaux sanguins qui contrôlent les réseaux capillaires dans les zones cutanées porteuses de lésions ou d'infections.

Naevus vasculaires
Il s'agit de zones de pigmentation causées par la dilatation permanente des capillaires

- Capillaire dilatés – petits capillaires rouges visibles dans les zones négligées ou sèches comme les joues.
- Angiomes stellaires – vaisseaux sanguins dilatés avec capillaires dilatés se propageant autour
- Angiomes plans – zones étendues de capillaires dilatés
- Angiomes tubéreux 'taches de vin' – marques rouges ou rougeâtres en relief apparaissant sur la peau à la naissance

Télangiectasie (rupture de vaisseaux capillaires)
Toute forme de rupture de vaisseaux capillaires peut empirer sous l'action aspirante de la microdermabrasion. Ces "veinules" sont très courantes autour du nez et sur les joues. La zone doit être totalement évitée ou le traitement doit être effectué à un niveau très bas.

Chéloïdes

Les chéloïdes sont des tissus cicatriciels contenant des dépôts excessifs de collagène. La peau apparait comme boursouflée, rouge avec des stries. Ce type de tissu cicatriciel ne peut pas être traité par microdermabrasion. Les vergetures et les cicatrices postopératoires peuvent cependant être traitées. Le tissu cicatriciel ne doit pas être traité tant que toute l'inflammation n'a pas disparu (environ 6 mois après l'intervention).

Dermatite

Une inflammation de la peau causée par un irritant ou un allergène. Il existe plusieurs types de dermatite. Les symptômes peuvent inclure une peau rouge, qui démange, pèle, s'écaille, suinte, qui est gonflée et parfois cloquée selon la gravité des cas.

La dermatite de contact irritant apparait rapidement après un contact avec un irritant puissant ou sur une durée plus longue après une exposition prolongée et répétée à un irritant léger. Les causes les plus communes de ce type de dermatite sont les savons, les shampooings et les détergents, l'huile et la graisse, le contact répété et prolongé avec l'eau.

La dermatite de contact allergique se manifeste lorsque la personne développe une allergie à une substance particulière. Des causes courantes de dermatite sont les teintures pour cheveux, les adhésifs et certains aliments tels que les fruits de mer.

Eczéma

Il existe deux principaux types d'eczéma, l'eczéma atopique et l'eczéma de contact.

L'eczéma atopique a tendance à se développer pendant l'enfance et disparaît généralement avec l'âge.

L'eczéma de contact affecte les adultes et est causé par le contact avec des allergènes tels que le nickel ou les détergents, les savons et les parfums.

Lorsqu'on souffre d'eczéma, la peau démange et devient sèche et écaillée. Elle est souvent rouge et douloureuse. Parfois elle suinte ou saigne. Les zones généralement touchées sont le visage, le cou et la peau, en particulier dans les plis intérieurs des coudes et derrière les genoux.

Psoriasis

Le psoriasis est une maladie auto-immune chronique qui touche la peau et les articulations. Le psoriasis provoque des plaques de peau squameuse appelées plaques psoriasiques qui sont des zones d'inflammation et de production de peau excessive, qui prennent rapidement un aspect blanc argenté en raison de l'accumulation de peau.

ANATOMIE ET PHYSIOLOGIE

Il est important que le thérapeute qui pratique le traitement possède des connaissances de base en matière d'anatomie et de physiologie.

LES OS DE LA TÊTE ET DU COU

Le visage est constitué de 14 os de la face, qui sont identifiés dans le schéma ci-dessous.

Os de la face

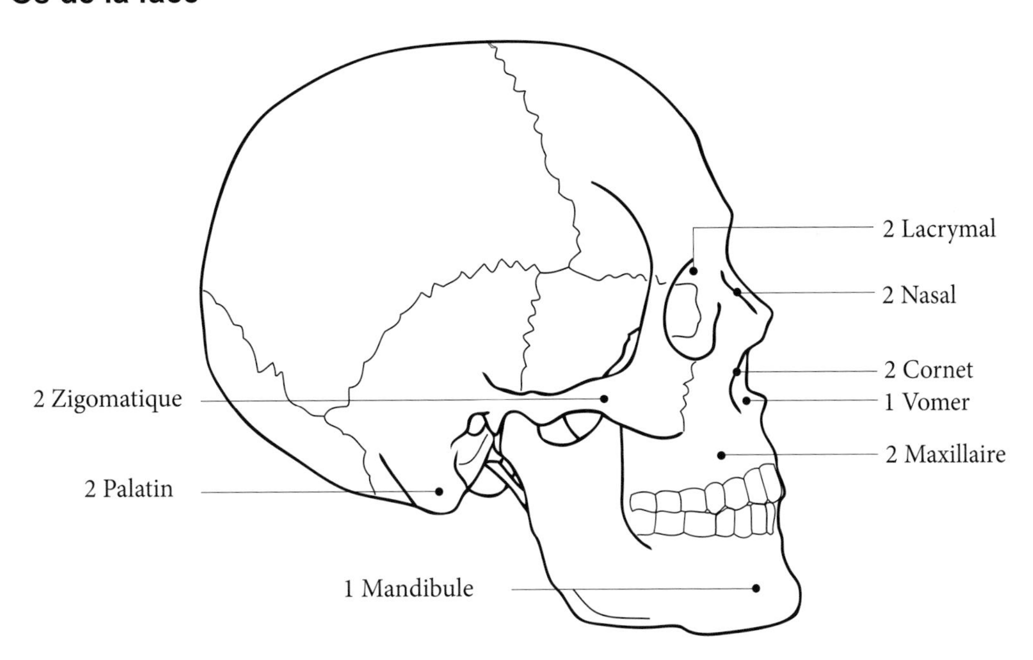

Os	
Palatin	x 2 Forment le plancher et la paroi du nez et le plafond de la bouche
Nasal	x 2 Forment l'arête du nez
Cornet	x 2 Ces deux os forment les parois extérieures du nez
Vomer	Paroi de division du nez
Lacrymal	x 2 Les parois intérieures des orbites
Maxillaire	x 2 Soudés pour former la mâchoire supérieure
Mandibule	La mâchoire inférieure
Zygomatique	Les pommettes

Français

Le reste du crâne est constitué des os du crâne qui sont au nombre de huit et sont indiqués dans le schéma ci-dessous.

Os du crâne

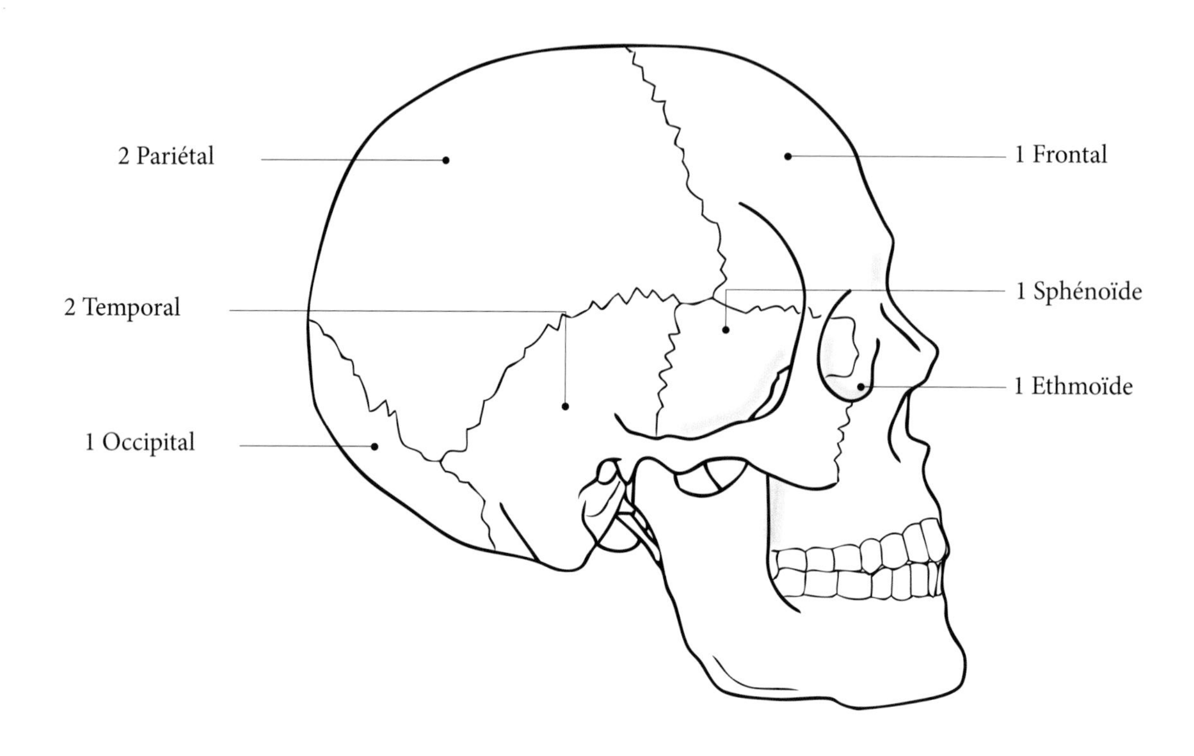

OS	
Occipital	Situé derrière le crâne, il contient l'orifice par où passent la moelle épinière, les nerfs et les vaisseaux sanguins.
Pariétal x 2	Soudés ensembles pour former la couronne
Frontal	Front et partie supérieure des orbites
Temporal x2	Les côtés de la tête
Ethmoïde	Forme la partie de la cavité nasale
Sphénoïde	Os en forme de chauve-souris qui unit ensemble tous les os du crâne.

Français

Os du cou, du torse, et des épaules

Vue de face

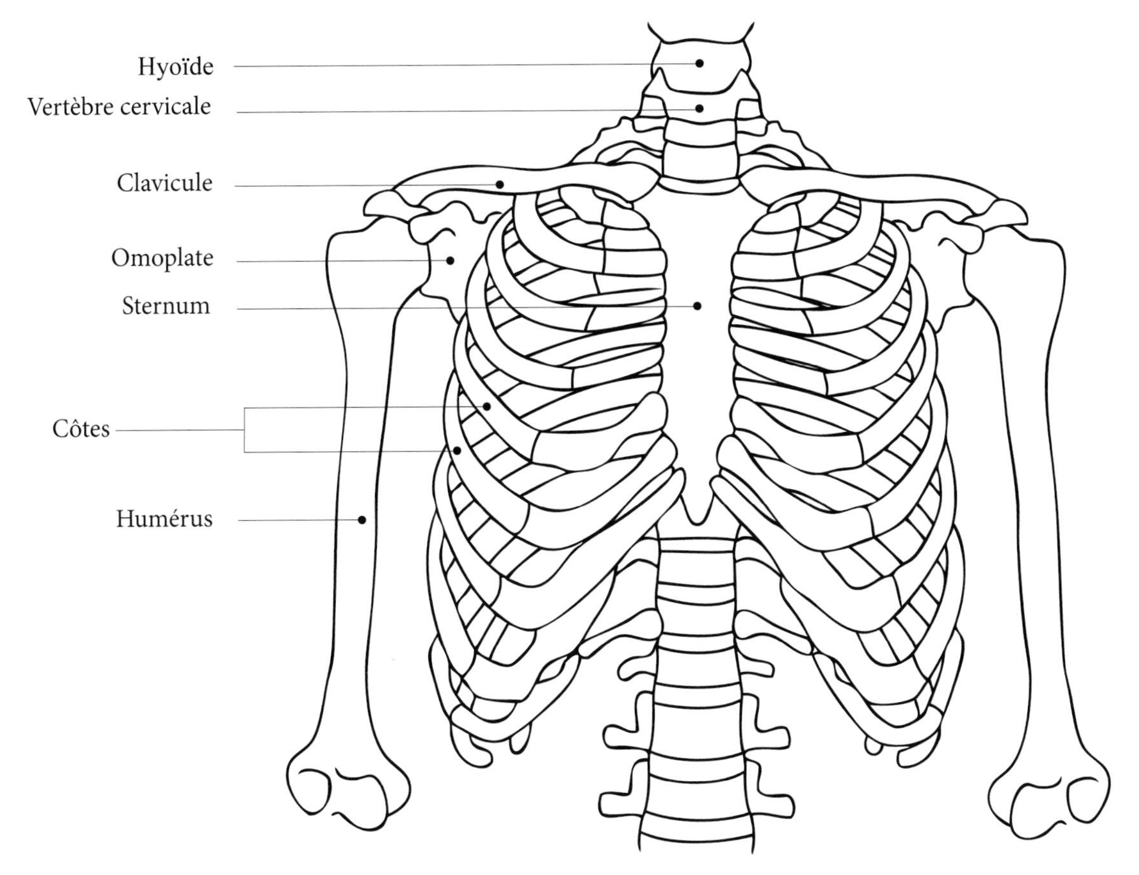

Vue de dos

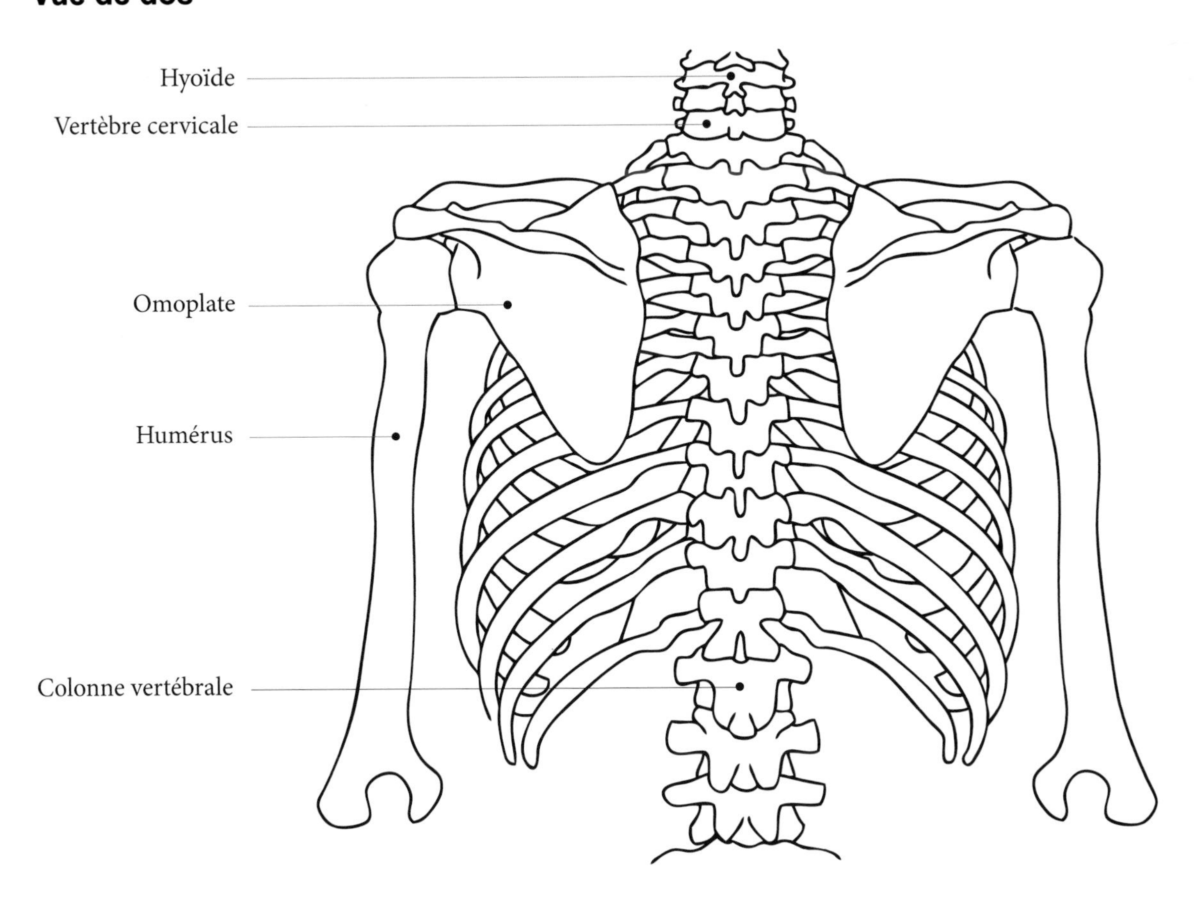

Français

MUSCLES DU VISAGE ET DU COU

Les muscles du visage et du cou sont responsables de nos expressions faciales. A mesure que nous vieillissons, les expressions que nous utilisons quotidiennement créent des lignes sur la peau, et nous commençons à montrer des signes extérieurs de vieillissement. La microdermabrasion élimine les cellules de peau morte de l'épiderme et améliore l'aspect de ces ridules et rides.

Muscles faciaux

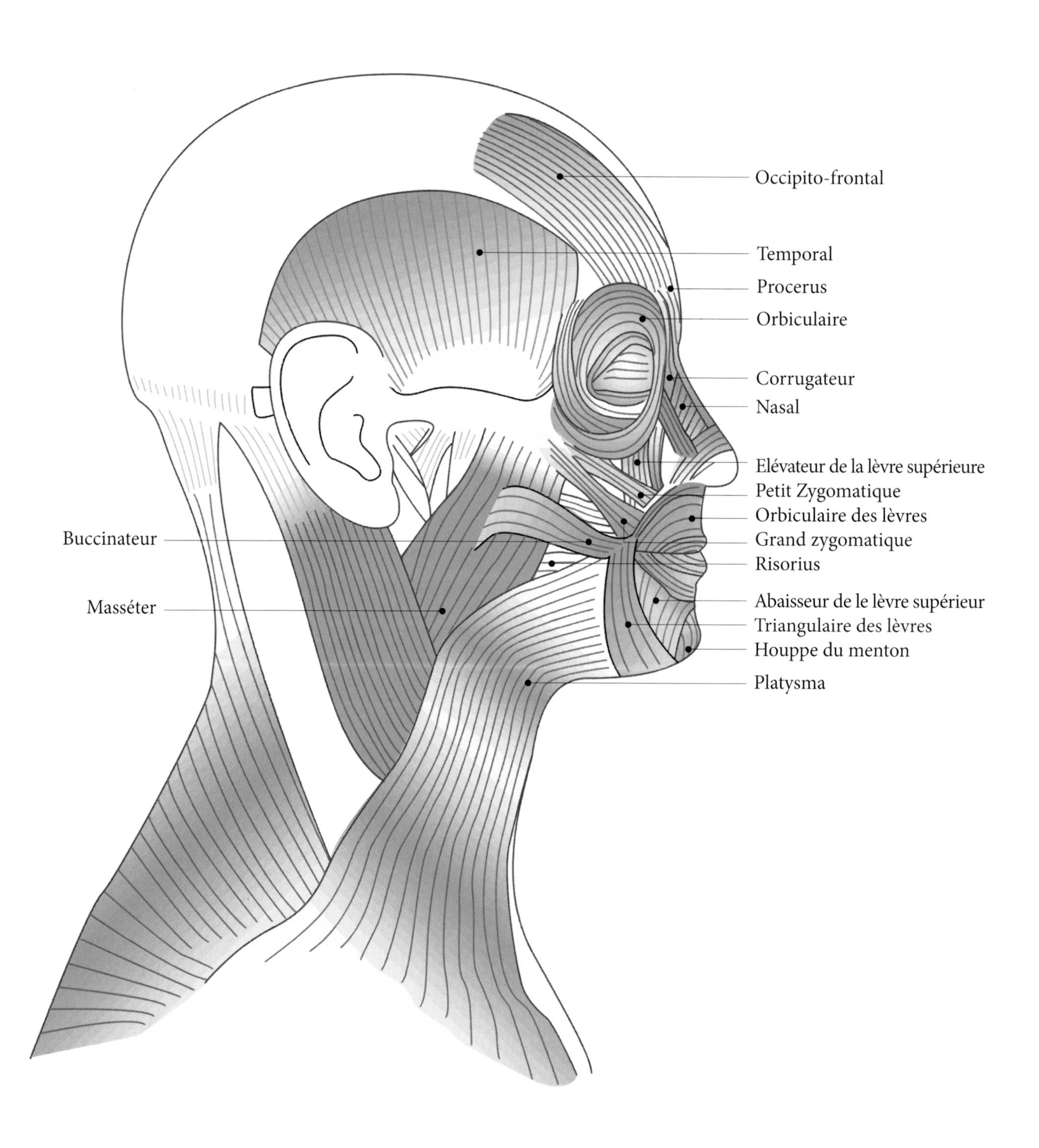

Français

Muscles du cou

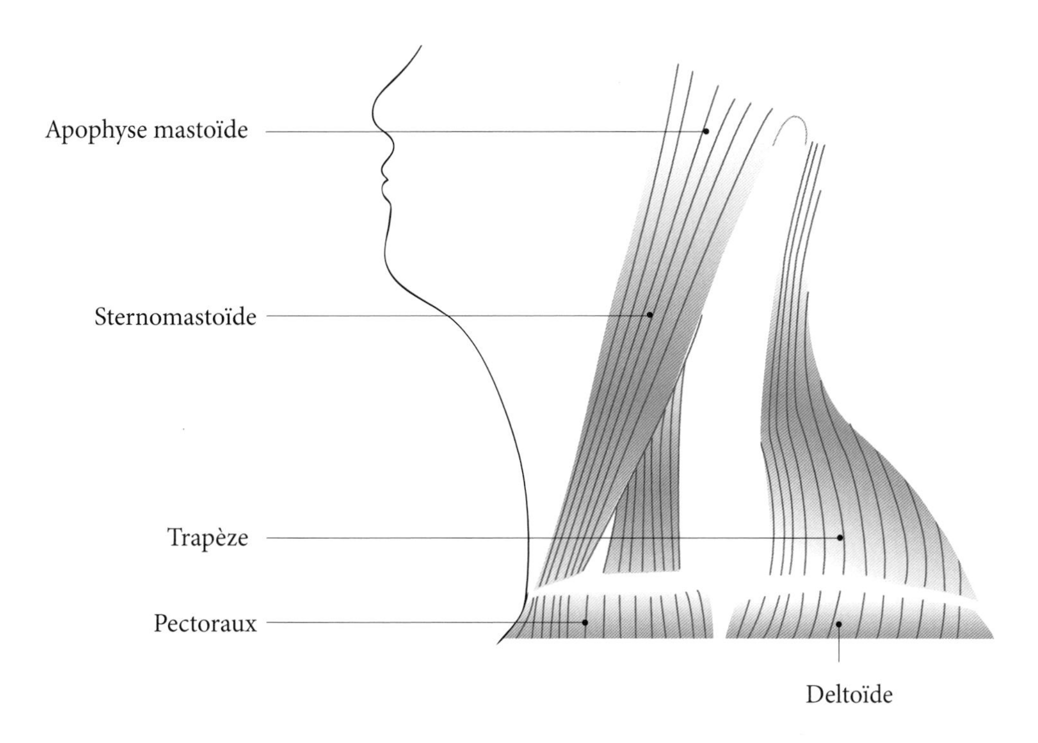

Français

NERFS CRANIENS

Le système nerveux permet au corps d'envoyer des messages d'information qui partent du cerveau vers les autres parties du corps.

Les nerfs du visage et du cou, ou nerfs 'crâniens' contrôlent les muscles de la tête et du cou ou acheminent les impulsions nerveuses (informations sensorielles) depuis les organes des sens vers le cerveau.

Les 5ème, 7ème et 11ème nerfs crâniens sont ceux qui nous concernent en tant que thérapeutes lorsque nous pratiquons des traitements faciaux.

5ème 'trijumaux'

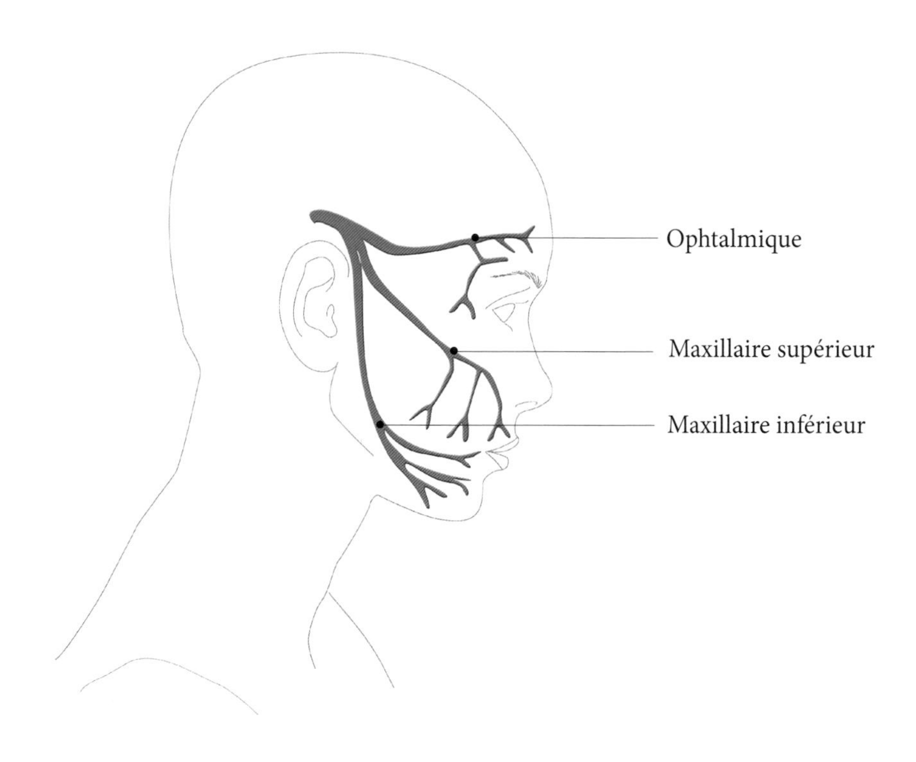

7ème nerf crânien - 'facial' **11ème nerf crânien - 'Accessoire'**

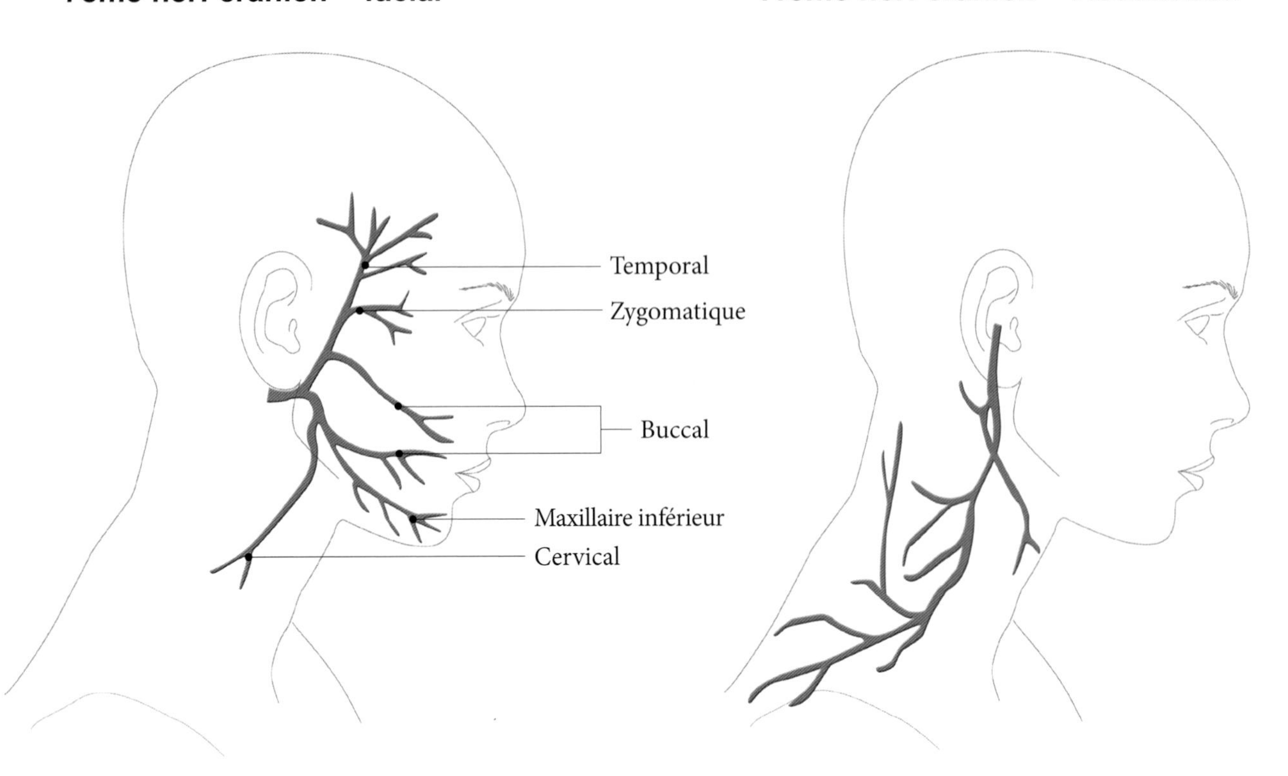

Nerfs	Fonctions	Branches nerveuses	Envoie des messages à
5ème 'trijumaux'	Contrôle les muscles de la mastiquation Transmet des informations sensorielles provenant du visage	Ophtalmique	Glandes lacrymales Peau du front Pomettes
		Maxillaire supérieur	Muscle supérieur de la mâchoire Bouche
		Maxillaire inférieur	Muscle inférieur de la mâchoire, Dents Muscles de la mastiquation
7ème 'facial'	Contrôle les muscles utilisés pour les expressions faciales	Temporal	Muscles autour des yeux Muscles du front
		Zygomatique	Muscles des yeux
		Buccal	Lèvre supérieure Côtés du nez
		Maxillaire supérieur	Lèvre inférieure Menton
		Cervical	Côtés du cou et du menton
11ème 'accessoire'	Bouge le cou et les épaules		

SESSION 2 – RÉSULTATS DE L'APPRENTISSAGE:

- Connaissance de base et compréhension de la structure et de la fonction de la peau
- Capacité d'identifier les différents types de peau
- Bonne compréhension du principe de microdermabrasion
- Capacité d'identifier les zones à problèmes qui peuvent être traitées par la microdermabrasion
- Compréhension du fonctionnement d'une série de traitements de microdermabrasion

LA PEAU

La peau est l'organe le plus grand du corps humain. La peau possède de nombreuses fonctions qui nous protègent des éléments extérieurs.

- Evite l'absorption de substances nocives
- Aide à réguler la température corporelle
- Agit comme une barrière pour éloigner les infections
- La mélanine de la peau nous protège des effets nocifs des rayons UV
- Fournit une protection imperméable qui nous évite de nous déshydrater
- Fournit une réserve d'énergie sous forme de graisse emmagasinée.

Français

La structure de la peau

La peau est constituée de deux couches distinctes: l'épiderme et le derme. Entre les deux se trouve la couche basale, qui maintient les deux couches ensemble. Sous ces couches se trouve l'hypoderme, une couche qui protège, amortit, isole et emmagasine le surplus d"énergie pour le corps.

L'épiderme

L'épiderme est la couche extérieure de la peau. Il est composé de cinq couches. Chaque couche de l'épiderme est reconnaissable par sa forme et par la fonction de ses cellules. Le principal type de cellules présentes dans l'épiderme sont les kératinocytes, qui produisent une protéine appelée kératine.

Le renouvellement cellulaire se produit sur une période de quatre semaines environ. Les cellules migrent de la couche inférieure de l'épiderme (couche basale) vers la couche supérieure (couche cornée) en changeant de forme et de structure à mesure qu'elles progressent. La couche supérieure de l'épiderme est la couche qui meurt et qui est éliminée par la 'desquamation' cutanée. C'est cette couche qui est éliminée lors du traitement de microdermabrasion. C'est aussi la couche qui aide à réfléchir les rayons UV de la surface de la peau, c'est pourquoi il est important que les clients utilisent une protection solaire après tout traitement de microdermabrasion.

L'épiderme

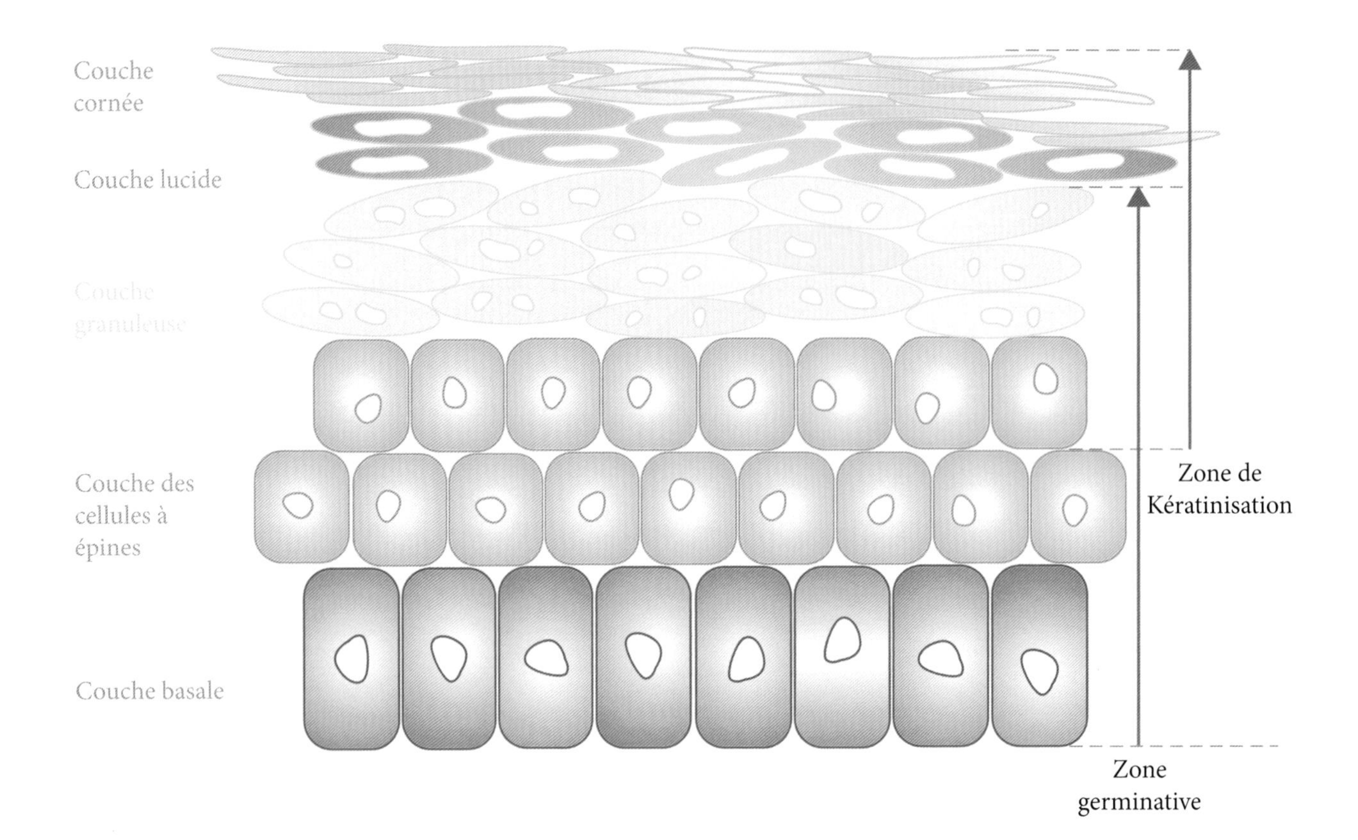

Les cinq couches de l'épiderme

1. Stratum Corneum ou 'couche cornée'

Il s'agit de la couche extérieure de l'épiderme, constituée de plusieurs couches de cellules aplaties, presque mortes, qui se chevauchent. Ces cellules permettent de réfléchir les rayons UV.

La peau noire, qui a évolué pour résister aux rayons UV puissants, possède une couche cornée plus épaisse que la peau caucasienne. Il faut environ 3 semaines aux cellules épidermiques pour atteindre la couche cordée depuis la couche basale; les cellules sont ensuite éliminées; ce procédé est appelé desquamation.

2. Stratum Lucidum ou 'couche lucide'

Cette couche ne se trouve que dans les zones les plus épaisses de la peau, telles que les paumes des mains ou la plante des pieds.

3. Stratum Granulosum ou 'couche granuleuse'

C'est dans cette couche que les cellules commencent à mourir. Ces cellules contiennent ce qui ressemble à des granulés, causés par la rupture des noyaux. Ces granulés sont connus sous le nom de granules kérato-hyalines et formeront plus tard la kératine.

4. Stratum Spinosum or 'Couche des cellules à épines'

Le stratum spinosum est constitué de cellules dont la surface épineuse (d'où leur nom) permet la connexion aux cellules environnantes. C'est cette couche qui commence à synthétiser la kératine.

5. Stratum Germinativum ou 'couche basale'

Cellules en forme de colonnes, responsables de la production de nouvelles cellules épidermiques. Les cellules se divisent et migrent vers les couches supérieures. Les cellules restantes se divisent pour combler les espaces. Ce procédé de division cellulaire est appelé mitose.

La couche basale de l'épiderme contient également deux autres cellules importantes, à savoir les cellules langerhan et mélanocyte.

Cellules de langerhans - elles absorbent et éliminent les corps étrangers qui pénètrent dans la peau. Elles sortent de l'épiderme pour rentrer dans le derme situé au-dessous, avant de pénétrer dans le système lymphatique, qui est le 'système d'évacuation' du corps.

Cellules mélanocytes – Elles sont responsables de la production de mélanine dans la peau. Elles protègent les autres cellules épidermiques des effets nocifs des UV. La mélanine permet de déterminer la couleur de notre peau. Plus il y a de mélanine, plus la peau est foncée.

Le derme

Le derme est la couche qui se trouve sous l'épiderme et qui est responsable de la résistance et de l'élasticité de la peau. Il contient aussi de nombreuses cellules et structures spécialisées, y compris des nerfs, des vaisseaux sanguins, des glandes et des follicules pileux. Le derme est constitué de deux couches: la couche papillaire et la couche réticulaire. La couche papillaire supérieure contient un réseau fin de fibres collagènes. La couche réticulaire située au-dessous est constituée de fibres collagènes denses qui sont parallèles à la surface de la peau.

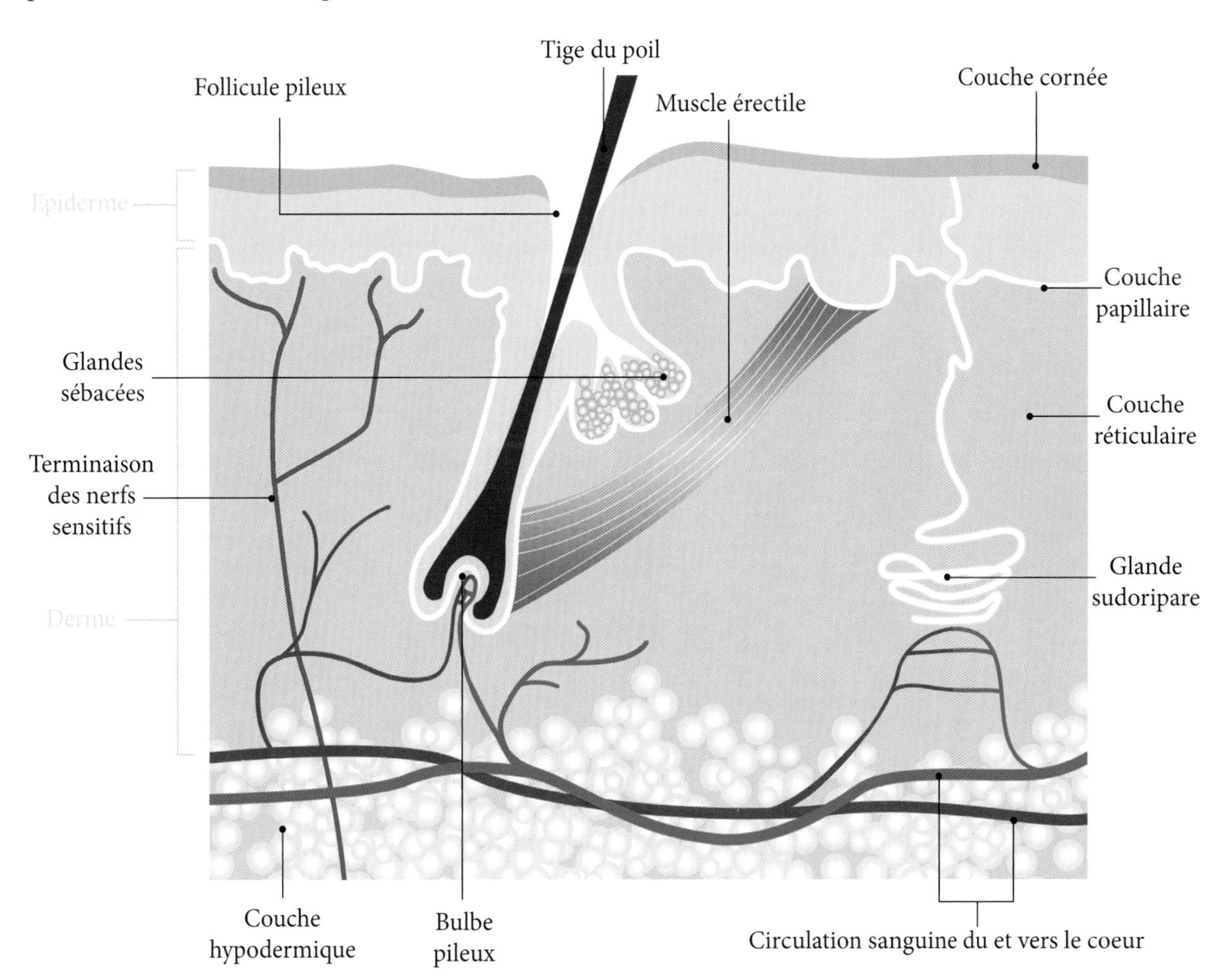

La couche réticulaire

La couche réticulaire est constituée de deux types de protéines: les fibres d'élastine, qui donnent à la peau son élasticité, et les fibres de collagène, qui donnent à la peau sa résistance. Ces fibres sont contenues dans une substance similaire à du gel, appelée substance fondamentale. Les fibres d'élastine et de collagène forment un réseau résistant qui nous donnent notre aspect jeune.

A mesure que nous vieillissons, ces fibres de la peau commencent à durcir et à se fragmenter; le réseau se dégrade, notre peau perd en élasticité et montre des signes de vieillissement. La circulation sanguine vers la peau diminue; les nutriments n'atteignent plus la surface et la peau devient jaunâtre. La couche graisseuse située sous la peau s'amincie et nos traits semblent plus tirés car notre structure osseuse est plus proéminente. La couche réticulaire est essentielle à la santé ainsi qu'à l'aspect de notre peau. Il est donc essentiel d'en prendre soin pour éviter l'apparition des signes de vieillesse.

Circulation sanguine

Le sang circule à travers le corps vers toutes les cellules, en transportant de l'énergie et des nutriments essentiels, tels que l'oxygène, le glucose et autres matières premières indispensables à la santé, à l'entretien et à la croissance du corps.

L'action d'aspiration du traitement de microdermabrasion favorise la stimulation de la microcirculation près de la surface de la peau. Cela améliore l'afflux sanguin vers la zone traitée, ce qui favorise la production de collagène et d'élastine ainsi que le renouvellement cellulaire (régénération cutanée), qui aide à réparer les tissus et révèle une peau plus lisse et plus fraiche.

Ce schéma indique comment le sang circule à travers les cellules, en apportant des nutriments et de l'énergie et en éliminant les déchets tels que le dioxyde de carbone.

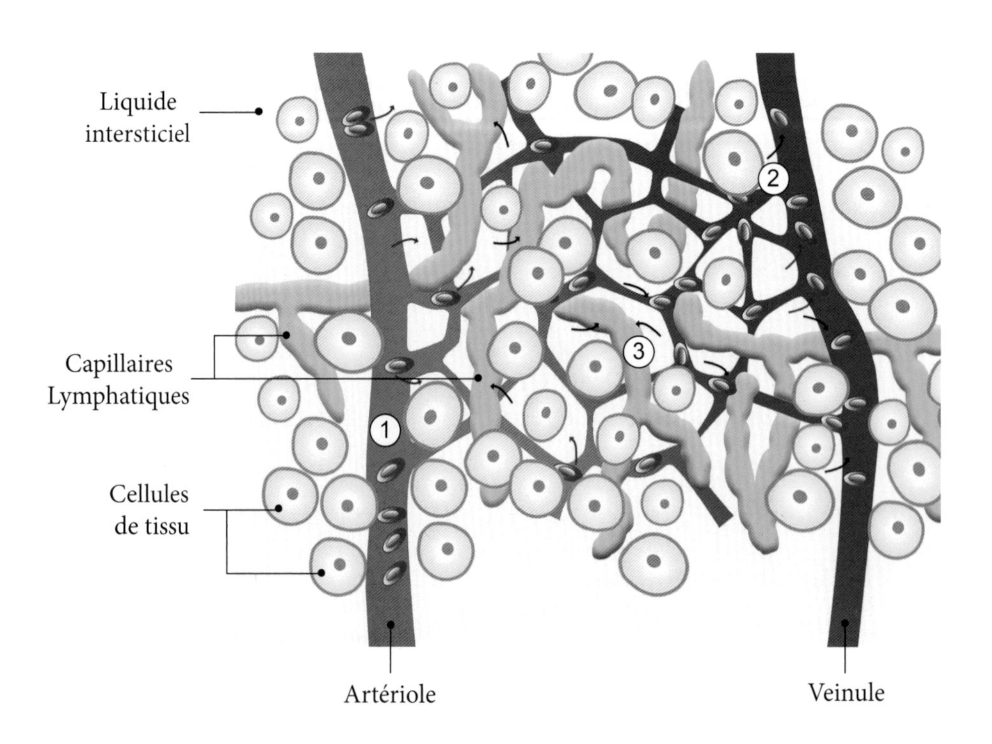

Français

① La pression sanguine est élevée lorsque le sang circule à travers le réseau capillaire, ce qui libère du liquide dans les tissus. C'est le liquide intersticiel. Ce liquide contient des substances utiles telles que de l'oxygène et des nutriments, essentiels aux cellules. Les cellules sanguines et les grandes protéines restent dans le capillaire.

② A mesure que le sang est désoxygéné, la pression est inversée et une partie du liquide contenant des déchets pénètre à nouveau dans les capillaires puis est éliminé.

③ L'excès de liquide, les déchets et les grandes molécules telles que les protéines qui sont incapables de retourner dans le sang, sont captés par les capillaires lymphatiques et transportés vers les noeuds lymphatiques, où le liquide est traité avant de retourner dans le sang plus près du coeur.

Circulation sanguine à travers la peau

La température corporelle normale est de 37°c. Le corps travaille pour maintenir cette température. Si la température corporelle commence à augmenter, le sang circulera près de la surface de la peau pour libérer un peu de sa chaleur. Lorsque la température du corps diminue, les capillaires se resserrent. Le sang passe alors à travers des 'vaisseaux shunt' plus profonds dans le derme, ce qui réduit la quantité de chaleur perdue à travers la peau.

La vasodilatation se produit lorsque vous avez:
Chaud – le sang passe près de la surface de la peau – la chaleur est libérée

La vasoconstriction se produit lorsque vous avez:
Froid – le sang passe par des vaisseaux shunt éloignés de la surface de la peau – la chaleur est retenue

TYPES DE PEAU

Il existe six types de peaux principaux. Cependant la peau du visage peut varier aux différents stades de la vie, en raison de maladies ou de déséquilibre hormonal.

Peau sèche

La peau sèche est causée par des glandes sébacées peu actives ou inactives qui ne produisent pas suffisamment de sébum pour maintenir la peau hydratée naturellement. Elle a généralement un aspect terne, est sèche et irritée au toucher et est parfois sensible. La peau sèche doit être hydratée régulièrement de l'intérieur (en buvant de l'eau) et de l'extérieur en utilisant des crèmes ou des lotions hydratantes riches.

Peau grasse

La peau grasse est causée par des glandes qui produisent trop de sébum. Dans ce cas, la peau apparait luisante avec de larges pores ouverts. Les peaux grasses ont tendance à développer des comédons (points noirs) et de l'acné. Malgré ces inconvénients, la peau grasse conserve un aspect plus jeune et reste plus souple que les autres types de peau. Les peaux grasses tirent un bénéfice considérable de la microdermabrasion, avec l'application de produits hydratants légers.

Peau sensible

Les peaux sensibles peuvent être sèches, normales ou grasses et sont caractérisées par leur délicatesse. La peau sensible réagit fréquemment de façon négative aux conditions environnementales et exige souvent des traitements spéciaux pour rester en bon état. La peau sensible s'entretient très bien avec des produits de soin et des traitements naturels pour la peau.

Peau normale

La peau normale produit du sébum en quantité modérée, d'où son état équilibré. La peau normale semble toujours rebondie, hydratée et dynamique. Un énorme avantage qui n'en exige pas moins de l'attention. Elle a besoin de l'application régulière de crème nettoyante, de tonique et de crème hydratante.

Peau mixte

La peau mixte est le type de peau le plus répandu. La peau mixte est fréquemment caractérisée par une zone grasse en forme de T, qui couvre le front, le nez et le menton, tandis que la peau des joues, des yeux et de la bouche est normale ou sèche. Les personnes à peau mixte doivent vérifier leur peau régulièrement et utiliser différents produits sur différentes zones du visage.

Peau mature

La peau mature a les caractéristiques suivantes: la peau devient sèche à mesure que les glandes sébacées deviennent moins actives. La peau perd son élasticité; des ridules et des rides apparaissent. La peau semble plus fine avec des ruptures de capillaires, en particulier sur les joues et autour du nez. Les contours du visage se détendent à mesure que le tonus musculaire diminue. La structure osseuse sous-jacente devient plus apparente, à mesure que la couche graisseuse sous la peau s'amincie. La circulation sanguine n'est plus aussi efficace, ce qui interfère avec la nutrition de la peau et lui donne un aspect jaunâtre. En raison du ralentissement du taux métabolique, les déchets ne sont pas éliminés aussi rapidement, ce qui entraîne un aspect bouffi de la peau. La peau mature doit être parfaitement hydratée en buvant de l'eau régulièrement et en utilisant des produits hydratants nourrissants.

TYPES DE COULEUR DE PEAU

La teinte de la peau humaine peut varier du brun foncé à une pigmentation presque incolore, qui peut apparaitre rougeâtre en raison du sang qui circule dans la peau. Les européens ont généralement une peau, des cheveux et des yeux plus clairs que les autres groupes, bien que ce ne soit pas toujours le cas. Pour des raisons pratiques, six types de couleurs de peau sont identifiés selon l'échelle Fitzpatrick (1975). Les couleurs de peau sont indiquées du plus clair au plus foncé.

TYPE	AUSSI APELLÉ	TOLÉRANCE AU SOLEIL	COULEUR DES CHEVEUX ET DES YEUX
I	Très claire, aussi appelée 'Nordique'	Brûle souvent, bronze rarement	Tendance aux taches de rousseur, cheveux roux ou blonds, yeux bleus ou verts
II	Claire	Brûle généralement	Tendance aux cheveux clairs, yeux bleus ou verts
III	Claire intermédiaire ou foncée, de type européen ou 'caucasien moyen'	Brûle parfois, bronze généralement	Tendance aux cheveux bruns et yeux marron
IV	Foncée intermédiaire, aussi méditerranéenne ou 'olive'	Brûle parfois, bronze souvent	Tendance aux cheveux bruns et yeux marron
V	Foncée ou 'brune'	Peau naturellement noire-brune	Souvent cheveux brun foncé et yeux marron foncé
VI	Très foncée ou 'noire'	Peau naturellement noire-brune	Généralement cheveux noir-brun et yeux noir-marron

LA MICRODERMABRASION - QU'EST-CE QUE C'EST ?

La microdermabrasion est un système contrôlé et sans danger d'exfoliation intense et de restructuration, qui utilise des cristaux ultrafins pour rajeunir la peau. Les cristaux agissent comme un abrasif doux sur la peau pour éliminer les cellules de peau morte, couche par couche. La forme irrégulière des cristaux permet de traiter des zones difficiles à atteindre, sans endommager le tissu cutané. Le traitement est progressif, ce qui signifie que les clients continuent à voir des résultats tout au long du traitement.

Le degré d'abrasion épidermique peut être modifié en réglant la vitesse d'impact des cristaux sur la peau. L'élimination de la couche cornée a pour effet de laisser la peau instantanément plus lisse et plus fraiche, tout en améliorant la production de peau neuve et de collagène. Pendant la durée du traitement, la peau acquiert un aspect 'lumineux' et semble plus jeune.

L'action d'aspiration élimine les cristaux utilisés et les cellules de peau morte. Elle stimule également la circulation et améliore l'afflux sanguin vers la zone traitée. La production de collagène et d'élas tine est stimulée, ce qui a pour effet de rendre la peau plus ferme et plus jeune d'aspect.

Français

La microdermabrasion peut être utilisée pour tous les types de peau et sur toutes les zones du corps et du visage. SkinBase recommande un traitement de 8 séances, généralement effectuées tous les 7 à 10 jours. Les personnes souffrant d'acné ou de cicatrices d'acné ont besoin de davantage de séances, et un traitement d'entretien mensuel est recommandé après la fin du traitement pour conserver les résultats. Après le traitement, il est possible de ressentir une sensation de tiraillement et la peau peut présenter de légères rougeurs. Il est par conséquent important que les clients utilisent une bonne crème hydratante. Ces effets disparaissent normalement au bout de 24 heures.

Quels sont les avantages de la microdermabrasion par rapports aux autres méthodes?

La microdermabrasion ne comporte qu'un inconfort minime et le patient est en mesure de reprendre ses activités normales immédiatement après la séance. La microdermabrasion aux cristaux utilise un composé totalement inerte et stérile qui ne présente aucun risque de réaction allergique.

- Il élimine les éventuelles réactions négatives souvent associées aux solutions chimiques
- Le client peut reprendre ses activités normales immédiatement après la séance (absence de rougeur extrême de la peau, etc.)
- La microdermabrasion peut traiter tous les types et toutes les couleurs de peau
- Grâce aux résultats visibles immédiatement, même après la première séance, le client reste motivé
- La microdermabrasion permet de traiter les premiers signes du vieillissement cutané et offre un rajeunissement total des peaux qui vieillissent
- L'action d'aspiration améliore l'élasticité de la peau et le tonus musculaire et stimule également les fibroblastes pour la production de collagène
- Améliore la pénétration des produits approuvés après le traitement
- Idéal pour les peaux congestionnées à pores ouverts et comédons et les peaux à tendance acnéique.

- Contrôle variable permettant une exfoliation plus profonde de la peau abimée et épaissie et les cicatrices d'acné

- Permet d'éliminer avec succès les marques de pigmentation indésirables

- Parfait pour les peaux abimées par le soleil

- L'exfoliation corporelle totale permet un traitement anticellulite car l'action d'aspiration favorise le drainage lymphatique.

Quels sont les risques associés à la microdermabrasion?

Une utilisation incorrecte ou des conditions non hygiéniques exposent à des risques pendant le traitement de microdermabrasion. C'est pourquoi nous insistons sur l'importance d'une bonne hygiène sur le lieu de travail. L'appareil MDPro utilise des buses jetables, qui éliminent tout risque de contamination croisée entre les clients, dans la mesure où la buse est le seul élément qui est en contact avec la peau pendant le traitement.

LES CRISTAUX

Les cristaux sont en oxyde l'aluminium, un minéral présent à l'état naturel. Stérile et non-toxique, sans réactions négatives au contact de la peau, nous recommandons cependant d'effectuer un test d'allergie avant le traitement par mesure de précaution.

L'oxyde d'aluminium est considéré à faible risque pour la santé par inhalation, et les normes industrielles traitent toute inhalation de cette nature comme une poussière nuisible. L'inhalation de particules de poussière, par exemple la poussière des ongles artificiels, peut causer des irritations et de la toux en cas d'exposition aux poussières pendant des périodes prolongées. L'oxyde d'aluminium ne contient pas de silice libre, ce qui signifie qu'il ne présente pas de risque respiratoire en cas d'inhalation.

Il est important d'effectuer un test de tolérance préalable pour vérifier que le client n'est pas sensible aux cristaux utilisés.

SENSIBILITÉ AUX CRISTAUX - TEST DE TOLÉRANCE

Il est très rare qu'un patient soit sensible aux cristaux utilisés, toutefois un test cutané doit être effectué avant le traitement, sur le dos de l'avant-bras. Si la zone devient irritable ou gonflée, ne pratiquez pas le traitement. Si le patient développe des marques rouges sur la peau après le traitement, cette réaction est généralement due à une trop forte pression appliquée par le thérapeute.

QUELS PROBLÈMES CUTANÉS PEUVENT ÊTRE TRAITÉS AVEC LA MICRODERMABRASION ?

Quiconque peut profiter du traitement de microdermabrasion. Il améliore l'aspect général de la peau en lui donnant un aspect jeune et éclatant. La microdermabrasion est également très efficace dans le traitement de nombreux problèmes cutanés. Elle peut être utilisée sur le visage et sur le corps et représente un excellent traitement pour les cicatrices d'acné sur le dos par exemple.

Acné et cicatrices d'acné

La microdermabrasion agit en éliminant les couches supérieures des cellules de peau morte de la surface de la peau, ce qui la rend particulièrement efficace dans le traitement de l'acné. L'élimination des cellules mortes désobstrue les pores et réduit les risques de formation de nouveaux boutons.

Ridules et rides

L'action d'aspiration de la microdermabrasion a pour effet de stimuler la production de collagène dans la peau. A mesure que nous vieillissons, la production d'élastine et de collagène commence à ralentir. L'association de la stimulation du collagène et du renouveau cutané permet d'améliorer la surface de la peau en atténuant les ridules et les rides.

Peau sèche et déshydratée
Teint irrégulier

Normalement, la peau se renouvelle environ tous les 28 jours. En éliminant les cellules mortes des couches supérieures de l'épiderme, la microdermabrasion accélère la fréquence à laquelle la peau se renouvelle normalement et permet ainsi de révéler une nouvelle peau fraiche et éclatante.

Cellulite 'effet peau d'orange'

La microdermabrasion ne peut pas soigner la cellulite, cependant elle permet de stimuler la circulation et d'améliorer ainsi l'afflux sanguin vers la zone traitée. Pour améliorer l'aspect de la cellulite, il est nécessaire de boire beaucoup d'eau et faire de l'exercice régulièrement.

Vergetures
Pigmentation et taches

La microdermabrasion peut améliorer considérablement l'aspect de la pigmentation et des vergetures. Le traitement de microdermabrasion stimule la zone ciblée pour qu'elle produise davantage de collagène et accélère le processus de renouvellement cutané, ce qui a pour effet d'améliorer la qualité de la peau et de réduire les marques de vergetures et de décoloration de la peau.

Le traitement de microdermabrasion n'élimine pas les vergetures. Toutefois, un traitement régulier permet une amélioration de la zone traitée et des marques de vergetures moins visibles. Le tissu cicatriciel ne doit pas être traité tant que l'inflammation n'a pas disparu de la zone (par exemple 6 mois après l'intervention).

Un traitement régulier de microdermabrasion permet d'améliorer l'aspect des vergetures en créant un effet de fusion avec le tissu cicatriciel situé autour. Il réduit également les problèmes de pigmentation qui rendent souvent les vergetures plus visibles.

Hyperpigmentation et sa cause (mélasme)

Les causes les plus évidentes sont l'utilisation de pilules contraceptives orales ou l'hormonothérapie substitutive, la grossesse ou l'interaction avec certains médicaments. Une exposition répétée ou excessive au soleil joue également un rôle, tout comme les inflammations ou traumatismes subis par la peau. Certains produits chimiques présents dans les parfums, etc., peut aussi provoquer des taches de pigmentation. Un traitement régulier de microdermabrasion peut être très bénéfique aux peaux endommagées par le soleil et permet d'éliminer les taches de pigmentation indésirables.

La microdermabrasion SkinBase permet d'obtenir des résultats bénéfiques dans le traitement des marques de pigmentation. Les clients doivent être informés qu'un traitement peut comporter entre 10-15 séances. Il est également important de conseiller aux clients d'appliquer une crème solaire en permanence.

Notez que le traitement de microdermabrasion ne permet pas d'améliorer les affections cutanées liées au vitiligo.

Le mélasme et le chloasme (brunissement de la peau dû à des changements hormonaux) peuvent être améliorés par la microdermabrasion. Le traitement permet au pigment emprisonné de migrer à travers les couches de l'épiderme pour être éliminé normalement. Cependant, de nombreuses séances peuvent être nécessaires pour améliorer la zone concernée.

COMMENT FONCTIONNE LE TRAITEMENT

La microdermabrasion est un traitement progressif plutôt qu'agressif. Les couches de l'épiderme sont éliminées en douceur et sans danger au cours des séances de traitement. Le traitement est effectué tous les 7 à 10 jours. Cela signifie que la couche cornée qui avait été éliminée lors de la séance précédente n'a pas eu le temps de se reformer et que la tolérance du client au traitement augmente. Par conséquent, à chaque séance suivante, l'intensité du traitement peut être augmentée pour atteindre les couches plus profondes de l'épiderme afin d'éliminer les cicatrices d'acné, réduire la pigmentation et lisser les ridules.

SESSION 3 – RÉSULTATS DE L'APPRENTISSAGE:

- Capacité d'effectuer une consultation complète du client avant le traitement
- Connaissance des principales contrindications au traitement de microdermabrasion
- Connaissance des soins post-traitement nécessaires et réactions possibles au traitement

CONSULTATION DU CLIENT

1. Vérifiez si le client peut suivre le traitement en vous basant sur la liste des contrindications.

2. Effectuez une analyse de la peau en identifiant les zones à éviter pendant le traitement, par exemple les contrindications mineures telles que les télangiectasies (rupture de capillaires)

3. Soulignez les zones qui ont besoin d'une attention particulière comme les cicatrices d'acné ou la pigmentation, les pores ouverts et le teint irrégulier

4. Suggérez un programme de traitement en ayant soin d'expliquer le coût, la durée et la fréquence nécessaire du traitement

5. Expliquez au client l'action du traitement et les sensations qu'il entraîne

6. Expliquez au client quelles sont les réactions possibles de la peau. Bien que les éventuelles réactions soient très réduites, veillez à ce que les clients sachent qu'une certaine sensibilité est possible.

7. Parlez au client des soins post-traitement pour qu'il sache exactement ce qu'il doit faire après le traitement pour prendre soin de sa peau.

8. Il est essentiel que le client comprenne l'importance d'un suivi correct à la maison entre chaque séance et le fait qu'il doit s'engager à atteindre les objectifs, par exemple l'utilisation d'indices de protection solaire corrects est impérative pour éviter d'autres problèmes de pigmentation.

9. **REMPLISSEZ TOUJOURS UNE FICHE CLIENT:**
   Elle vous permet de mieux connaitre le besoins spécifiques de chaque client. Expliquez les contre-indications du traitement et demandez au client de signer la fiche.

Les parents/tuteurs (de plus de 18 ans) doivent signer la fiche de consultation pour les enfants âgés de moins de 16 ans.

CONTRE-INDICATIONS DU TRAITEMENT DE MICRODERMABRASION

CONTRE-INDICATIONS MAJEURES
- NE PAS PROCÉDER

- Rosacée
- Acné de niveau 4 (attendre 6 mois après un traitement “Roaccutane”)
- Diabètes. Les clients doivent fournir une autorisation écrite de leur généraliste avant de pouvoir effectuer le traitement.
- Cancer et maladies auto-immunes
- Grossesse - les dérèglements hormonaux peuvent provoquer des mélasmes.

CONTRE-INDICATIONS MINEURES
- PROCÉDER AVEC PRÉCAUTION ET EVITER LES ZONES AFFECTÉES

- Psoriasis
- Télangiectasie
- Cicatrices chéloïdes
- Herpès Simplex (boutons de fièvre)
- Eczéma chronique et dermatite séborrhéique
- Conjonctivite
- Grains de beauté en relief, verrues, papillomes

Français

CONSEILS POST-TRAITEMENT

Il est recommandé aux clients de se conformer aux conseils suivants après avoir reçu un traitement de microdermabrasion

- Le traitement MD peut être répété à des intervalles de 7-10 jours. Un traitement de 15 à 20 séances à intervalles hebdomadaires est considéré comme un maximum. A ce stade, le client peut suivre un programme d’entretien toutes les 4/6 semaines.

- Ne pas utiliser d’acide de fruits, d’acide glycolique et de rétinol après le traitement MD; la peau fraichement abrasée est réceptive aux produits appliqués, par conséquent l’utilisation d’exfoliants après le traitement peut irriter la peau

- Pas de sauna ou de lit solaire pendant 48 heures après le traitement

- Pas de baignade pendant 24 heures après le traitement

- Pas de ‘Botox’ ou de produits de comblement dermique pendant 48 heures après le traitement

- Attendre 14 jours après l'application de produits de comblement dermique avant effectuer le traitement de microdermabrasion

- Pas de maquillage lourd pendant 12 heures après le traitement

- Un indice de protection solaire minimum de 15 doit être appliqué

- L'application régulière de crème hydratante est indispensable pour assurer l'hydratation de la peau et l'empêcher de devenir sèche et de peler.

- Les produits doivent avoir un pH compris entre 4,5 et 7

- Les produits de soin pour la peau contenant un pourcentage élevé de produits d'herboristerie et d'huiles essentielles ne sont PAS ADAPTES à l'usage après un traitement de microdermabrasion dans la mesure où certains des ingrédients peuvent provoquer une réaction allergique. Si cela se produit, il existe un réel risque que le thérapeute et le client pensent que c'est le traitement qui provoque l'allergie, alors qu'il s'agit en réalité des ingrédients contenu dans les produits de soin. Il est important d'utiliser les produits qui redonnent ou ajoutent de l'hydratation à la peau pour empêcher la peau de se dessécher ou de peler.

SESSION 4 – RÉSULTATS DE L'APPRENTISSAGE:

- Capacité d'identifier les différentes parties de l'appareil de microdermabrasion et ses fonctions
- Capacité de préparer l'appareil et de vérifier qu'il est en bon état de marche
- Capacité de sélectionner le traitement approprié en fonction du type de peau du client

PRÉPARATION DE L'APPAREIL SKINBASE MDPRO

1. Ouvrez le couvercle et sortez:
   - le câble électrique
   - la pièce à main avec le tube
   - le flacon de stockage vide avec raccord encliquetable

2. Branchez ensuite le raccord encliquetable en vérifiant qu'il est enfoncé à fond et que le manchon de verrouillage est en position correcte. S'il n'est pas correctement fixé, il risque d'y avoir une chute de la pression à vide.

3. Vérifiez que la pièce à main est reliée au flacon de stockage par le tube argenté et serrez à fond aux deux extrémités.

4. Fixez une cartouche de cristaux neuve à la pièce à main et serrez à fond.

5. Branchez ensuite le câble électrique, mettez la source d'alimentation sous tension et actionnez l'interrupteur situé sur le tableau.

6. Enfin, fixez une buse propre à la pièce à main. En plaçant votre index sur l'orifice de la buse, tournezla vanne de régulation jusqu'à obtention de la pression désirée pour le traitement facial. Assurez-vous de bien comprendre les niveaux de pression corrects avant de commencer tout traitement MD.

IMPORTANT: EN AUCUNE CIRCONSTANCE LE BOITIER MÉTALLIQUE NE DOIT ÊTRE DÉVISSÉ ET SOULEVÉ AVANT D'AVOIR COMPLÈTEMENT DÉBRANCHÉ L'ALIMENTATION DE SECTEUR

NIVEAUX DE TRAITEMENT

Les descriptions suivantes fournissent des indications permettant de sélectionner le niveau de traitement approprié pour chaque client.

PREMIER NIVEAU -0,3 bar

Ce niveau doit être utilisé par les thérapeutes formés depuis peu jusqu'à ce qu'ils sachent comment utiliser l'appareil avec la pression appropriée.

Ce niveau permet une exfoliation totale douce et doit toujours être sélectionné pour la première séance du traitement.

Toujours utiliser ce niveau pour les types de peaux asiatiques, noires et foncées.

SECOND NIVEAU -0,4 bar

Ce niveau doit être sélectionné progressivement pour intervenir sur les cicatrices d'acné ou la peau plus épaisse.

Ne pas dépasser ce niveau pour les types de peau V et VI de l'échelle Fitzpatrick.

TROISIÈME NIVEAU -0,5 bar

Ce niveau ne doit être utilisé sur les clients que vers les dernières séances du traitement lorsque la peau est plus tolérante.

Utilisé pour les interventions sur les cicatrices d'acné, la pigmentation, les ridules et les rides.

Egalement adapté à l'exfoliation corporelle, aux vergetures et à la cellulite.

QUATRIÈME NIVEAU -0,6 bar

pour le corps uniquement, **ne jamais utiliser sur le visage.**

SESSION 5 – RÉSULTATS DE L'APPRENTISSAGE:

- Capacité d'utiliser l'appareil et d'appliquer le traitement sans danger et efficacement pendant la durée de traitement prévue
- Capacité de travailler dans des limites de temps acceptables dans le secteur

MÉTHODE DE TRAITEMENT

1. Installez le client en position semi-inclinée
2. Assurez-vous que le visage soit bien dégagé
3. Nettoyez parfaitement la peau du client – utilisez un nettoyant en gel
4. Séchez parfaitement la peau
5. Etirez la peau avec le pouce et le majeur
6. Tenez la pièce à main comme si vous teniez un stylo, et déplacez-le dans un mouvement de balayage sur le visage (voir schéma page suivante)
7. Pratiquez une exfoliation douce de la totalité du visage et du cou
8. Une fois l'exfoliation douce terminée, revenez sur les zones qui exigent une attention plus particulières, telles que cicatrices d'acné, marques de pigmentation, ridules et rides.
9. Une fois la séance terminée, éliminez les résidus de cristaux qui restent sur la peau en essuyant avec des disques de coton humide (eau froide)
10. Tonifiez avec un tonique doux
11. Masque en option
12. Hydratez
13. Appliquez une protection solaire indice 15

INSTRUCTIONS D'APPLICATION DU TRAITEMENT

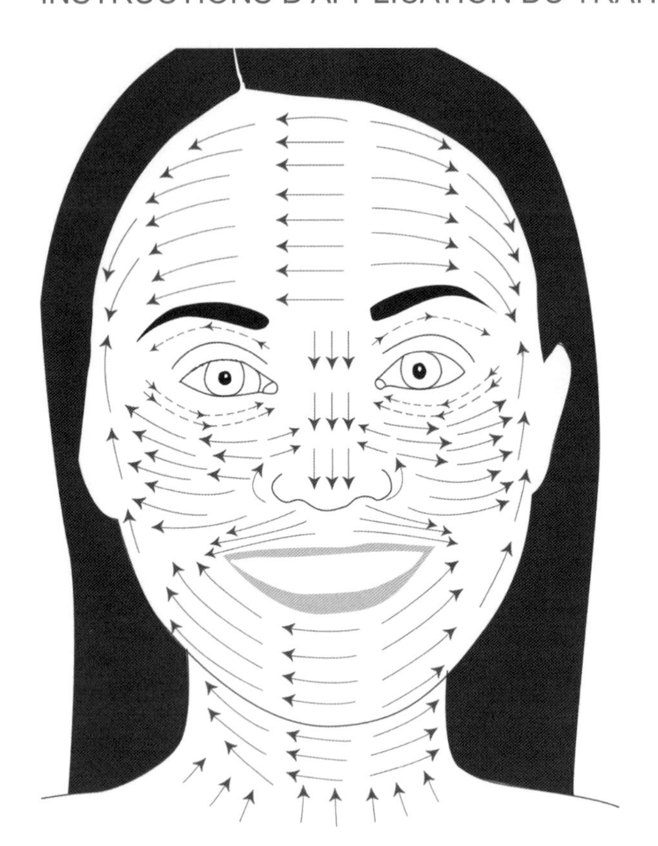

Le schéma indique le sens du mouvement lorsque vous traitez le visage. Les lignes en pointillés autour de la zone délicate des yeux suggèrent des passages rapides et légers.

Chaque flèche (passage) fait 4 cm de longueur

Lignes en pointillés autour des yeux
- Action amortie
- Toujours utiliser le niveau 1 autour des yeux

Conseils pour le traitement

1. Comprendre la peau du client et sa réaction avant d'aller plus loin.

Très souvent, les thérapeutes veulent impressionner le client dès leur première séance et appliquent trop de pression et de façon trop agressive. Cela a pour effet sensibilise la peau du clien, qui tirée avec trop de pression, peut provoquer des traces des traces rouges. Cela est dû au fait que le thérapeute est trop ambitieux et ne comprend pas la peau du client. Il est essential que les thérapeutes maîtrisent le mouvement de passage de la buse sur la peau de façon douce et contrôlée.

2. Le traitement doit rester léger lors de la première séance et peut évoluer progressivement vers un traitement plus agressif au fur et à mesure des séances.

De cette façon, la peau a le temps de s'habituer au traitement et le client comprend ce qui se passe. Un client qui rentre chez lui avec des traces rouges ou une peau sensible et rouge n'est pas un client satisfait et il est très probable qu'il annulera la suite de son traitement car le thérapeute ne lui a pas expliqué ou n'a pas appliqué le traitement correctement.

3. N.B. Toujours utiliser une aspiration légère sur les peaux noires ou asiatiques, et un niveau ne dépassant pas le niveau 2 sur les peaux de type V et VI de l'échelle Fitzpatrick

4. Le secret d'un traitement réussi réside dans la pression des passages.

Des passages rapides et légers doivent être effectués pour une exfoliation douce (action amortie autour des yeux), des passages plus lents pour se concentrer sur des zones à problèmes. Les zones présentant des télangiectasies mineures (ruptures de capillaires) doivent être traitées très délicatement en effectuant des passages rapides et légers sur la zone. Les passages ne doivent jamais s'étendre sur plus de 4 cm.

SESSION 6 – RÉSULTATS DE L'APPRENTISSAGE:

- Capacité d'apprécier les problèmes et santé et de sécurité relatifs au traitement et à l'entretien de l'équipement

- Capacité de mettre à jour efficacement les fiches clients

ARRÊT DE L'APPAREIL

- Après chaque traitement – arrêtez l'appareil et débrancher le câble électrique de l'alimentation secteur et du boîtier

- Retirez la cartouche de cristaux et tapotez la pièce à main sur la paume de votre main pour éliminer les éventuels résidus de cristaux présents dans la chambre de la pièce à main

- Retirez la buse et mettez-la au rebut

- Dévissez le flacon de stockage du couvercle et videz les cristaux utilisés avec soin puis éliminez-les conformément aux réglementations en vigueur

- Veillez à revisser le flacon de stockage à fond

- Détachez le tube du raccord encliquetable

- Rangez soigneusement tous les tubes et les accessoires dans le boîtier et vérifiez que tous les éléments sont propres et prêts pour la prochaine utilisation

ENTRETIEN QUOTIDIEN OBLIGATOIRE

- Videz le flacon de stockage après CHAQUE traitement

- Vérifiez que le couvercle du flacon est serré à fond (s'il n'est pas serré à fond, la puissance d'aspiration sera réduite)

- Chaque fois que vous remplacez la cartouche de cristaux, secouez l'excès de cristaux qui peut se trouver dans le canal intérieur de la pièce à main. Cela permet de maintenir la propreté de la chambre intérieure de la pièce à main en permanence.

- Retirez la cartouche de cristaux à la fin de la journée et secouez l'excès de cristaux qui peut se trouver dans le canal intérieur de la pièce à main.

IMPORTANT:

Le flacon de stockage DOIT être remplacé une fois par mois. Si un flacon neuf n'est pas installé tous les mois, la puissance d'aspiration risque de diminuer. Dans ce cas, les cristaux risquent d'être aspirés depuis le filtre en papier situé dans le flacon directement dans la pompe située à l'intérieur de l'unité, ce qui peut gravement endommager l'appareil et invalider la garantie.

INDEX

SkinBase™

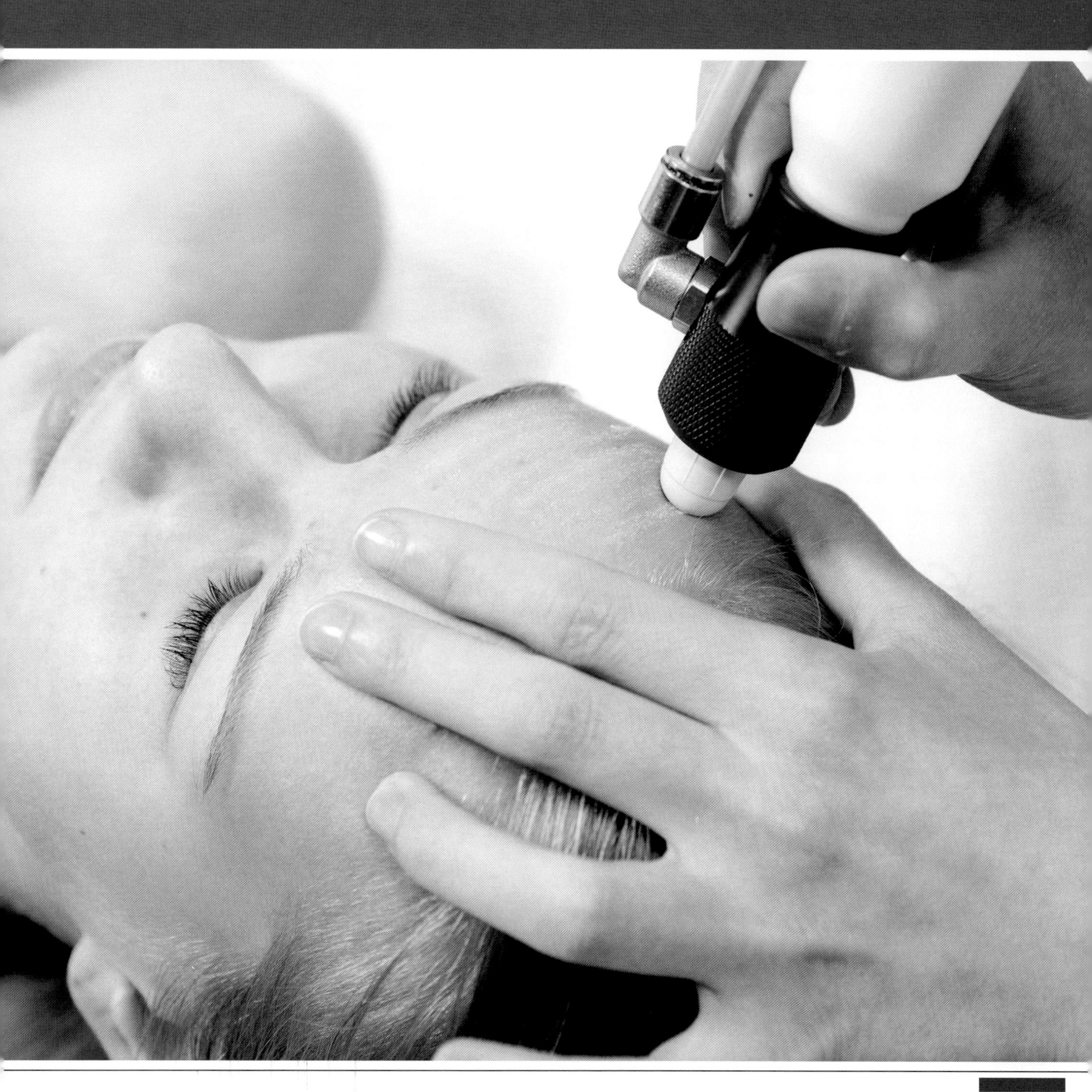

La microdermoabrasión de SkinBase: Manual de Instrucciones

INDICE	PAGINA

LA MICRODERMOABRASIÓN DE SKINBASE: MANUAL DE INSTRUCCIONES

Este manual de instrucciones está organizado de tal manera, que garantiza al cliente obtener toda la información necesaria para el tratamiento de microdermoabrasión. Es imprescindible, que el practicante tenga las calificaciones de belleza o de esteticista requeridas o que tenga experiencia laboral significativa en ese campo. El manual cubre los aspectos teóricos y prácticos de la microdermoabrasión.

El SkinBaseMDPro es un sistema profesional (para efectuar tratamientos) de microdermoabrasión. Ha sido diseñado y fabricado en el Reino Unido por una empresa, que tiene considerable experiencia a raíz de trabajar cercanamente con centros de medicina estética. Eso les permitió una larga experimentación en el campo y les ayudó a idear un sistema con una prestación, calidad y fiabilidad excepcional.

SECCIÓN 1 – RESULTADOS DEL APRENDIZAJE

- Al terminar esta sesión entenderá cuáles serán sus responsabilidades referente a las normas de sanidad y seguridad en el trabajo y cómo realizarlas
- Será capaz de reconocer las diferentes molestias o enfermedades de la piel y conocerá las contraindicaciones al tratamiento
- Mejorará su conocimiento sobre la anatomía y la fisiología de la cara y el cuello

SALUD Y SEGURIDAD EN EL LUGAR DE TRABAJO

La sección trata de las responsabilidades (del titular, de los empleados -en su caso-, y de los clientes) referentes a la salud, la seguridad y el bienestar en el lugar de trabajo. Es importante, que sea consciente de esas responsabilidades y que sean aplicadas cuando sea razonablemente posible. Un extenso conocimiento sobre los temas de salud y seguridad le ayudará a efectuar el tratamiento de forma segura, mostrando una apariencia y actitud profesional.

La norma relativa a la sanidad y la seguridad, que concierne a los centros de belleza define unas reglas mínimas de salud, seguridad y bienestar, que son requeridas en e l trabajo. Quién trabaje en el sector de los servicios está automáticamente obligado por ley de proporcionar un entorno seguro e higiénico.

Para evitar potenciales peligros y riesgos en el trabajo es necesario:

- conocer la responsabilidad legal propia en relación a la aplicación de las normas de sanidad y seguridad en el trabajo.
- garantizar, que la presencia laboral cumpla con los requisitos legislativos de sanidad y seguridad, de acuerdo con las políticas del trabajo.
- seguir las políticas laborales de su profesión y las instrucciones del fabricante para el uso adecuado de los materiales.
- avisar o manejar inmediatamente cualquier riesgo, que pueda ser un peligro en el trabajo.
- tener una instalación de primeros auxilios, en caso de un accidente o una enfermedad.
- Tener un procedimiento de evacuación y asegurarse de que todos los empleados sepan cómo utilizarlo
- Minimizar la posibilidad de contagio de una infección o de una enfermedad, manteniendo la higiene al máximo

NORMAS RELATIVAS AL USO DE ENERGÍA ELÉCTRICA EN EL LUGAR DEL TRABAJO

Las normas cubren la instalación, el mantenimiento y el uso de los aparatos eléctricos en el puesto de trabajo. Los aparatos eléctricos deben ser controlados regularmente por un electricista cualificado, para asegurar que cumplan con las normas de salud y seguridad. Mantener un registro sobre esos controles. También es importante que sean conscientes sobre los posibles peligros asociados con los aparatos eléctricos: cables expuestos, clavijas agrietadas y enchufes sobrecargados.

Aunque sea la responsabilidad del patrón asegurarse de que los instrumentos sean seguros al uso, también es responsabilidad del empleado controlar siempre si son totalmente seguros antes de utilizarlos y nunca hacerlo si resultasen defectuosos.

POSIBLES RIESGOS ELÉCTRICOS:

- Cables expuestos
- Clavijas agrietadas o enchufes rotos
- Enchufes sobrecargados

PRIMEROS AUXILIOS

Aunque haya tomado todas las medidas para asegurar que el lugar de trabajo esté lo más seguro posible, pueden ocurrir accidentes. Es necesario tener un procedimiento de primeros auxilios en el puesto de trabajo y que todos los empleados sepan cómo proceder en el caso de un accidente, una enfermedad o una emergencia.

Todos los puestos de trabajo deben disponer de un botiquín de primeros auxilios y de una persona designada a la responsabilidad de realizar la manutención del botiquín. Registre todas las lesiones en un log de accidentes.

TODOS LOS EMPLEADOS DEBEN SABER:

- Donde se puede localizar el botiquín de primeros auxilios
- Quién es responsable de la manutención del botiquín de primeros auxilios
- A quién informar en caso de un accidente, una enfermedad o una emergencia

Eliminación De Residuos

La basura debe ser eliminada en un contenedor recubierto con una bolsa de polietileno, que sea resistente a la rotura. Esterilice el contenedor regularmente con un desinfectante usando guantes protectores.

Las Normas De Higiene En El puesto De Trabajo

La esterilización del aparato entre clientes es esencial para destruir bacterias, hongos y virus dañinos, que puedan causar una infección. Una higiene adecuada en el lugar de trabajo evitará infecciones cruzadas e infecciones secundarias.

Las infecciones cruzadas ocurren cuando microorganismos son transferidos a través de contacto personal o contacto con boquillas infectadas que no hayan sido esterilizadas.

Las infecciones secundarias pueden ser provocadas por una herida al cliente durante el tratamiento o si el cliente ya tenía una herida sobre la piel. En tal caso, las bacterias pueden penetrar la piel y causar una infección.

Higiene Personal

Un alto estándar de higiene personal es esencial. Lávese las manos regularmente, y también antes y después de cada cliente. El pelo largo debe ser recogido y evite tocarse la cara. Cubra heridas o rozaduras con un vendaje limpio.

TRASTORNOS O ENFERMEDADES DE LA PIEL

Las enfermedades infecciosas que sean contagiosas contraindican el tratamiento. Personas con ciertos trastornos de la piel (aunque no sean contagiosos) no deben ser tratadas, ya que el tratamiento puede conducir a una infección secundaria. El esteticista tiene que ser capaz de distinguir entre una piel sana y otra que sufra de enfermedad o trastorno.

IMPORTANTE : Si no está seguro, o es incapaz de identificar la condición de una piel, no debe tratar al cliente y aconséjele consultar a un médico.

Ciertos trastornos o ciertas enfermedades de la piel contraindican un tratamiento: éste podría exponer al esteticista y a otros clientes al riesgo de una infección cruzada. De ese modo es importante estar familiarizado con los trastornos o enfermedades de la piel con las que pueda entrar en contacto.

Infecciones bacterianas

Las bacterias pueden estar en grandes cantidades sobre la piel sin causar ningún daño. Sin embargo, algunos tipos de bacterias son dañinos para nuestra salud; estos son conocidos como 'patógenos'. Las bacterias patógenas pueden causar infecciones en la piel que son contagiosas, por lo cual el cliente no debe ser tratado, si resulta que sufre alguna de las siguientes infecciones bacterianas:

Impétigo
Extremamente infeccioso y muy fácil de transmitir a través de contacto. Suele aparecer primero en la cara, alrededor de la nariz, la boca y las orejas, y puede distribuirse a otras zonas. Inicialmente la piel se vuelve roja y produce picor, luego se forman ampollas, que progresivamente crean una costra húmeda.

Conjuntivitis
La conjuntivitis no siempre es infecciosa y puede ser causada por una reacción alérgica o como resultado de una irritación. Como es imposible para usted de determinar la causa, debe tratarla siempre como infecciosa. El ojo aparece rojo e inflamado. Llos ojos también pueden estar lacrimosos y puede salir pus de la zona ocular.

Orzuelos
Los orzuelos son una infección de la glándula sebácea en la raíz de una pestaña. Esto causa una inflamación, dejando la zona contigua roja y al folículo afectado con un pequeño bulto lleno de pus.

Forúnculos
Los forúnculos son provocados por la inflamación de los folículos pilosos como resultado de una acumulación de pus y de tejidos muertos. Los forúnculos son bultos rojos, llenos de pus, que son suaves, cálidos y/o dolorosos. Un punto amarillento o blanco en el medio del bulto se hace visible cuando está a punto de vaciarse.

Infecciones virales

Las partículas de un virus son tan pequeñas, que no pueden crecer o reproducirse por sí mismos, de modo que necesitan una célula huésped. Los virus invaden las células sanas y vivas del cuerpo con el objetivo de reproducirse. Entran en nuestro cuerpo de cualquier forma posible: a través de la inhalación, la saliva o mediante el contacto sexual. Nuestro sistema inmunitario está diseñado para lidiar con la mayoría de virus, siendo capaz de combatir naturalmente a la mayoría de las infecciones. Clientes que sufran de las siguientes infecciones virales no deben recibir el tratamiento de microdermoabrasión:

Úlceras del herpes simplex
Las úlceras son transmitidas a través de contacto directo con alguien que esté afectado. Se caracterizan por una sensación de hormigueo en la piel, seguida de llagas que forman costras. Se suele encontrar en las membranas mucosas de la nariz y de los labios, aunque también pueden ocurrir en otras partes del cuerpo.

Herpes zóster (culebrilla)
La culebrilla es una infección del nervio y de la parte contigua. En general el virus afecta un nervio, habitualmente en el pecho, abdomen o en la parte superior de la cara. Los síntomas ocurren en la zona de la piel inmediata al nervio, causando rojez, llagas y costras.

Infecciones fúngicas

Los hongos son plantas parasitarias y microscópicas, que se alimentan de los residuos de nuestra piel. Algunas infecciones fúngicas se encuentran sobre la superficie de la piel, otras se localizan en tejidos cutáneos más profundos. Clientes con infecciones fúngicas no deben ser tratados, debido a que las infecciones puedan transmitirse.

Tiña (Tineacorporis)
La tinea corporis è un infezione da fungo della pelle che si evidenzia sul torace, sugli arti e sul volto. Ha li aspetto a scaglie, con chiazze rosse sulla pelle che si allargano. Le chiazze si cicatrizzano dal centro lasciando un anello sulla pelle.

Otras enfermedades de la piel no son infecciosas pero deben ser tratadas con mucho cuidado y en algunos casos deben ser evitadas por completo.

Trastornos de las glándulas sebáceas

Las glándulas sebáceas son glándulas pequeñas, que secretan una sustancia grasienta llamada 'sebo', en los folículos pilosos para lubricar la piel. Se encuentran en gran abundancia en la cara y el cuero cabelludo. Trastornos de glándulas sebáceas incluyen el acné, la rosácea, y la milia. Los trastornos de las glándulas sebáceas son provocados normalmente debido a una sobreproducción de sebo.

Milia
La milia son quistes benignos, rellenos de queratina, que se pueden encontrar alrededor de la nariz y los ojos. Son pequeños, duros, blancos o de un color amarillo pálido. No son contagiosos y pueden ser eliminados, usando una aguja estéril, pinchando la piel, liberando la queratina.

Comedones (espinillas)
Son provocados por una producción excesiva de sebo y un blanqueamiento del folículo piloso a causa de células queratinadas. Se encuentran en la cara, la parte de la espalda superior y el pecho. No son contagiosos.

Seborrea
Provocada por una producción excesiva de sebo, ocurre normalmente durante la pubertad a causa del cambio hormonal. Los afectados tienen los folículos dilatados y sebo excesivo. No es contagioso y suele encontrarse en la cara y en el cuero cabelludo. También puede afectar el pecho y la espalda.

Quistes sebáceos
Estos se forman en el folículo piloso, cuando el sebo se encuentra bloqueado y crea un bulto. No son contagiosos.

Acné vulgar
Desequilibrio hormonal durante la pubertad, provoca un aumento de la producción del sebo. Esto a su vez causa la congestión de los conductos sebáceos, lo que resulta en una inflamación de la piel y la formación de comedones, pústulas y pápulas. El acné vulgar no es contagioso y se suele encontrar en la cara, la nariz, la barbilla y en la frente. También puede aparecer en el pecho y la espalda. Fases activas del acné deberían ser evitadas durante el tratamiento de microdermoabrasión.

Rosácea
Causada por la combinación de una secreción excesiva de sebo y una inflamación crónica, la piel se vuelve gruesa, los poros se dilatan, las mejillas y la nariz enrojecen y se inflaman. El color de la piel puede aparentar violeta por causa de una circulación sanguínea escasa. La rosácea no se puede tratar con la microdermoabrasión.

Pigmentación

Hiperpigmentación: aumento de la pigmentación

- Cloasma 'manchas cutáneas' – el aumento de la producción de pigmentación puede ser causado por los rayos UVA. También aparecen durante el embarazo (se cree que el estrógeno estimula la producción de melanina) y como resultado de tomar la píldora anticonceptiva. Las manchas se forman en las manos, los antebrazos, la parte superior del pecho, las sienes y en la frente.

- Efélides 'pecas' – son causadas por la exposición a los rayos UVA, que estimulan la producción de melanina. Se encuentran sobre la nariz y las mejillas de las personas con la tez blanca. También ocurren encima de las manos, los brazos, los hombros y la espalda.

- Lentigo – manchas de hiperpigmentación más grandes que las pecas. Ocurren en la niñez o en personas de mediana edad, como consecuencia de la exposición al sol. Se encuentra en la cara, las manos y los hombros.

Hipopigmentación: pérdida de pigmentación

- Vitíligo – manchas en la piel, que no contienen ningún pigmento y de ese modo parecen completamente blancas.

- Albinismo – piel, que no contiene ningún pigmento. Por lo tanto la piel, el pelo y los ojos escasean color. La piel es de un color rosa pálido, los ojos son rosas y el pelo es blanco.

Eritema

Eritema es el enrojecimiento de la piel causado por la dilatación de los vasos sanguíneos, que controlan las redes capilares en las zonas de la piel, que estén afectadas por una lesión o infección.

Nevos vasculares

Son áreas de pigmentación causadas por la dilatación permanente de los capilares sanguíneos.

- Capilares dilatados – capilares pequeños y rojos, visibles en zonas descuidadas o secas, como las mejillas.
- Nevo arácneo – vasos sanguíneos dilatados con capilares dilatados proliferando alrededor de ellos.
- Hemangioma capilar 'marca de fresa' – marcas abultadas de color rojo o violeta que aparecen en la piel desde el nacimiento.
- Hemangioma oporto - áreas grandes de capilares dilatados.

Telangiectasia (capilares rotos)

Cualquier tipo de capilares rotos puede empeorar a través de la acción de succión de la microdermo-abrasión. Estas 'venas varicosas' son bastante comunes alrededor de la nariz y por la zona de las mejillas. Esa zona debe ser evitada por completo o el tratamiento debe ser realizado a un nivel muy bajo.

Queloides

Queloides son tejidos cicatriciales con depósitos excesivos de colágeno. La piel parece estar elevada, roja y con ranuras. Este tipo de tejido cicatricial no puede ser tratado con la microdermoabrasión. Estrías y cicatrices postoperatorias pueden ser tratadas, sin embargo, no se debe hacer hasta que toda la inflamación haya desaparecido (6 meses después de la operación por ejemplo).

Dermatitis

La dermatitis es una inflamación de la piel causada por un irritante o una alergia. Hay varios tipos de dermatitis. Los síntomas pueden incluir una piel roja, que produce picor, forma escamas y costras húmedas, se hincha y posiblemente forma ampollas según la gravedad del trastorno.

La dermatitis de contacto irritante ocurre inmediatamente después de tener contacto con un irritante fuerte o a lo largo de un periodo prolongado después de una exposición repetitiva con un irritante débil. Causas comunes de ese tipo de dermatitis son: jabones, champús y detergentes, polvo, aceite y grasa, contacto repetitivo y prolongado con agua.

La dermatitis alérgica de contacto es provocada cuando el afectado desarrolla una alergia a una sustancia. Causas comunes son tintes de cabello, adhesivos y comidas como el marisco.

Eccemas

Hay dos tipos de eccemas: los eccemas atópicos y los eccemas de contacto.

El eccema atópico se suele desarrollar en la niñez y a muchos niños lo superan.
El eccema de contacto suele afectar a adultos y es provocado por el contacto con un alérgeno, como el níquel, detergentes, jabones o perfumes.

En el caso de un eccema, la piel produce picor, se seca y se escama. También puede ponerse roja y ser dolorosa. A veces puede humedecer o sangrar. Las partes comúnmente afectadas son la cara, el cuello y la piel especialmente en la parte inferior del codo o detrás de las rodillas.

Psoriasis

La psoriasis es una enfermedad crónica y autoinmune que afecta la piel y las articulaciones. La psoriasis causa partes escamosas, llamadas 'placas psoriásicas', que son zonas inflamadas y de producción excesiva de piel, que se vuelven de color blanco-plateado debido a la acumulación de piel.

ANATOMÍA Y FISIOLOGÍA

Como esteticista, que realiza el tratamiento, es importante tener cierto conocimiento básico de la anatomía y la fisiología del cuerpo humano.

LOS HUESOS DE LA CABEZA Y EL CUELLO

La cabeza está compuesta de 14 huesos, como se observa en el diagrama, que figura a continuación.

Huesos faciales

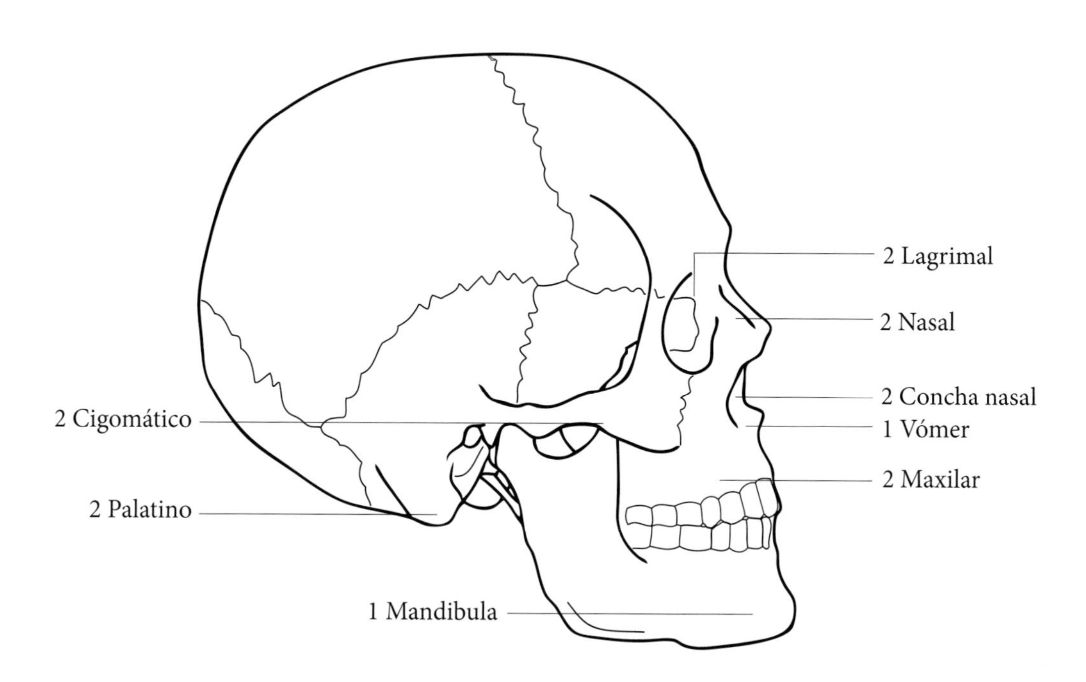

Hueso	
Palatino x 2	Forma la parte inferior y superior de la nariz y la parte superior de la boca
Nasal x 2	Forma el puente de la nariz
Concha nasal x 2	Estos dos huesos forman las paredes externas de la nariz
Vómer	La pared que divide la nariz en dos
Lagrimal x 2	Paredes internas de las cuencas de los ojos
Maxiliar x 2	Fusionados para formar la mandíbula superior
Mandibula	Representa la parte inferior de la mandíbula
Cigomático x 2	Los huesos de las mejillas

Español

El resto del cráneo está formado de los huesos craneales, 8 en total, como muestra el diagrama.

Huesos Del Cráneo

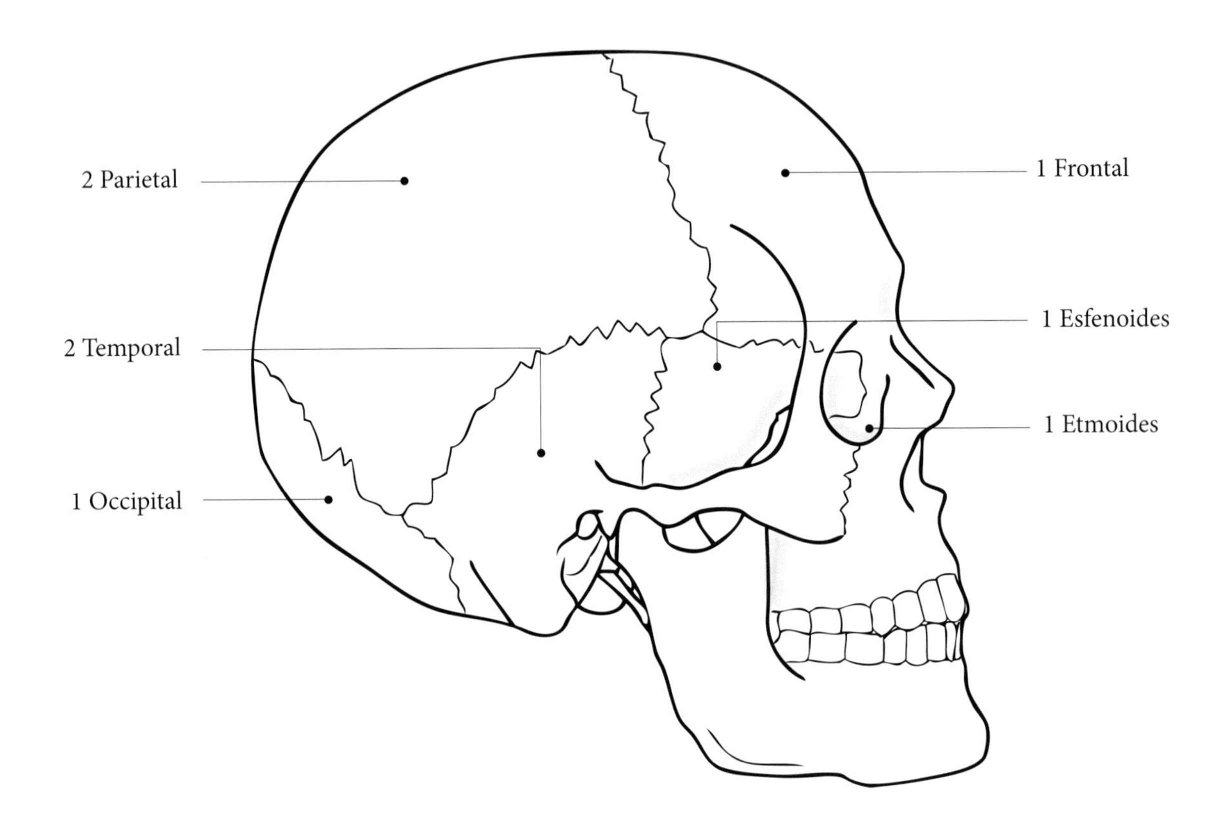

Hueso	
Occipital	Situado en la parte trasera del cráneo, contiene el agujero por el que pasan la médula espinal, nervios y vasos sanguíneos
Parietal	x2 fusionados para formar la bóveda craneal
Frontal	Frente y cuencas de los ojos superiores
Temporal	x2 las partes laterales de la cabeza
Etmoides	forma parte de las fosas nasales
Esfenoides	hueso con forma de murciélago, que une todos los huesos craneales

Español

Huesos Del Cuello, Del Pecho y De La Espalda

Delante

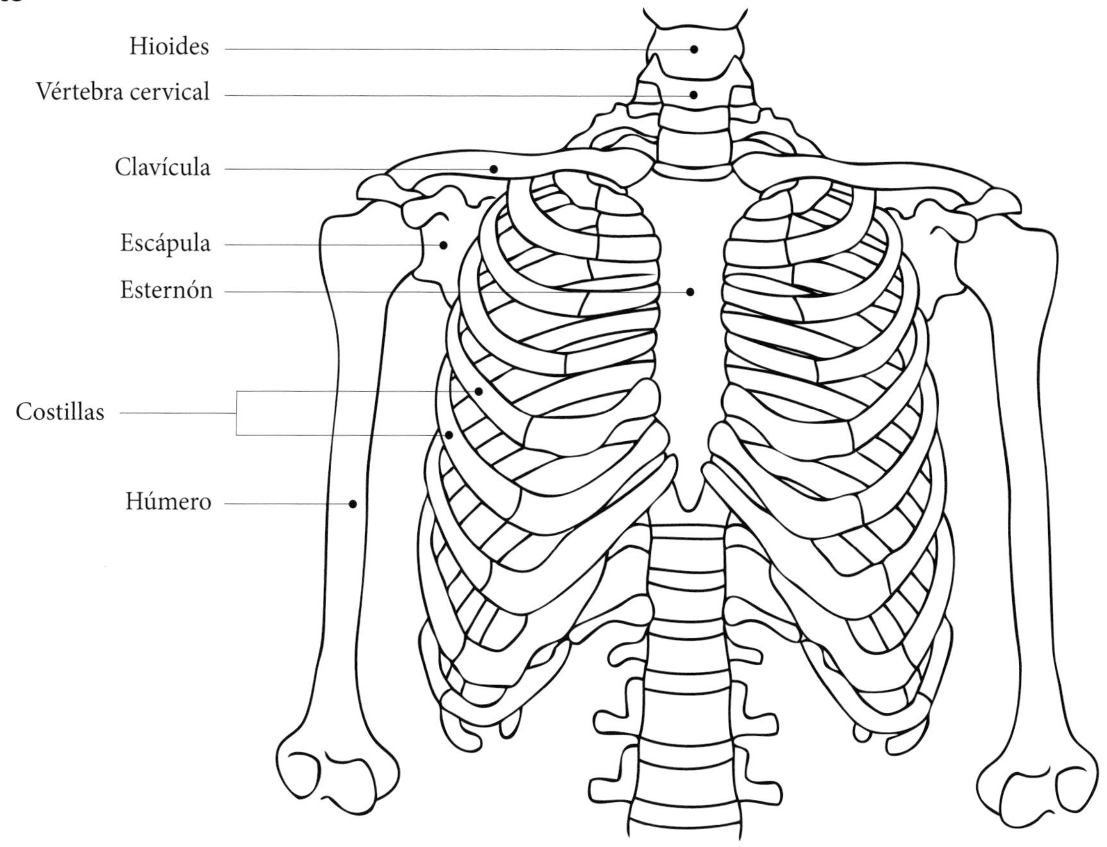

Atrás

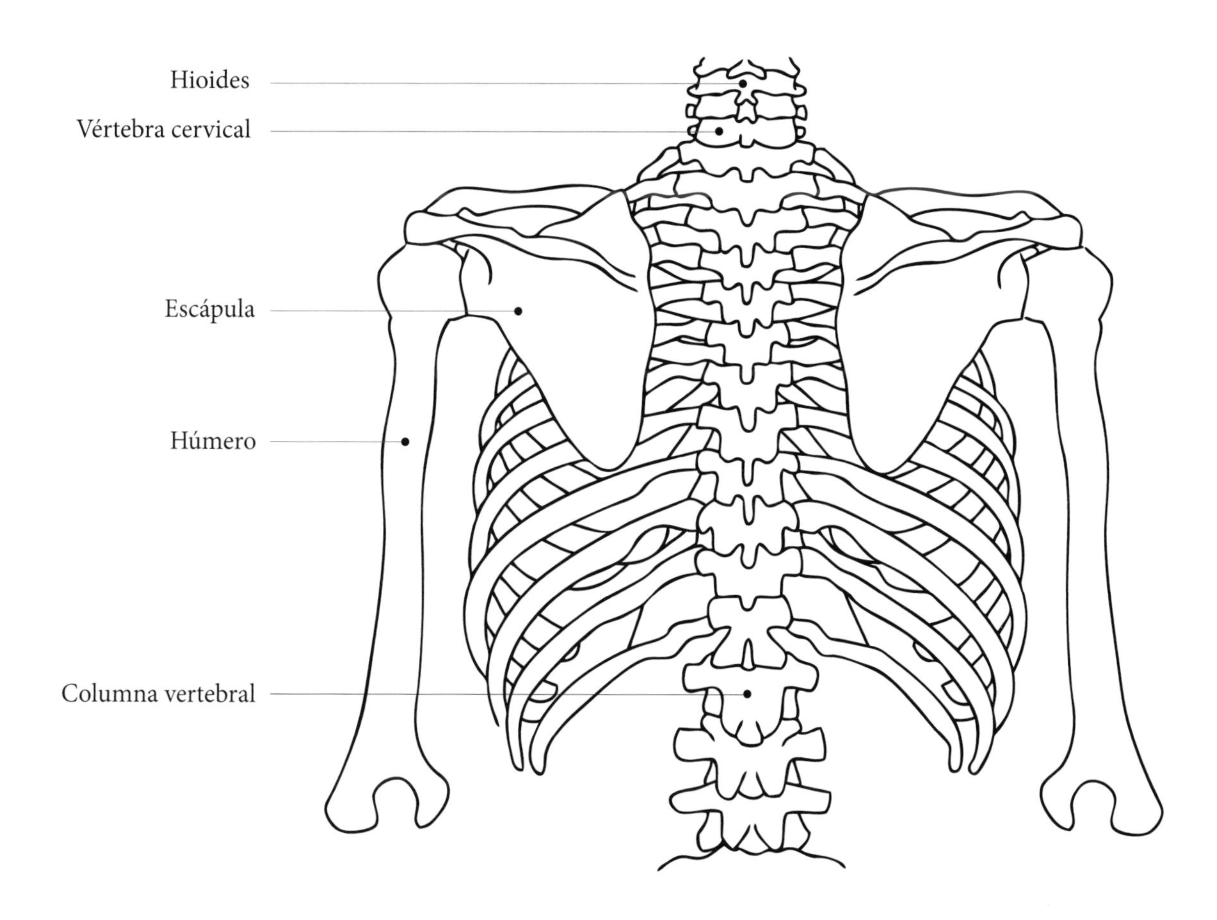

MÚSCULOS DE LA CARA Y EL CUELLO

Los músculos de la cara y el cuello son responsables para nuestras expresiones faciales. A medida que uno envejece, las expresiones faciales, que usamos a diario producen arrugas en la piel y empezamos a enseñar los primeros signos del envejecimiento. Microdermoabrasión elimina las células muertas de la epidermis, mejorando la apariencia de las arrugas.

Músculos Faciales

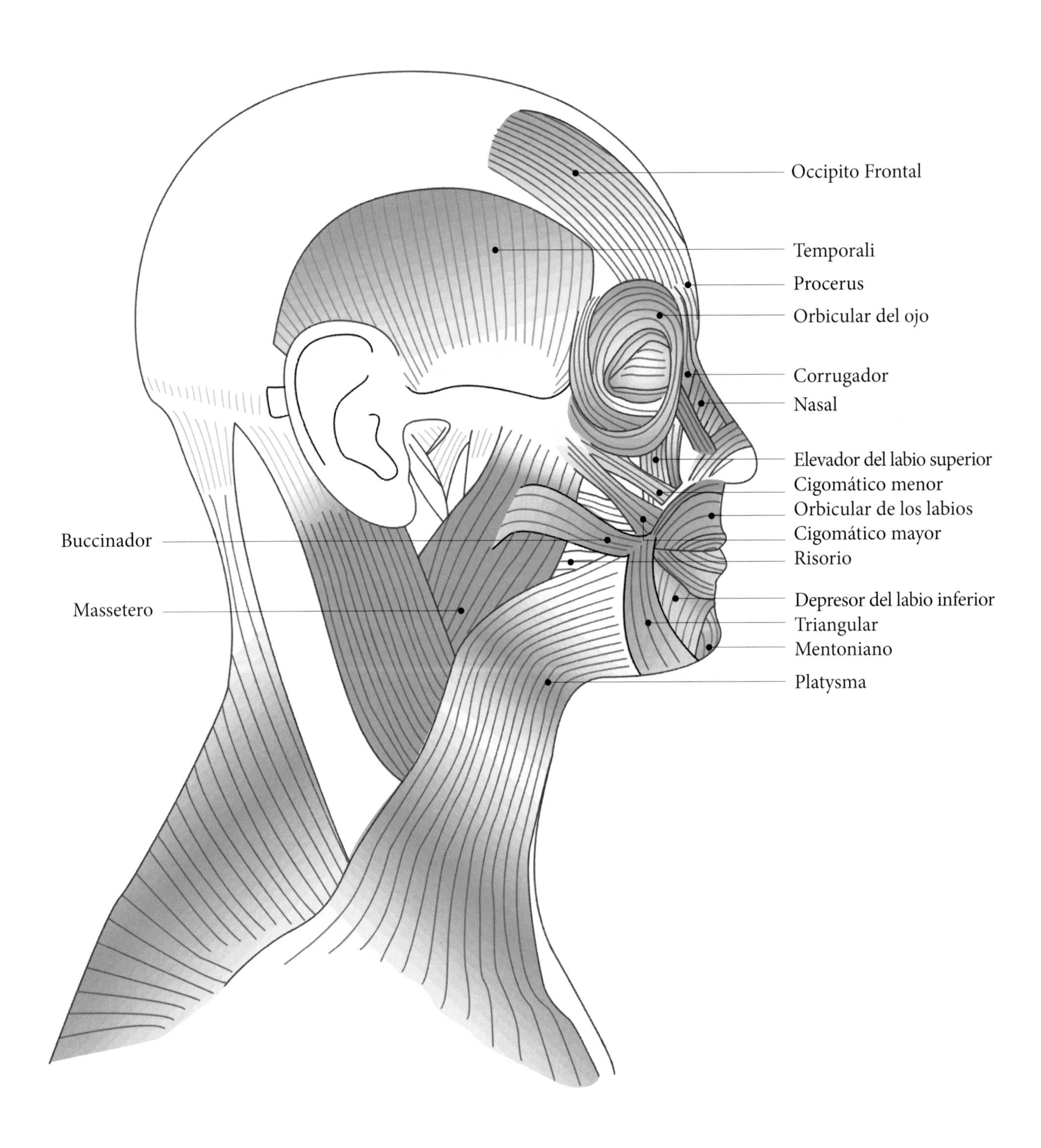

Músculos Del Cuello

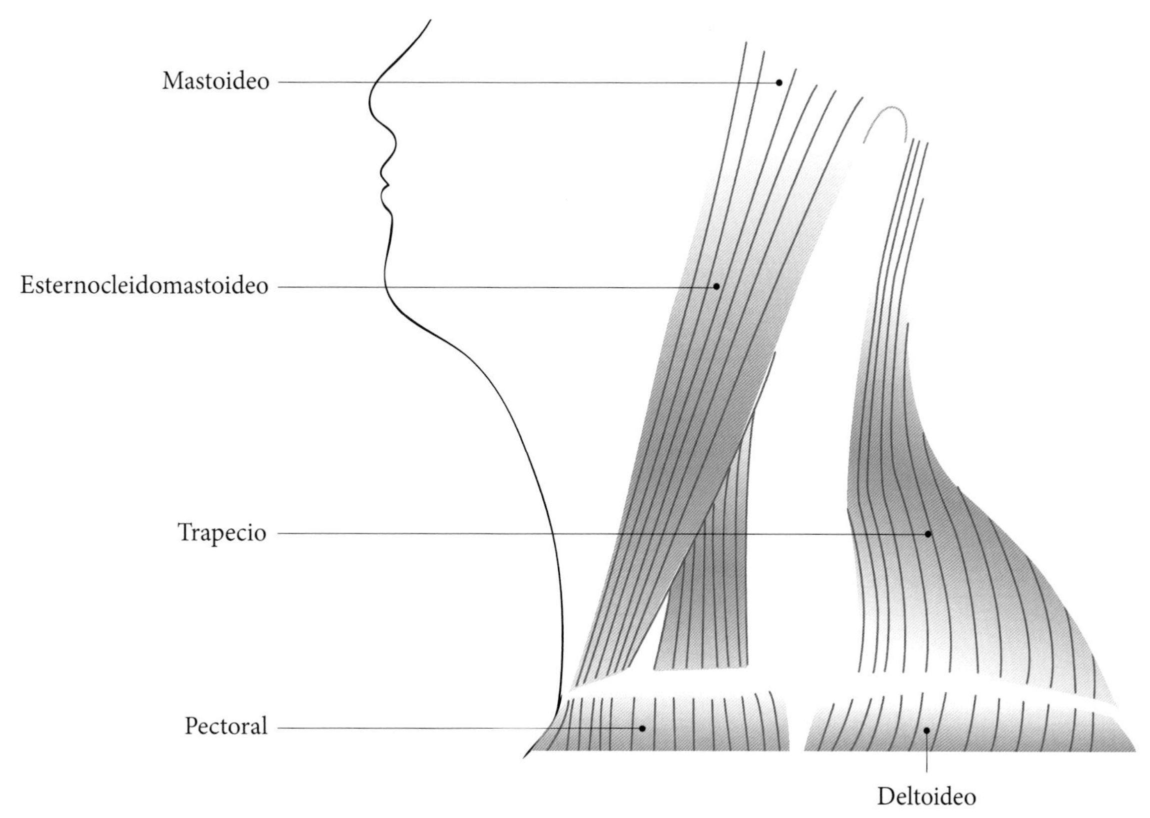

NERVIOS CRANEALES

El sistema nervioso es el método que utiliza el cuerpo para mandar mensajes de información del cerebro a otras partes del cuerpo. Los nervios de la cara y el cuello o también llamados nervios craneales controlan los músculos de la cabeza y el cuello o transportan impulsos nerviosos (información sensorial) de los órganos sensoriales al cerebro. El 5°, 7° y 11° nervio craneal son críticos para los esteticistas, en el momento de realizar un tratamiento facial.

5º Nervio Craneal - 'Trigémino'

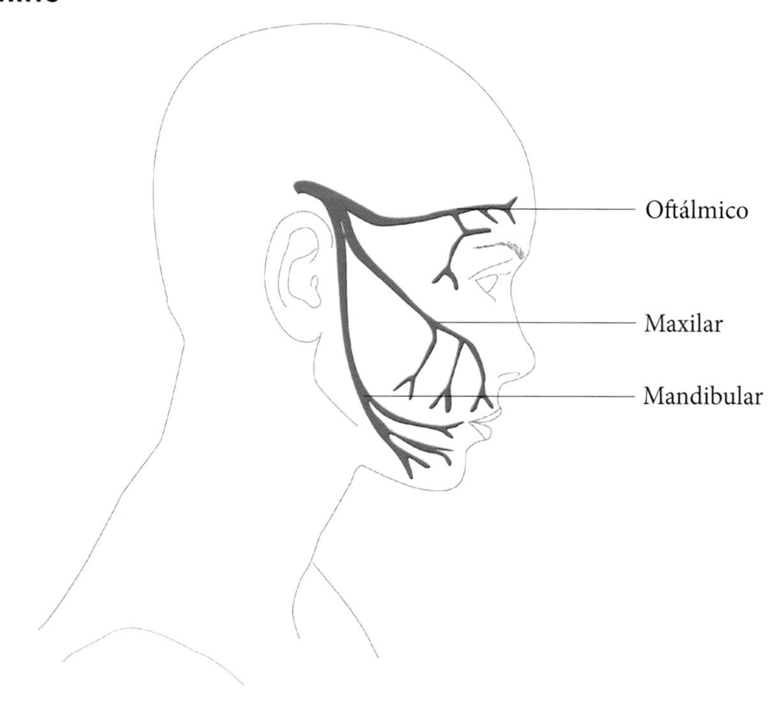

7°Nervio Craneal - 'Facial'

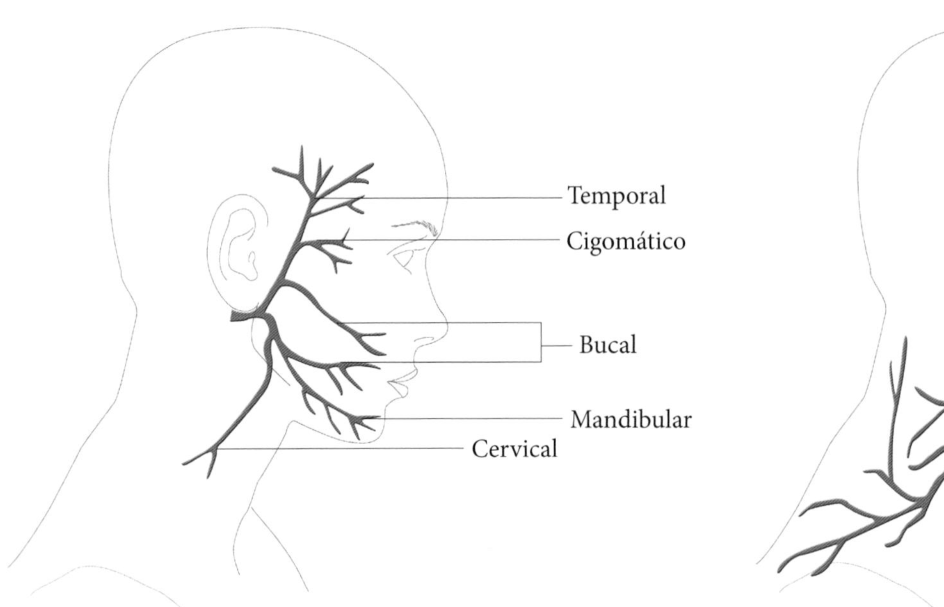

11° Nervio Craneal - 'Accesorio'

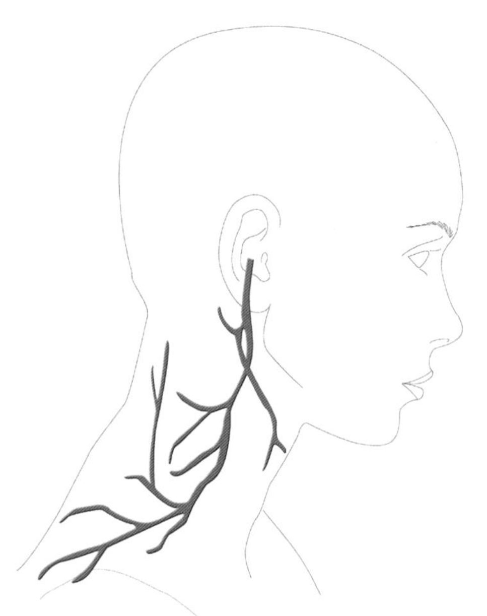

Nervio	Función	Ramos del Nervio	Manda Mensajes a:
5° trigémino	Controla los músculos de la masticación	Oftálmico	glándulas lacrimales, piel de la frente, zona superior de las mejillas
	Transmite información sensorial de la cara	Maxilar	Músculo superior de la mandíbula; la boca
		Mandibular	Músculo inferior de la mandíbula; dientes; Músulos de la masticación
7° facial	Controla los músculos, que se usan para las expresiones faciales	Temporal	Músculos alrededor de los ojos; Músculos de la frente
		Cigomático	Músculos de los ojos
		Bucal	Labio superior: Lados de la nariz
		Mandibular	Labio inferior; Barbilla
		Cervical	Lados de cuello y barbilla
11° accesorio	Mueve el cuello y la barbilla		

SECCIÓN 2 - RESULTADOS DEL APRENDIZAJE

- Conocimiento básico sobre la estructura y la función de la piel
- Identificación de los diferentes tipos de piel
- Buen conocimiento sobre la teoría de la microdermoabrasión
- Identificación de las partes de la piel, que pueden ser tratadas con la microdermoabrasión
- Conocimiento sobre el funcionamiento de un ciclo de tratamientos de microdermoabrasión

LA PIEL

La piel es el órgano más grande del cuerpo humano. Esta utiliza diversas funciones para protegernos de los elementos externos.

- Previene la absorción de sustancias dañinas
- Ayuda a regular la temperatura corporal
- Actúa como una barrera contra las infecciones
- Contiene melanina, que nos protege de los efectos dañinos de los rayos UVA
- Crea una capa impermeable, que impide la deshidratación
- Dispone de una reserva energética en forma de grasa almacenada

La Estructura De La Piel

La piel está compuesta de dos capas distintas: la epidermis y la dermis. Entre ellas se encuentra la membrana basal, que mantiene las dos capas unidas. Por debajo de las dos capas se encuentra la capa subcutánea, una capa de grasa, que protege, amortigua, aísla y almacena energía aditiva para el cuerpo.

La Epidermis

La epidermis es la capa más externa de la piel. Está compuesta de cinco capas. Cada capa de la epidermis es reconocible por su forma y la función de sus células. El tipo de célula más común en la epidermis es el queratinocito, que produce la proteína queratina.

La renovación celular ocurre durante un periodo de aproximadamente 4 semanas. Las células pasan de la capa inferior de la epidermis (capa basal) a la capa superior (capa córnea), cambiando su forma y estructura a medida que avanzan. La capa superior de la epidermis, es la capa que muere y se desprende de la piel a través de descamación. Es esta la capa que es eliminada en el tratamiento de microdermoabrasión y también la que ayuda a reflejar los rayos UVA de la piel. Por eso, es muy importante que los clientes usen protección solar después de un tratamiento de microdermoabrasión.

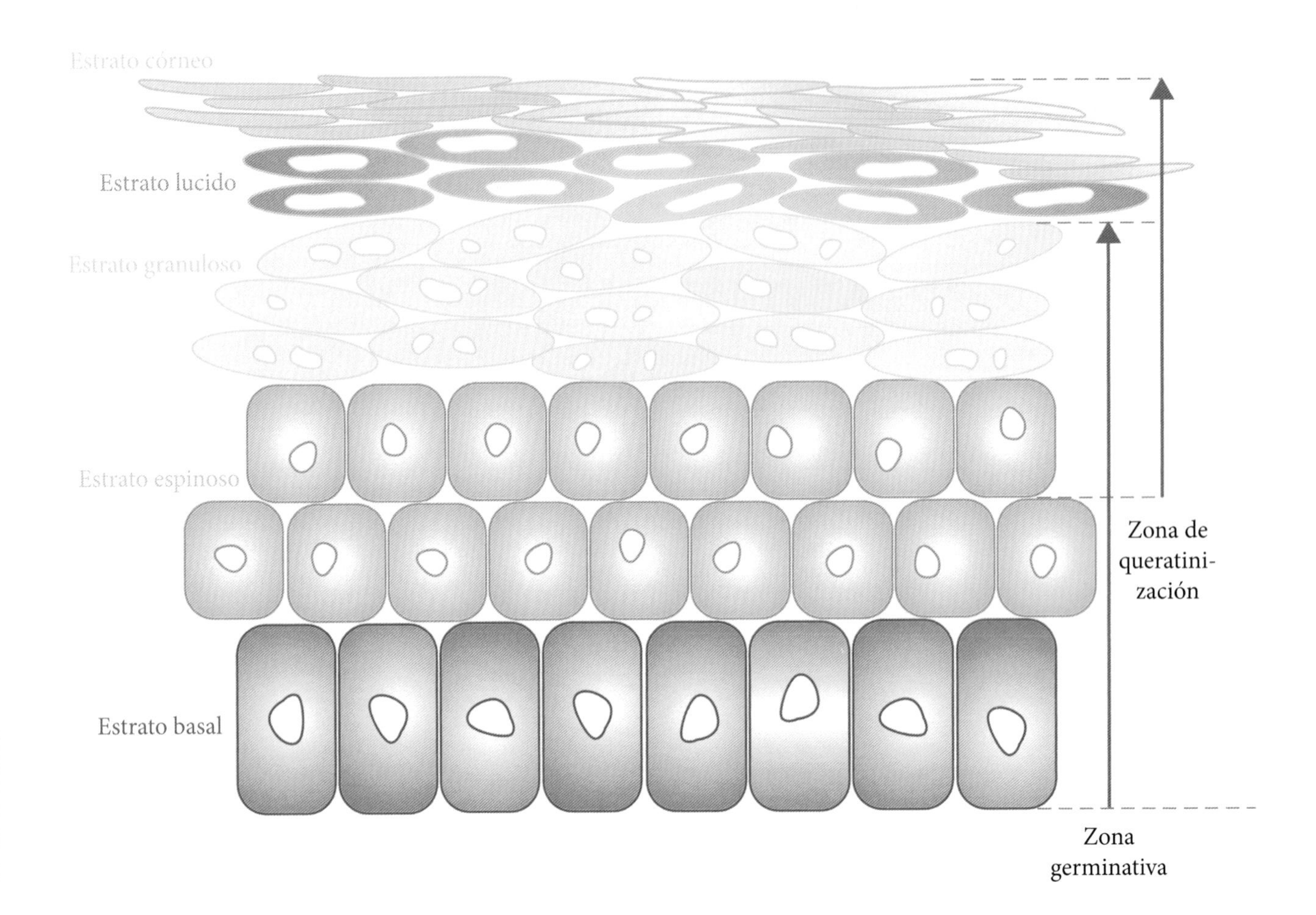

Las Cinco Capas De La Epidermis

1. Estrato córneo o 'capa córnea'

Esta es la capa más exterior de la epidermis y está compuesta de varias capas de células aplanadas, en su mayor parte muertas y que se solapan entre sí. Estas células ayudan a reflejar los rayos UVA.

Piel oscura que evolucionó para resistir a alta radiación UV, tiene un estrato córneo más dura que la piel caucásica. Las células epidérmicas tardan aproximadamente unas tres semanas en llegar al estrato córneo desde el estrato germinativo. Luego se desprenden las células, un proceso llamado descamación.

2. Estrato lucido

Esta capa solamente se puede encontrar en zonas más gruesas de la piel, como en las palmas de las manos y las plantas de los pies.

3. Estrato granuloso

En esta capa las células empiezan a morir. Estas células tienen, lo que parecen ser gránulos dentro de ellos causados por la división de los núcleos. Esos gránulos se conocen comúnmente como gránulos de queratohialina, que luego forman la queratina.

4. Estrato espinoso

El estrato espinoso está compuesto de células que tienen una superficie puntiaguda para conectarse con células adyacentes. Esta es la capa que inicia la síntesis de la queratina.

5. Estrato germinativo o 'capa basal'

Estas células en forma de columna son responsables de la producción de nuevas células epidérmicas. Células se dividen y pasan a capas superiores. Las células restantes se dividen para cubrir los huecos. El proceso de la división celular es conocido por mitosis. vuoti. Questo processo di divisione cellulare è conosciuto come mitosi.

La zona germinativa de la epidermis también contiene otras dos células importantes, melanocitos y células de Langerhans.

Células de Langerhans – absorben y eliminan los cuerpos extraños que penetran por la piel. Pasan de la epidermis a la dermis y desde allí al sistema linfático (el sistema de eliminación de residuos del cuerpo).

Melanocitos – responsables de la producción de melanina en la piel. Estas células protegen a las otras células epidérmicas de los efectos dañinos de los rayos UVA. La melanina ayuda a determinar el color de la piel. Cuanta más melanina haya presente, más oscuro será el tono de piel.

La Dermis

La dermis es la capa que se encuentra por debajo de la epidermis y es responsable de la fuerza y elasticidad de la piel. También contiene muchas células especializadas y estructuras, como nervios o vasos sanguíneos, glándulas y folículos pilosos. La dermis consiste en dos capas: la capa papilar y la capa reticular. La capa superior (papilar) contiene una lámina fina de fibras de colágeno. Por debajo, la capa reticular está compuesta de fibras de colágeno densas proporcionadas paralelamente a la superficie de la piel.

Español

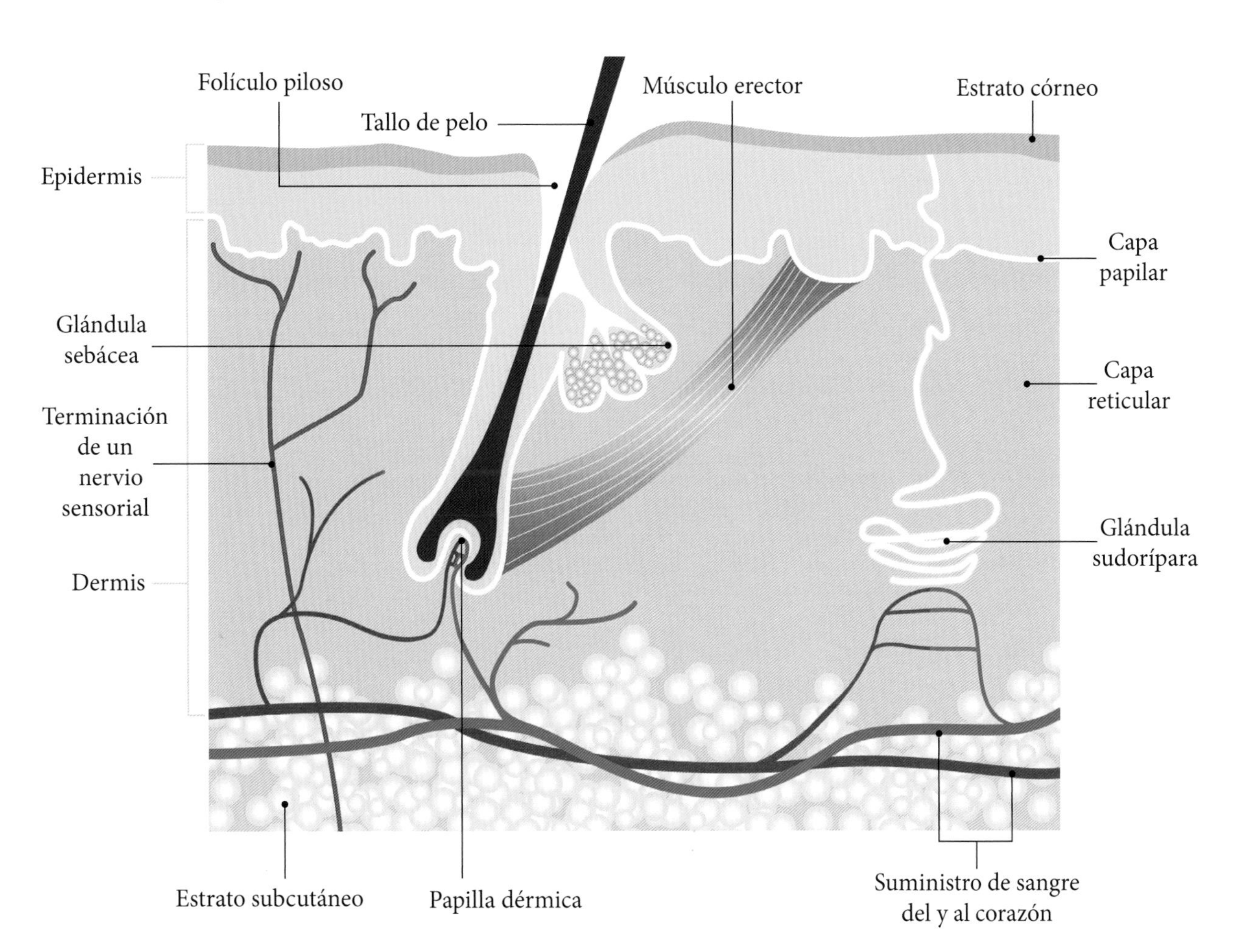

La Capa Reticular

La capa reticular consiste de dos tipos de proteína: fibras de elastina, que le dan a la piel su elasticidad, y fibras de colágeno, que le dan a la piel su fuerza. Estos dos tipos de fibras se mantienen en una sustancia gelatinosa llamada 'sustancia básica'. Las fibras de elastina y colágeno forman una fuerte red, que nos da una apariencia juvenil.

A medida que envejecemos, estas fibras de la piel empiezan a endurecerse y fragmentarse; la red comienza a derribarse y nuestra piel pierde su elasticidad y enseña los signos visibles del envejecimiento. La circulación sanguínea hacia la piel disminuye; los nutrientes no llegan a la superficie, lo que resulta en una piel cetrina. La capa de grasa que se sitúa por debajo de la piel crece más fina de lo normal y hace destacar más nuestra estructura de huesos, lo que nos hace parecer más demacrados. La capa reticular es vital para la salud y el aspecto de nuestra piel. Por eso es esencial, que la cuide, para prevenir los signos del envejecimiento.

El Flujo Sanguíneo

La sangre circula a través del cuerpo hacia todas las células, transportando nutrientes vitales y energía, como el oxígeno, la glucosa y otras materias primas esenciales para la salud, el mantenimiento y el crecimiento del cuerpo humano.

La acción de succión del tratamiento de microdermoabrasión favorece la estimulación de la microcirculación cerca de la superficie de la piel. Esto ayuda el aumento del flujo sanguíneo y favorece la producción de colágeno y elastina en la piel, como también la renovación celular (regeneración de la piel), ayudando la reparación de los tejidos y mostrando una piel más sabe y sana.

Este diagrama muestra el flujo de la sangre a través de las células; primero transportando nutrientes y energía y luego eliminando productos de desecho, como el dióxido de carbono.

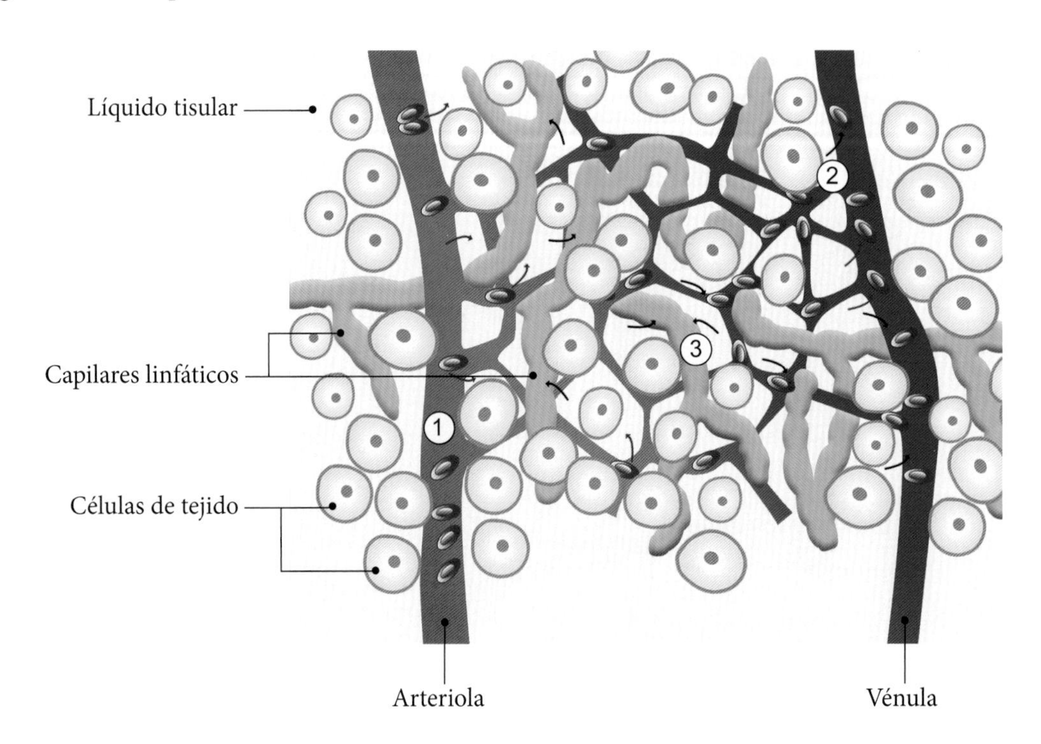

① La sangre está sometida a gran presión cuando fluye a través de la red capilar, forzando el fluido a través del tejido, convirtiéndose en líquido tisular. Este líquido contiene sustancias útiles, como el oxígeno y nutrientes esenciales para las células. Las células de la sangre y proteínas grandes se quedan en el capilar.

② A medida que la sangre pasa por un proceso de desoxigenación, la presión se invierte y algo del líquido, que contiene productos de desecho volverá a entrar por el capilar, dejándose llevar.

③ Exceso de líquidos, productos de desecho y moléculas grandes, como las proteínas que han sido incapaz de volver a entrar en la sangre, son recogidos por los capilares linfáticos y transportados a los ganglios linfáticos, donde el fluido se procesa y donde vuelve a entrar en la sangre, cerca del corazón.

El Flujo Sanguíneo A Través De La Piel

La temperatura corporal normal es de 37°C. El cuerpo se ocupa de mantener esa temperatura. Si la temperatura corporal empieza a subir, la sangre pasa cerca de la piel para eliminar el calor. Cuando la temperatura corporal baja, los capilares se oprimen y la sangre pasa por 'vasos de derivación', que se sitúan en lo profundo de la dermis, reduciendo de esa manera la pérdida de calor a través de la piel.

Vaso-dilatación ocurre, cuando tiene:
Calor – la sangre pasa cerca de la superficie – el calor es eliminado

Vaso-constricción ocurre cuando tiene:
Frio – la sangre fluye a través de 'vasos de derivación', alejándose de la superficie – el calor es mantenido

LOS TIPOS DE PIEL

Hay seis tipos diferentes de piel. Sin embargo, la piel de la cara de una persona puede variar en varias épocas de su vida, debido a enfermedades o desequilibrio hormonal.

Piel Seca

La piel seca es provocada por glándulas sebáceas inactivas o hipofuncionantes, que no producen suficiente sebo como para mantener la piel hidratada de modo natural. Suele tener un aspecto opaco, se siente seca, produce picor y a veces es sensible. La piel seca debe ser hidratada regularmente desde dentro (bebiendo agua) y desde fuera (con cremas o lociones hidratantes).

Piel Grasa

La piel grasa es provocada por glándulas que producen demasiado sebo, resultando en una piel con aspecto graso con poros grandes y abiertos. Piel grasa tienden a desarrollar espinillas y acné. A pesar de estas desventajas la piel grasa suele mantenerse más joven y más pulposa a lo largo del tiempo, que otros tipos de piel. Piel grasa beneficia mucho de microdermoabrasión y lociones ligeras.

Piel Sensible

La piel sensible puede ser seca, normal o grasa y es caracterizada por su delicadeza. Normalmente este tipo de piel reacciona de manera adversa a determinadas condiciones medioambientales y es precisa de un tratamiento especial para mantener la piel sana. La piel sensible beneficia mucho de tratamientos y productos naturales para el cuidado de la piel.

Piel Normal

La piel normal produce sebo a un ritmo moderado, llevando a cabo un estado equilibrado. Piel normal tiene un aspecto voluminoso, húmedo y vibrante. Este tipo de piel parece una bendición, pero siempre requiere una atención determinada. Se beneficia de limpieza regular, productos tonificantes e hidratación.

Piel Mixta

Este tipo de piel es el más común. Piel mixta está caracterizada por una "zona T" grasienta, que cubre la frente, la nariz y la barbilla. Sin embargo las zonas alrededor de las mejillas, los ojos y la boca suelen ser normal o seca. Personas con pieles mixtas deben evaluar la piel a menudo y usar diferentes productos en las diferentes zonas de la piel.

Piel Madura

La piel madura resulta cada vez más seca con el avance de la edad, porque las glándulas sebáceas se vuelven menos activas. De ese modo la piel pierde elasticidad y las arrugas empiezan a formarse. La piel aparenta más delgada y presenta capilares rotos, sobre todo por la zona de las mejillas y alrededor de la nariz. Los contornos faciales se aflojan al reducirse el tono muscular. La estructura ósea subyacente se vuelve más visible, porque la capa grasa por debajo de la piel se vuelve más fina. El flujo sanguíneo es más débil, lo que interfiere con la nutrición de la piel, provocando una piel amarillenta. Debido a la disminución del índice metabólico, los productos de desechos no son eliminados tan rápidos, llevando a una hinchazón de piel. Hay que hidratar bien a la piel madura bebiendo agua y usando lociones y cremas hidratantes.

COLOR DE LA PIEL

El tono de la piel humana puede variar de un marrón oscuro a casi una pigmentación incolora, que puede parecer roja, debido a la sangre en la piel. Los europeos suelen tener la tez, el pelo y los ojos más claros que cualquier otro grupo, no obstante, esto no siempre es así. A efectos prácticos, seis tipos de piel son distinguidos, siguiendo la escala de Fitzpatrick (1975). La tonalidad de la piel aparece en orden decreciente.

LA ESCALA DE FITZPATRICK

Tipo	También llamado	Comportamiento del bronceado	Color de pelo y ojos
I	Muy claro, 'nordico'	Se quema a menudo, rara vez se broncea	Suelen tener pecas, pelo rojo o rubio, ojos azules o verdes
II	Claro o 'piel clara'	Suele quemarse	Suelen tener pelo claro, ojos azules o verdes
III	Medio claro, 'europeos de piel oscura" o "caucásico medio"	Se quema a veces, se suele broncear	Suelen tener el pelo moreno y ojos oscuros
IV	Medio oscuro, 'mediterranea' o 'tono de oliva'	Se quema a veces, se broncea a menudo	Suele tener el pelo moreno oscuro y los ojos marrones oscuros
V	Oscuro o 'tipo marrón'	piel negra/marrón natural	A menudo tienen pelo moreno oscuro y ojos marrones oscuros
VI	Muy oscuro o 'tipo negro'	piel negra/marrón natural	Suelen tener pelo negro-moreno y ojos negro-marrones

Español

MICRODERMOABRASIÓN - ¿QUÉ ES?

La microdermoabrasión es un sistema, que realiza una exfoliación intensiva y una regeneración de la piel de manera segura y controlada, usando cristales ultra finos, que rejuvenecen la piel. Los cristales funcionan como un abrasivo suave sobre la piel, eliminando células muertas capa por capa. La forma irregular de los cristales permite el acceso a zonas difíciles de alcanzar, sin dañar la piel. Los tratamientos son progresivos, lo que significa, que los clientes podrán ver buenos resultados a lo largo del ciclo de tratamientos.

El grado de abrasión epidérmica puede variar, cambiando la velocidad de los cristales, con la que impactan sobre la piel. La eliminación del estrato córneo tiene como resultado una piel inmediatamente más suave y refrescada, facilitando a la vez el crecimiento de piel nueva y de colágeno. A lo largo de un ciclo de tratamientos la piel quedará resplandeciente y se sentirá rejuvenecida.

La acción de aspiración succiona los cristales usados y las células muertas. A su vez estimula la circulación y facilita un aumento de flujo sanguíneo a la zona. La producción de colágeno y elastina es estimulada, lo que resulta en una piel más firme y juvenil.

La microdermoabrasión puede tratar todos los tipos de piel, en todas las partes del cuerpo y de la cara. SkinBase recomienda un ciclo de 8 tratamientos, realizados cada 7-10 días. Puede ser, que las personas afectadas del acné o de las cicatrices del acné necesiten más tratamientos. Recomendamos un tratamiento de mantenimiento al mes, una vez que haya terminado con el ciclo de tratamientos, para mantener los resultados obtenidos. Después de un tratamiento, la piel puede sentirse algo tensa y suavemente irritada. Por eso, es importante, que los clientes usen una buena crema hidratante. Los efectos disminuirán en menos de 24 horas.

¿Cuáles son las ventajas de la microdermoabrasión en comparación con otros métodos de tratamiento?

El tratamiento de microdermoabrasión produce una incomodidad mínima para el cliente, lo que significa, que puede volver a su rutina diaria, después del tratamiento, sin ningún problema. La microdermoabrasión de cristales utiliza un componente inerte y estéril, que produce ninguna reacción alérgica.

- Elimina posibles reacciones adversas, que normalmente son relacionadas con soluciones químicas
- Los clientes pueden volver inmediatamente después del tratamiento con su estilo de vida normal (no provoca una irritación extrema)
- Puede tratar de forma segura a todos los tonos de color y a todos los tipos de piel
- Los resultados son visibles inmediatamente, incluso después del primer tratamiento (ayuda tener a los clientes motivados)
- Trata los primeros signos del envejecimiento y ofrece un rejuvenecimiento total para las pieles envejecidas
- La acción de aspiración mejora la elasticidad y el tono muscular de la piel, como también estimula los fibroblastos para la producción de colágeno
- Facilita la penetración de productos autorizados después del tratamiento
- Ideal para pieles congestionadas con poros abiertos y espinillas y para pieles propensas al acné
- Control variable permite una exfoliación más profunda en pieles defectuosas y con cicatrices de acné
- Ayuda con éxito la eliminación de marcas de pigmentación no deseadas
- Ideal para pieles dañadas por el sol
- La exfoliación corporal total ofrece un tratamiento contra la celulitis, porque la acción de succión mejora el drenaje linfático

¿Hay algún riesgo asociado con la microdermoabrasión?

El uso inadecuado o condiciones poco higiénicas suponen un riesgo durante el tratamiento de microdermoabrasión. Por eso abogamos por la importancia de una buena higiene en el puesto de trabajo. La máquina MDPro utiliza boquillas desechables; de esa manera se evita el riesgo de una contaminación cruzada entre clientes, ya que la boquilla es el único componente, que entra en contacto con la piel durante el tratamiento.

LOS CRISTALES

Los cristales son de óxido de aluminio, un mineral natural. Al ser estéril y no ser tóxico, no produce reacciones adversas alguna en contacto con la piel. De todos modos recomendamos un test de alergia cutánea antes del tratamiento como medida de precaución.

El óxido de aluminio se considera un riesgo bajo para la salud cuando se inhala y reglamentos industriales tratan este tipo de inhalación como polvo molesto. La inhalación de cualquier tipo de partículas de polvo fino, como por ejemplo polvo de uñas artificiales, puede causar irritación y tos, si se expone a ellos durante largos periodos. El óxido de aluminio no contiene cuarzo/silicio libre, lo que significa, que no supone un riesgo respiratorio por inhalación.

SENSIBILIDAD A LOS CRISTALES

Es necesario realizar una prueba de parche, para comprobar si el cliente tiene sensibilidad a los cristales empleados durante el tratamiento. Aunque sea muy inusual que un cliente sea sensible a los cristales, se debe de hacer un test de parche por la parte trasera del antebrazo antes de tratamiento. Si la zona está irritada o inflamada no debe proceder con el tratamiento. Si el cliente desarrolla marcas rojas después del tratamiento, es debido normalmente al esteticista por aplicar demasiada presión.

¿Qué problemas de la piel se pueden tratar con la microdermoabrasión?

Todos pueden beneficiarse de los tratamientos de microdermoabrasión. El tratamiento mejora el aspecto de la piel, dándole un resplandor sano y un aspecto joven. La microdermoabrasión también es muy eficaz en tratar numerosos problemas de la piel. Puede ser usado en la cara y en el cuerpo, permitiendo un tratamiento para mejorar las cicatrices del acné en la espalda, por ejemplo.

Acné Y Catrices Del Acné
La microdermoabrasión elimina las capas superiores de células muertas situadas en la superficie de la piel, lo que es muy eficaz para tratar el acné. Eliminando las células muertas de la superficie de la piel, desbloquea los poros, reduciendo la posibilidad de un nuevo desarrollo de granos.

Líneas de expresión y arrugas
Piel envejecida
La acción de aspiración de la microdermoabrasión estimula la producción de colágeno en la piel. A medida que envejecemos la producción de elastina y colágeno empieza a disminuir. La combinación de una estimulación de colágeno y un aumento de renovación de piel mejorará la condición de la superficie de la piel, suavizando las líneas de expresión y las arrugas.

Piel seca y deshidratada
Tono de piel irregular
Normalmente la piel se renueva aproximadamente cada 28 días. Eliminando las células muertas de las capas superiores de la piel, la microdermoabrasión acelera el ritmo, con el que suele renovar la piel, presentando una piel nueva y refrescada, resplandeciente.

Celulitis, efecto ‘piel de naranja’
La microdermoabrasión no puede curar la celulitis, sin embargo puede estimular la circulación, mejorando el flujo sanguíneo en esa zona. Para mejorar el aspecto de la celulitis, clientes deben beber abundante agua y hacer ejercicio regularmente.

Estrías, Pigmentación E imperfecciones

La microdermoabrasión puede mejorar enormemente el aspecto de la pigmentación y de las estrías. El tratamiento de la microdermoabrasión estimula la zona tratada a producir más colágeno y a acelerar el proceso de renovación de la piel, mejorando así la condición de la piel y disminuyendo la aparición de estrías y decoloración de la piel.

El tratamiento de microdermoabrasión no eliminará las estrías. Sin embargo, tratamientos regulares mostrarán un mejoramiento de la zona tratada, ayudando, a que las marcas sean menos visibles. El tejido cicatrizante no debe ser tratado, hasta que toda la inflamación haya desaparecido de la zona (6 meses después de la cirugía, por ejemplo).

Tratamientos regulares de microdermoabrasión ayudarán a mejorar el aspecto de las estrías, creando un efecto de uniformidad alrededor del tejido cicatrizante y reduciendo a su vez cualquier problema de pigmentación, que muchas veces hacen las estrías más notables.

Hiperpigmentación y su causa (Melasma)

Las causas más obvias son el uso de pastillas anticonceptivas o la terapia de reemplazo hormonal, embarazo o la interacción con ciertos medicamentos. Exposición excesiva o una exposición repetida al sol pueden causarlo, como también lo hacen una inflamación o un trauma de la piel. Ciertas sustancias químicas presentes en perfumes etc., también pueden causar marcas de pigmentación. Tratamientos regulares de microdermoabrasión mostrarán beneficios significantes a pieles dañadas por el sol y ayudarán a eliminar las marcas de pigmentación no deseadas.

Un ciclo de tratamientos de microdermoabrasión SkinBase puede lograr resultados beneficiosos, referente al tratamiento contra las marcas de pigmentación. Los clientes deben ser aconsejados, de que un ciclo de entre 10-15 tratamientos será necesario. También es imprescindible aconsejarles de llevar protección solar a todas horas.

Por favor tome nota de que el tratamiento de microdermoabrasión no puede ayudar a clientes con vitíligo.

Melasma y cloasma (oscurecimiento de la piel, debido a un cambio hormonal) puede ser tratado con microdermoabrasión. El tratamiento ayudará a levantar el pigmento atrapado a través de las capas epidérmicas para ser desprendido de la piel de la manera habitual. Sin embargo se necesitarán muchos tratamientos, para mejorar el área afectada.

¿CÓMO FUNCIONA UN CICLO DE TRATAMIENTOS?

La microdermoabrasión es un tratamiento progresivo, más que agresivo. Las capas epidérmicas son eliminadas de forma suave y segura a lo largo de un ciclo de tratamientos. En un ciclo, los tratamientos se realizan cada 7-10 días. De esta manera, el estrato córneo, que fue eliminado durante el tratamiento anterior, no tuvo tiempo para restablecerse y la tolerancia del cliente referente al tratamiento aumenta. Por lo tanto, la intensidad del tratamiento puede ser aumentada con cada tratamiento sucesivo, para alcanzar capas epidérmicas más profundas y eliminar las cicatrices del acné, levantar la pigmentación y suavizar las arrugas con éxito.

En general, los clientes optan por un ciclo de seis tratamientos, realizados cada 7-10 días para obtener el máximo efecto. Después de completar un ciclo, el cliente puede recibir un tratamiento mensual de mantenimiento, para ayudar mantener los resultados obtenidos. Es probable, que clientes que tengan la piel más problemática necesiten un ciclo de tratamientos más largo, aunque 15-20 tratamientos se considera lo máximo, transcurridos los cuales deben someterse a un programa de mantenimiento cada 4-6 semanas.

SECCIÓN 3 – RESULTADOS DEL APRENDIZAJE

- Capacidad de efectuar una consulta al cliente antes del tratamiento
- Conocimiento sobre las contraindicaciones del tratamiento de microdermoabrasión
- Conocimiento sobre el seguimiento requerido después del tratamiento y las posibles reacciones al tratamiento

CONSULTA AL CLIENTE

1. Compruebe la idoneidad del cliente al tratamiento refiriéndose a la lista de contraindicaciones.
2. Efectúe un análisis de piel señalando cualquier zona que necesite ser evitada durante el tratamiento, por ejemplo contraindicaciones menores, como la telangiectasia (capilares rotos).
3. Localice las partes, que requieran atención especial, como las cicatrices del acné, pigmentación, poros abiertos o tonos irregulares.
4. Sugiera un programa de tratamiento y asegúrese de explicar el precio, la duración y la frecuencia requerida del ciclo.
5. Explíquele al cliente las posibles reacciones de la piel. Aunque las reacciones (si las hay) son menores, asegúrese de que el cliente comprenda, que puede haber sensibilidad.
6. Explíquele al cliente las posibles reacciones de la piel. Aunque las reacciones (si las hay) son menores, asegúrese de que el cliente comprenda, que puede haber sensibilidad.
7. Trate a fondo el seguimiento después del tratamiento, para que comprenda el cliente lo que debe hacer después del procedimiento para cuidar la piel.
8. Es vital, que el cliente entienda la importancia de hacer el régimen correcto en casa entre tratamientos y que se comprometa a obtener buenos resultados, por ejemplo usando la protección solar adecuada para evitar aún más problemas de pigmentación.

9. SIEMPRE COMPLETE LA FICHA DEL CLIENTE

Esto garantizará que las necesidades específicas del cliente obtendrán atención especial. Explique las contraindicaciones del tratamiento y asegúrese, de que el cliente firme su ficha.

Padres/Tutores (mayor de 18) deben firmar la ficha de consulta para niños menores de 16 años.

CONTRAINDICACIONES AL TRATAMIENTO DE MICRODERMOABRASIÓN

Contraindicaciones mayores – no proceda con el tratamiento

Embarazo
Un aumento de hormonas puede afectar la piel durante el embarazo, por lo cual puede provocar pigmentación. Por eso no le recomendamos la microdermoabrasión, ya que la piel reaccionar de un modo inesperado, empeorando el problema. Recomiende a los clientes usar buena protección solar, para evitar la aparición de pigmentación.

Cáncer
No le recomendamos, que trate a un cliente con cáncer. Los clientes deben estar en remisión por lo menos por 6 meses, antes de comenzar un ciclo de tratamientos. La microdermoabrasión estimula el flujo sanguíneo y el drenaje linfático.

Acné Grado 4
Clientes con este grado de acné no deben ser tratados con microdermoabrasión. Si la piel está muy congestionada con pústulas y pápulas, el tratamiento podría aumentar la irritación de la piel y propagar las bacterias.

Roacutan
Roacutan causa el debilitamiento de la piel. Si su cliente está recibiendo un tratamiento de roacutan contra el acné, tiene que esperar 6 meses después de dejar de tomar roacutan, antes de recibir el tratamiento de microdermoabrasión.

Enfermedad Autoinmune
Describe una enfermedad causada porque el sistema inmunitario ataca las células del propio organismo. Evite tratar a un cliente afectado de una enfermedad autoinmune.

Diabetes
La diabetes afecta los nervios y la circulación y es probable, que la piel necesite más tiempo para curarse de lo normal. Clientes con diabetes deben presentar un permiso por escrito de su médico, antes de realizar el tratamiento.

Impétigo
Impétigo es una infección bacteriana de la piel. No realice el tratamiento de microdermoabrasión.

Rosácea
La rosácea no puede ser tratada con microdermoabrasión.

Contraindicaciones menores – proceda con cuidado y evite zonas afectadas:

- Infecciones oculares, por ejemplo conjuntivitis, orzuelos, quistes
- Trastornos de piel (p. ej. Acné, seborrea, dermatitis, úlceras, eccemas, psoriasis
- Queloides
- Telangiectasia (capilares rotos)
- Lunares elevados, verrugas, papilomas cutáneos
- Cortes, moratones, abrasiones

Si está inseguro o es incapaz de identificar el problema de la piel, no debe tratar al cliente y recomendarle que consulte a su médico.

CONSEJOS PARA DESPUÉS DEL TRATAMIENTO

Hasta 12 horas después del tratamiento:

Evite el maquillaje pesado

Hasta 24 horas después del tratamiento:

No vaya a nadar
No se someta a inyecciones de botox ni colágeno ni a rellenos dérmicos

Hasta 48 horas después del tratamiento:

No vaya a la sauna, al solario y evite la exposición al sol
No reciba inyecciones de Botox, colágeno ni rellenos dérmicos

Hasta 72 horas después del tratamiento:

No utilice cremas antiedad
No utilice productos, que contengan AHAs (ácidos alfa hidróxidos), glicólicos o retinol
No use productos exfoliantes. La piel recién tratada es sensible hacia cualquier producto. El uso de productos exfoliantes puede irritar a la piel.

Use a todas horas durante un ciclo de tratamientos

Protección solar de un mínimo de 15 y la exposición a los rayos UVA debe ser evitada por completo.
Hidratación regular es vital para restaurar la humedad y prevenir una piel reseca, que se pela.

Los productos tienen que tener un pH entre 4.5 y 7

Productos para el cuidado de la piel que contengan un porcentaje alto en botánicos y aceites esenciales NO SON ADECUADOS para el uso después del tratamiento de microdermoabrasión, ya que algunos de los ingredientes, que contienen pueden causar una reacción alérgica. En el caso de que esto ocurra, existe el peligro, que los dos, el esteticista y el cliente piensen que la alergia es debida al tratamiento, cuando realmente son los ingredientes del producto usado para el cuidado de la piel. El uso de productos que reponen o agregan hidratación es importante, para evitar que la piel se seque o empiece a pelarse.

Botox/rellenos dérmicos

Permita 14 días antes de someterse a un tratamiento de microdermoabrasión, para dejar, que el botox o los rellenos dérmicos se.

Hombres

Hombres deben afeitarse a ras la noche anterior al tratamiento, si el tratamiento es por la mañana. Si el tratamiento es por la tarde, deben afeitarse por la mañana.

Tratamientos láser

Un ciclo de tratamientos láser no puede ser efectuado paralelamente con un ciclo de tratamientos de microdermoabrasión. Por favor permita por lo menos 2 semanas, entre la finalización del ciclo de láser y el comienzo de la microdermoabrasión.

SECCIÓN 4 – RESULTADOS DEL APRENDIZAJE

- Conocimiento sobre los componentes de la máquina de microdermoabrasión y sus funciones
- Conocimiento sobre el montaje y el control del aparato
- Capacidad de seleccionar la intensidad adecuada según el tipo de piel del cliente

MONTAJE DEL SISTEMA SKINBASE MDPRO

1. Compruebe siempre que el contenedor del filtro esté completamente vacío antes de comenzar el tratamiento
2. Asegúrese de que el dispositivo esté conectado con el frasco de eliminación de residuos del tubo plateado y que esté conectado firmemente por los dos lados.
3. Adjunte una boquilla limpia y una botellita nueva de cristales a la pieza de mano y ciérrelo firmemente
4. Conecte el cable eléctrico, encienda el interruptor y el botón en el panel para comenzar. Si tiene una máquina alquilada, siga las instrucciones dentro de la máquina.

CÓMO AJUSTAR EL GRADO DE TRATAMIENTO

Asegúrese de que la botella de cristales esté conectada con la pieza de mano. Ponga su dedo índice encima del agujero de la boquilla. Gire la válvula de regulación, hasta que obtenga la presión deseada para su tratamiento facial.

Asegúrese de que comprenda los grados de presión correctos, antes de comenzar los tratamientos de microdermoabrasión.

TOME EN CUENTA: EN NINGÚN CASO DEBE SER DESTORNILLADA NI LEVANTADA LA CUBIERTA METÁLICA SIN HABER DESCONECTADO EL CABLE PREVIAMENTE.

NIVELES DE TRATAMIENTO

Las siguientes descripciones ofrecen una guía para seleccionar el nivel apropiado para el cliente.

NIVEL UNO - 0,3 bar

Este nivel lo deben usar esteticistas recién entrenados, hasta que estén seguros de efectuar los trazos con la suavidad adecuada. El nivel uno permite una suave exfoliación general y debe ser seleccionad siempre para el primer tratamiento de los clientes. Siempre use el nivel uno cuando trate la zona alrededor de los ojos.

Nivel uno:

- 0,3 bar

- esteticistas recién entrenados
- primer tratamiento
- zona de los ojos

NIVEL DOS - 0,4 bar

Este nivel debe ser seleccionado gradualmente, cuando se trata las cicatrices del acné o piel más dura. Piel negra o asiática no pueden ser tratadas con un nivel más alto que el nivel dos. (Refiérase a la escala de Fitzpatrick).

Nivel dos:

- 0,4 bar

- Trata la zona con más atención
- No supere el nivel dos al tratar piel negro o asiática

NIVEL TRES - 0,5 bar

Este nivel solo puede ser usado en clientes llegando al final del ciclo de tratamientos, cuando la piel es más tolerante/tolerable. El nivel tres se utiliza para tratar las cicatrices del acné, pigmentación, líneas de expresión y arrugas. También se usa para una exfoliación corporal, para tratar estrías y celulitis.

Nivel tres:

- 0,5 bar

- Al final del ciclo de tratamientos
- Exfoliación corporal
- Piel problemática
- Solo para tratar zonas con más atención
- Nunca sobre piel negra o asiática

NIVEL CUATRO - 0.6 bar

Sólo para tratamientos corporales. Nunca debe ser usado en la cara.

SECCIÓN 5 – RESULTADOS DEL APRENDIZAJE

- Habilidad de utilizar el aparato y efectuar un tratamiento de modo seguro y eficaz durante el tiempo recomendado
- Capacidad de operar dentro del tiempo aceptado en el sector estético

MÉTODO DE TRATAMIENTO

1. Sitúe al cliente en una posición semi-reclinada.
2. Asegúrese de que el pelo del cliente esté fuera de la cara.
3. LIMPIE la cara del cliente afondo (Tiene que usar un limpiador de gel o espumoso).
4. La piel tiene que estar completamente limpia.
5. Estire la piel con su pulgar y su dedo corazón.
6. Coja la pieza de mano como si fuera un lápiz, haga un movimiento suave similar al de una escoba sobre la cara.
7. Efectúe una exfoliación general sobre la cara entera y el cuello.
8. Después de la exfoliación general, vuelva a las zonas que necesiten más atención, como las cicatrices del acné, marcas de pigmentación, líneas de expresión o arrugas.
9. Al terminar con el tratamiento, limpie los restos de los cristales que aún permanecen sobre la piel, usando un algodón (agua fría).
10. Use un tonificador suave.
11. Ponga una mascarilla (opcional).
12. Hidrate la piel.
13. Aplique una crema de protección solar de 15.

INSTRUCCIONES PARA LA APLICACIÓN DEL TRATAMIENTO

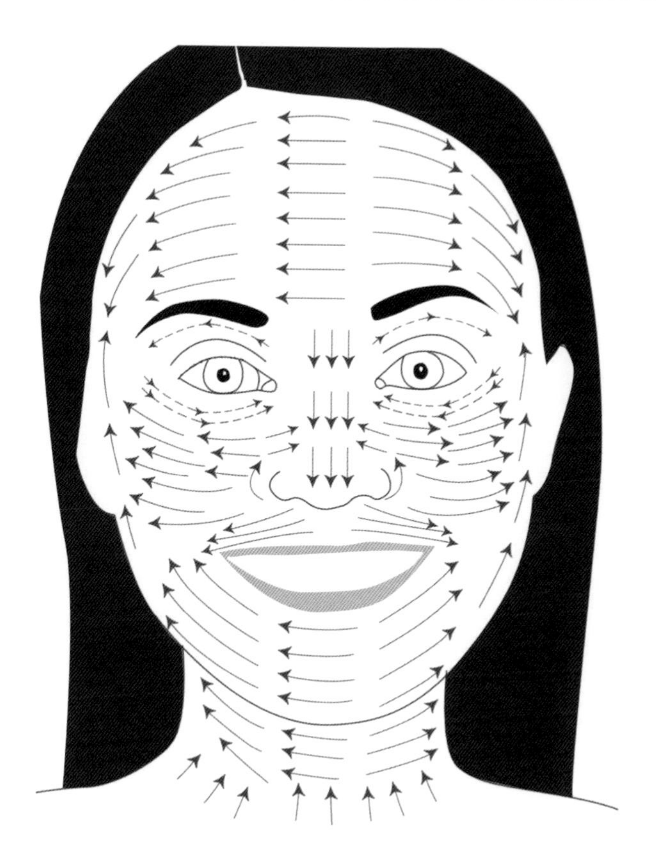

El diagrama muestra las direcciones, en las que debe efectuar el tratamiento, para tratar la cara.

Las líneas punteadas alrededor de la zona de los ojos sugieren trazos rápidos y suaves. Cada flecha (trazo) es aproximadamente 4 cm de largo.

ZONA DE OJOS:

- Use movimientos ligeros
- Siempre use el nivel uno alrededor de los ojos

Consejos De Utilización

1. Debe intentar de comprender la piel del cliente y cómo reacciona antes de empezar a ser algo venturoso con el tratamiento. Muchas veces los esteticistas quieren impresionar tanto a sus clientes en el primer tratamiento, que utilizan demasiada presión y trabajan de manera algo agresiva. En consecuencia, la piel del cliente se sensibiliza y al ser trata con mucha presión, se pueden hacen visibles marcas rojas. Esto es debido al esteticista, por ser muy ambicioso y no entender la piel del cliente. Es importante que los esteticistas efectúen el movimiento de la boquilla sobre la piel de una manera suave y controlada.

2. Mantenga siempre la presión ligera durante el primer tratamiento y proceda despacio a niveles más altos y a tratamientos más agresivos a medida que el curso progresa. Esto garantiza, que la piel del cliente se acostumbra al tratamiento y el cliente comprende lo que ocurre. Un cliente que se va a casa con marcas rojas o una piel roja y sensible, será un cliente insatisfecho, que probablemente cancele el resto del ciclo de tratamientos, porque el esteticista fue incapaz de explicar o efectuar el tratamiento correctamente.

3. Use una acción de aspiración ligera para pieles negras y asiáticas. No sobrepase el nivel dos en tipos de piel V y VI de la escala de Fitzpatrick.

4. El secreto de un tratamiento exitoso está en la presión de los trazos. Trazos ligeros y rápidos deben ser usados ara una exfoliación general (muy suave alrededor de los ojos), trazos más despacio para tratar zonas problemáticas con más atención. Zonas, que presentan telangiectasia menor (capilares rotos) deben ser tratadas con cuidado, efectuando trazos ligeros y rápidos sobre esa zona. Los trazos nunca deben ser más largos de 4 cm.

SECCIÓN 6 – RESULTADOS DEL APRENDIZAJE

- Buen conocimiento sobre los aspectos de salud y seguridad relacionados con el tratamiento y el mantenimiento del equipo
- Capacidad de actualizar las fichas de los clientes con precisión

MANTENIMIENTO ESENCIAL DE LA MÁQUINA

- Después de cada tratamiento – apague el sistema y desconecte el cable de la red eléctrica y de la carcasa.
- Saque el contenedor de los cristales y compruebe, poniendo la pieza de mano encima de la palma de la mano, si quedan cristales en la cámara de la pieza de mano. Cada vez que cambie la botella de cristales, elimine el exceso de cristales que puedan quedar en el conducto interior. De este modo se garantiza, que la cámara interior del dispositivo se mantiene limpia a todas horas.
- Quite la boquilla y tirela.
- Vacíe el contenedor de residuos después de CADA tratamiento, desenrosque la tapadera del contenedor de residuos, vacíe los cristales usados y tírelos responsablemente.
- Asegúrese de que el contenedor de residuos esté posicionado seguramente y que esté enroscado perfectamente. Si no está bien enroscado, la intensidad de la aspiración será reducida.
- Recoja todos los tubos y accesorios y métalos en la caja. Asegúrese de que todo el equipo esté limpio, listo para el próximo uso.

IMPORTANTE:

El filtro desechable de plástico hay que cambiarlo por lo menos cada 80 tratamientos. Si no conecta un nuevo filtro, la intensidad de la aspiración disminuirá y puede causar, que los cristales sean aspirados directamente hacia la bomba en el interior de la unidad, cosa que podría dañar la máquina e invalidar la garantía.

INDICE

Notes